9

STAGE SCENERY and LIGHTING

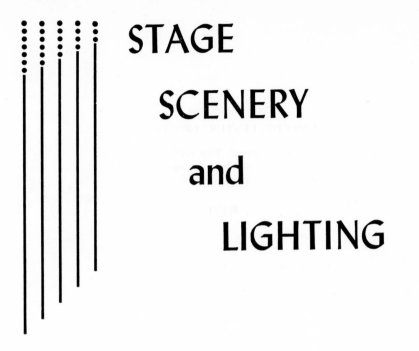

STAGE
SCENERY
and
LIGHTING

By SAMUEL SELDEN *and* HUNTON D. SELLMAN

Third Edition

APPLETON-CENTURY-CROFTS

Division of Meredith Publishing Company

NEW YORK

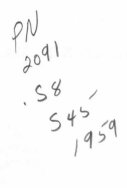

PREFACE

OUR PURPOSE in preparing this manual is to satisfy the need for a short, but comprehensive handbook of scenery and lighting for college, school, and community theatres. It is addressed primarily to those who are designing, building, and painting scenery, as well as those who are lighting the set and the actors. It should be of interest also to the director and actor themselves, as well as to the general student of the theatre.

The book is planned first to be a reference manual for the individual of some experience who wishes to find specific information on particular problems. For this person the material is arranged in major and minor divisions with a system of titles, subtitles, and cross-references for convenience in finding needed information quickly.

The book is designed second as a text for the person with little or no experience who wishes to study the subject of scenery and lighting step by step from the beginning. For this person, the material is arranged under separate topics and chapters which present the elements of each subject in a progressive sequence. After an explanation of what scenery is, the reader is led to examine the topography of a stage, the elements of scenery, some common arrangements of these elements into stage settings, and some methods of planning settings by means of drawings and models. Then follow the study of the construction and painting of scenery and the assembling and shifting of the completed parts on the stage. There is a chapter on how to provide scenery in a theatre where there are tight budgetary restrictions, and a final chapter dealing with experimental staging.

Part II begins with a statement of the meaning, functions, and demands of stage lighting and proceeds to a detailed description of lighting instruments. Following these are an explanation of the nature and use of color, and a brief review of the theory of electricity and light for those who have had no technical background. The two final chapters deal with lighting control and lighting practice. New terms are defined along the way, and related or explanatory material is made easy to find by means of the cross-references. There is a full glossary of stage terms at the end of the book.

The equipment and methods outlined are essentially those employed in Broadway playhouses and scenic studios. Slight changes, however, are occasionally advised to adapt the "standard" methods and equipment to the special requirements of simplicity and economy peculiar to the school or community theatre.

This third edition has been revised throughout. Part I has been extended in text and drawings, the section on color has been rewritten and there is a new section on perspective drawing, and a new chapter on recent developments in theatre architecture and staging methods. Part II has been completely rewritten to bring all sections of the text up to date. Almost all of the technical illustrations in this part are new. The photographs of stage settings in both parts are new.

We wish to acknowledge once more our indebtedness to the many professional associates and other friends who helped us prepare this book. In the case of Part II the author wishes particularly to acknowledge his appreciation and indebtedness to Herbert Kliegl, George Gill, and Lee Watson, who gave him opportunities to observe equipment and lighting practice in New York City. For photographs and diagrams in Part II, he is indebted to Kliegl Bros., Century Lighting Inc., Davis Mfg. Co., Ward Leonard Electric Co., Superior Electric Co., Major Equipment Co., Art Institute of Light, General Electric Co., General Radio Corp., and Metropolitan Electric Co.

S. S.
H. D. S.

CONTENTS

Part II: STAGE LIGHTING

ILLUSTRATIONS

FIGURES

STAGE SCENERY

By SAMUEL SELDEN

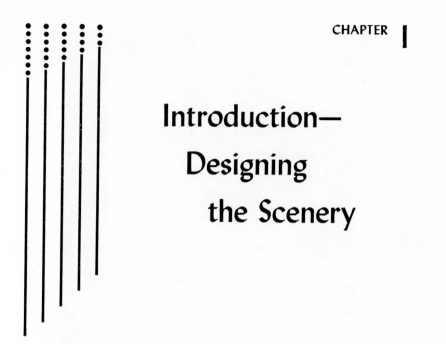

CHAPTER 1

Introduction— Designing the Scenery

1. THE ORGANIC THEORY OF PLAY PRESENTATION

THE "ART" OF the theatre, as it is generally understood, consists of two parts: the writing of a play and the presenting of a play. An author conceives a pattern of physical and vocal images which he puts into words. A group of fellow artists, following the directions they find in his script, re-create his images for an audience. They make his phantom ideas visible and audible by translating the author's written words into acting, music, dancing, costumes, scenery, and lighting. The same thought and the same spirit govern the re-created vision as governed the original—if the artists who have done the translating have understood the directions in the text and been intelligent about carrying them out.

Words in a text, however, are only symbols for ideas, and it is often possible to interpret symbols in a number of different ways. Several experts in the arts of speech, pantomime, stage design, and lighting may read an author's directions for a stage presentation and from them make quite dissimilar translations. Because the essential thing in creating a vision is the idea, or the effect, and not the precise form, each of these artists, if he is a good interpreter, will in his way be right; if his translation alone is placed

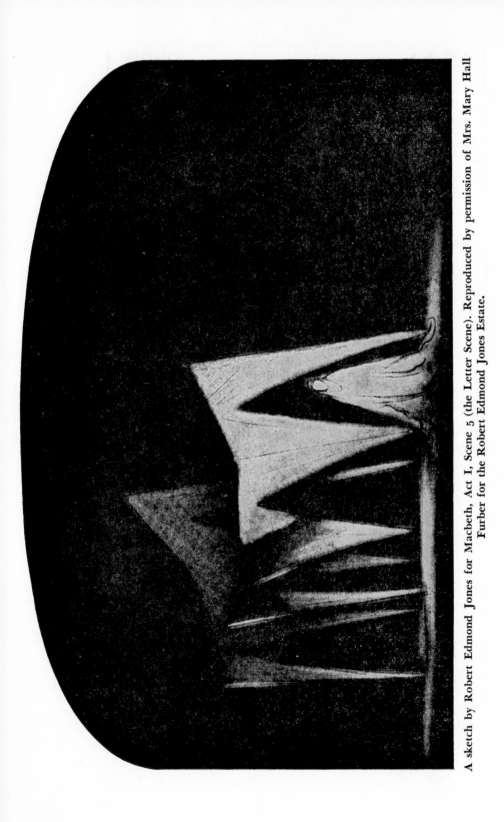

A sketch by Robert Edmond Jones for Macbeth, Act I, Scene 5 (the Letter Scene). Reproduced by permission of Mrs. Mary Hall Furber for the Robert Edmond Jones Estate.

on the stage, an audience will feel and see in it a true re-creation. If several dissimilar translations are placed on the stage at the same time, however, there can be only confusion; the effect produced will be like that of the proverbial orchestra composed of many excellent musicians but with no conductor. Re-created imagery then, if it is to be understood, must be unified in all its elements. In other words, the impression or effect a performance as a whole produces upon an audience must be *one*.

Herein lies the difference between the old and the new concept of the art of the theatre. Half a century ago dramatic art was considered to be a composite thing made by bringing together a number of loosely related, lesser arts. Sometimes the members of this group co-operated in a performance, but more often they competed against each other. Today the art of the theatre is better understood to be a single thing, a great art produced by the complete fusion of its several component arts—acting, dancing, music, costumes, scenery, properties, and lighting—all carefully orchestrated before they are placed before an audience. They are designed for the perfect co-ordination of emotional appeals. The conductor of this projected dramatic symphony is the director.

2. THE ELEMENT OF ACTION IN THE PRESENTATION

Play presentation, as we have said, is the business of re-creating an author's vision for his audience. The most important element of this re-created vision is *action*. By action we do not mean purely physical pantomime and speech; we mean the spirit of acting, that vital flow or *dramatic movement* which, through the medium of rhythmic speech and gesture, brings a play to life on the stage. The art of the actor (who is the special instrument of action) becomes naturally, then, the central art of play presentation. All the other interpretative arts of the theatre—music, scenery, lighting, and the rest—must be complementary and contributive to this first art. Says Sheldon Cheney in *Stage Decoration:* [1]

Any working definition of the art of the theatre today has to emphasize the presentation of a play by actors on a stage, through a flow of action, *with that fusion of all the contributive stage arts which makes the*

[1] Sheldon Cheney, *Stage Decoration* (New York, The John Day Company, Inc., 1928).

drama live for its audience at its highest possible emotional intensity.
Within this larger definition there should be special emphasis on
action as the essentially theatric core of the arts; but either action in
the sense of movement (as in early ritual drama and in the recently
highly developed dance-dramas), or in the sense of the unfolding of a
story or drama by actors using speech largely for expressiveness.

The study of scenery is, then, the study of one of those contributive arts that develop and enrich dramatic action.

But what does it contribute?

3. SCENERY, THE ENVIRONMENT OF ACTION

What exactly must scenery do for action?

One will be able to answer this question clearly only if he decides at the start just what is meant by the term *scenery*. The word
in the theatre today is used to represent two things. Employed in a
strictly technical sense it stands for painted draperies, screens, and
frames, and certain of their mechanical accessories, forms that
create the images of skies, walls, trees, and platforms. Used in a
broader sense, it means what Gordon Craig calls *scene:* all those
visual elements that surround an actor in his performance on the
stage—furniture and incidental objects (*properties*), costumes and
lighting, as well as the larger forms just mentioned. For the purpose of the study of scenery in relationship to play presentation,
let us in this chapter use the term in its broader sense.

Searching the written thoughts of the artists and critics of
modern stagecraft for their answers to the question of what is the
relationship between scenery and action in a play, one finds some
interesting opinions. The most quotable are those given in the
form of definitions. Scenery, or *scene,* says Gordon Craig, should
be the visual expression of the dynamic spirit of a play "in all that
comes before the eye." Adolphe Appia feels that scenery, in its
best sense, is the pattern of light and form which surrounds and
supports a living and active presence on the stage and adds to its
vitality. Lee Simonson has much the same view. Scenic art, he be-
lieves, is "the creation of plastic forms and spaces that are an
integral part of acting and project its meaning." Scenery, declares
Sheldon Cheney, must be "an adequate and appropriate background for theatric action." Kenneth Macgowan offers a similar

thought when he says that scenery should function as "an emotional envelope appropriate to the dramatic mood of the author, a visualization in color, line and light of the dominant emotions to be pictured by the actors." Robert Edmond Jones, one of America's leading designers, said simply that scenery should be an "environment" of action.

If one examines the array of ideas here presented he finds that through it all runs a single thought, a thought which is probably most clearly suggested by Jones's one word *environment*. A definition of the purpose of scenery that is representative of the best expression in the theatre today might be this: *In the organic design of play presentation, scenery should function as the helpful environment of theatric action.* Because most artists think of action and acting—from the practical standpoint of a performance —as being essentially the same thing, it may safely be concluded that it is the duty of scenery, through the use of suggestive and significant surrounding forms, to aid the actor in translating the spirit of the author's vision in the most effective manner possible.

Robert Edmond Jones frequently declared that he was most content when his settings (he created many beautiful ones) fitted a performance so perfectly that they were not noticed. In a foreword to his *Drawings for the Theatre* he said that a finished scene is one that will cause a spectator to remark to himself as the curtain rises, not, What a magnificent picture! but *"It is evident that this play we are about to see is no common play. It is evident that these men and women who will appear before us are no common mummers. These are Actors, Seers, Sayers. Let us honor them. For by their inspiration they intimate immortality."* [2]

4. FUNCTIONS OF THE ENVIRONMENT: PLACING THE ACTION

Scenery, as environment, assists the actor in several ways.

Environment implies place. The first function of scenery, then, is to locate the action—to give it a home. This it may do in one, or a combination of four different manners to suit the particular requirements of the play for which it is designed.

[2] Robert Edmond Jones, *Drawings for the Theatre* (New York, Theatre Arts, 1925).

A "realistic" setting, for instance, may be created to give a definite, lifelike portrayal of an actual or imaginary locality appropriate to the action:

The parlor of Abraham Lincoln's house at Springfield, Illinois, early in 1860. (John Drinkwater's *Abraham Lincoln*)

Exterior of the Farmhouse. (Eugene O'Neill's *Desire Under the Elms*)

Such a scene builds up an illusion of place by making use of purely imitative forms—"real" walls, "real" doors and windows, "real" moldings, furniture, and pictures. The artist who creates the setting attempts to make the spectator feel that he is gazing into the kind of sitting room or farmyard that actual people, not mere characters in a play, might use. The realistic and semirealistic plays of today and the near past—plays by such authors as Ibsen, Shaw, Galsworthy, the two Andersons, and Miller—are usually presented in settings of this type. To produce an effect of reality an imitative scene does not have to be a complete portrayal of natural forms. A good artist always avoids over-detailed, elaborate, photographic representation because it tends to clutter the stage and interfere with the acting. The best of the realistic settings today are very simple, with many elements of the scene left to the imagination of the spectator.

Then, a scenic environment may be created to place the action in a "suggestively realistic" way by intimating a locality without fully describing it.

Another chamber. (Almost any of Shakespeare's plays)

High in the hills, a late afternoon in spring. (Paul Green's *Wilderness Road*)

The scenery for this kind of a setting makes use of a few simple forms to stand for a complete picture—a Gothic bench and a chest in front of a tapestry may create the image of a room in an early English castle, or a rocky shape and a bit of sky may suggest a hilltop. Each form in the setting is a symbol for a whole group of other forms called up in the mind of the spectator; he is made to *feel* the presence of that which is not actually shown. In the production of *Romeo and Juliet* in which Jane Cowl and Rollo Peters played a few years ago, Capulet's house in the orchard was represented by a plain little balcony placed in a single panel in the center of the stage. The rest of the set consisted merely of soft, dark, neutral draperies and an effective lighting arrangement. That was all; but as soon as Romeo spoke, the sense of place was complete. Many types of plays, among them the classics and modern realistic works requiring considerable scene shifting, are set very effectively in environments which are only suggested by the scenery.

Again, the action may be placed "nonrealistically." In such a scene the emphasis is placed not on the representation of natural forms, but on the expression of an idea. The artist, in designing the scene, makes use of a distinct mode, or style—exaggerating or otherwise distorting certain colors, shapes, or proportions—in an effort to imply some inner characteristic of the author and his theme. The artist who interprets *Rip Van Winkle* as a fairy story and designs his settings for it in the whimsical manner of an illustration for *Jack and the Bean Stalk* employs a nonrealistic style. So does the artist who surrounds the action of Strindberg's *The Dream Play* with shapes suggesting the grotesque images seen in a nightmare. Everyone is familiar with the leaning walls, crooked doorways, and twisted shadows in the famous old German film, *The Cabinet of Dr. Caligari,* which indicate the distorted mental and emotional reactions of the central character to the world around him. All strongly expressionistic works—like Strindberg's *The Spook Sonata,* Walter Hasenclever's *Beyond,* Eugene O'Neill's *The Hairy Ape;* fantasies like J. M. Barrie's *Peter Pan;* burlesques like Beaumont and Fletcher's *Knight of the Burning Pestle;* psychological studies like Shakespeare's *Hamlet* and *Macbeth* or Paul Green's *Tread the Green Grass*—call for nonrealistic settings.

In a fourth manner the action of a play may be placed in a purely "formal" setting. This type of scene marks a place for the action, but does not attempt to represent any given locality. It is always designed very simply, usually in plain architectural forms such as walls, steps, and platforms. This type of scenery adapts itself to the presentation of certain classical and romantic plays, as well as some modern poetic works.

Two ways of placing the action of a play. Above: realistic scenery in *Sabrina Fair*, produced by Oregon State College. Below: suggestively realistic scenery in *Billy the Kid* (an original play) produced by the Carolina Playmakers, University of North Carolina.

Two additional ways of placing the action. Above: a non-realistic setting in *Tiger Rag,* produced by the University Theatre, University of Illinois, and designed by George W. McKinney. Below: formal scenery in *Murder in the Cathedral,* presented by the Carolina Playmakers and designed by Robert Burrows.

5. FUNCTIONS OF THE ENVIRONMENT: REINFORCING THE ACTION

The second general function of scenery as environment is to help explain and to give significance to the action of a play. This might be called *reinforcing* the action.

Well-designed scenery may support the action of a play in a number of ways. It may supplement the action by reflecting the characters' personalities. The general appearance of a room, for example, may tell something about the tastes and habits of the people who live in it. The general tidiness in which the characters keep the room, the color they paint the walls, the kind of chairs they like to sit in, the kind of tools and utensils they use, the incidental, intimate objects they have lying about—all may indicate personality, just as in real life. There are a hundred ways in which surroundings may reveal the thought and explain the behavior of the characters. An example of character explanation through scenery was offered in two rooms which Robert Edmond Jones once designed for Philip Barry's *Holiday*. One, a sitting room, was a large rectangular room of the Stanford White period, with heavily paneled walls, massive moldings, tall windows, formal curtains, and stern portraits. It was "a handsome room, and quite a comfortable room, but very, very rich." The other, a playroom, was an airy, low-ceilinged place with white woodwork, pale blue walls covered with story-book designs, trapezes, and toys; it was a thoroughly unconventional, casual room. The two rooms characterized perfectly the two elements of the family of Seton that lived in them.

Scenery may also explain action by symbolizing it in such forms as the falling leaves and fading daylight at the close of Cyrano's romance in *Cyrano de Bergerac,* or in the rock and mist of Gordon Craig's conception of a set for *Macbeth.*

I see two things. I see a lofty and steep rock, and I see a moist cloud which envelops the head of this rock. That is to say, a place for fierce and warlike men to inhabit, a place for phantoms to nest in. Ultimately the moisture will destroy the rock; ultimately these spirits will destroy the men.

In his interpretation of the same play for Arthur Hopkins, Robert Edmond Jones hung three large masks above the stage in several scenes to remind the audience of the ever-present influence of the three witches.

Scenery helps to describe conditions surrounding the action. By the use of appropriate lighting and certain indicative objects, such as fireplaces and lamps, scenery may describe the time of day and season, and the general weather conditions. By the shape, color, and physical condition of the scenery—walls, furniture, clothes, and so on—the economic and social status of the characters might be indicated. Or again, scenery may tell or intimate some of the dramatic circumstances in the situation. Consider the gallows with its background of redcoat uniforms in the last act of Shaw's *The Devil's Disciple,* or the tomb filled with its dense shadows in *Romeo and Juliet.* Forms that describe physical and dramatic conditions in this way help also to reveal personality by supplying a framework on which the characters can base their reactions. The two rooms in *Holiday,* just described, served this purpose. Linda revealed herself constantly by her contrasting reactions to the two rooms.

Then, too, scenery may create *atmosphere* for the action. For example, it may cause the audience to view the action in a warm, sympathetic frame of mind. Consider, for instance, a setting for the famous little love scene in the avenue to Portia's house in the last act of *The Merchant of Venice,* suggested by Lorenzo's lines to Jessica:

> How sweet the moonlight sleeps upon this bank!
> Here we will sit and let the sounds of music
> Creep in our ears. Soft stillness and the night . . .

A setting designed in the spirit of these lines would itself build up a romantic attitude toward the two lovers even before Lorenzo spoke. It would create the *atmosphere.* It would make each spectator think to himself: "A moonlit garden is a place for love; in such unusually soft and expressive moonlight, in such a beautiful garden, these two young people must be very deeply in love." Atmospheric scenery is what might be called emotional scenery. Its elements, both individually and collectively, convey an emotional impression. Each of these scenic elements symbolically suggests sadness, or loneliness, or weariness, or joy, or laughter, and puts the spectator in the proper mood for the action of the play. In a setting for the scene in the convent park in the last act of

Cyrano de Bergerac, for example, the soft fall of leaves, the quiet movement of black-gowned nuns, and the light slowly fading through the trees, all help the audience to understand how the old soldier's poetical life is finally drawing to a close. All scenery that suggests in one way or another the thoughts and feelings of the characters that move within it has *atmosphere.* Gordon Craig's mist-covered rock in *Macbeth,* the two contrasting rooms in *Holiday,* as well as the strange surroundings of *The Cabinet of Dr. Caligari*—all are atmospheric. They attune the audience to the proper mood for drama.

6. FUNCTIONS OF THE ENVIRONMENT: DRESSING THE ACTION

The third (and by no means least important) function of scenery is to make the action of a play pictorially attractive. This function of scenery might be termed *dressing* the action. By means of an appealing composition in line and color, scenery provides a background of pleasant design, and so adds greatly to the appreciation of the action. This is a very important function of scenery. If scenery does not adorn, because it is ugly, it cannot properly be called environmental. Flat, monotonous backgrounds painted in lifeless browns and grays are both tiresome and irritating to look at; they detract attention from the acting, and thus weaken instead of strengthen it. For this reason even the setting for a play that demands drab surroundings is rightly designed with life and interest in its elements of line and color. The artist handles these two elements in such a way as to *intimate* the subdued mood of the action without actually lowering the warmth of the picture. In fact, he may make use of those very details which indicate age and poverty—stained walls, worn woodwork, broken furniture, and shadows—to heighten, instead of to lower, the picturesque qualities of his design.

It is perhaps significant that many English-speaking artists have, for three hundred years, employed the term *stage decoration* as a synonym for scenic art. Continental artists have made use of a similar word, *décor.*

7. THE FOUR ELEMENTS OF THE STAGE SETTING

Designing a "stage setting" (a complete set of scenery in the comprehensive sense—see Section 3) involves planning and co-ordinating four related elements: (1) scenery (in the limited technical sense)—background forms that represent walls, archways, the sky, trees, fences, and the like; (2) properties—furniture and incidental objects; (3) costumes—clothes worn by the actors; and (4) lighting—specialized illumination.

1. Scenery (in its limited sense) forms a physical background for, and places the location of, the action.

2. Properties make the scene intimate by relating it directly to human action. Properties have a strong dramatic value as the objects which the characters handle, and as those upon which they sit or lie and about which they talk. Properties can frequently place the action quite specifically. Also, by entering into the mass and line composition of the scene they become an integral part of the total set design. A bookcase, cupboard, or mirror in an interior setting, for instance, may be as important a feature in a wall arrangement as a door. A long, low table or couch may be employed to give the right line of contrast to a tall, narrow panel —and so on. Properties also enter very obviously into the color composition of a scene. With the present tendency to keep the larger areas of the background fairly neutral and to accent only the smaller objects placed in it or in front of it, a set generally looks very bare until it has been dressed up with furniture, window hangings, table covers, books, or flowers.

3. Costumes, too, play a vital part in the composition of a stage design. Color here, if properly handled, has the same value as color in properties—often more, because it has the added advantage of being constantly in motion. Costumes have been termed, very appropriately, "scenery worn by actors." The most pronounced accents in the whole scene are often found in these bits of moving scenery.

4. Light is one of the artist's most valuable means of design; it is placed first by some designers. By the manipulation of color, highlights, and shadows, light helps powerfully to compose the tone, mass, and line elements of the scene and so to intensify its

dramatic values. (The principles of designing by light are outlined in Part II of this book.)

In the ideal, and the only fully logical plan of scenic design, a single artist conceives the entire setting. He designs the scenery, selects the properties (or has them made), plans the costumes, and works out the lighting. Because of certain difficulties in modern production, however, especially in the preparation of elaborate costume plays, it is not always possible for one man to do all of the detailed, creative planning in each of the four departments of design. Nevertheless, if the final environmental expression is to be unified, it is imperative that the initial conception and the general supervision of the entire work be that of one artist.

The study of scenic art in Part I of this book is centered on the construction, painting, and assembling of scenery (in the limited sense of the term). But because the planning of scenery cannot very easily be disengaged from a consideration of properties, costumes, and lighting (especially the first), these three complementary elements must always be felt to be involved at least indirectly in any consideration of scenic design mentioned in the following chapters.

8. REQUIREMENTS OF THE STAGE SETTING

The stage setting—the visual environment of the action of a play—should be so designed, as has been stated, that it will place, reinforce, and dress the action. The designer should, therefore, plan the set so that it (1) places the action, (2) expresses the mood and spirit of the play, (3) is pleasing to look at, (4) can be seen and understood by the audience, (5) is simple in design, (6) can withstand continued usage by the actors, (7) can be efficiently constructed, assembled, and handled, and (8) is related in design to the other contributive elements in the proposed presentation of the play. In brief, the designer should aim to make the setting:

1. locative	5. simple
2. expressive	6. utilitarian
3. attractive	7. practicable
4. clear	8. organic

9. MAKING THE SETTING LOCATIVE AND EXPRESSIVE

A stage setting should be first, *locative,* and second, *expressive.* That is, (*a*) it should place the action realistically, suggestively realistically, nonrealistically, or formally; and (*b*) it should reinforce the action by explaining it, describing the conditions surrounding it, and creating atmosphere for it. How the artist may design a locative and expressive scene has already been dealt with in Sections 4 and 5 of this chapter. Several typical arrangements of expressive settings are illustrated in Chapter 2, Sections 4 through 7.

10. MAKING THE SETTING ATTRACTIVE

Third, a stage setting designed to be the environment of the action of a play (Section 3) should be *attractive.* By the use of pleasing shapes and colors it should set off the action and make it appear at all times visually appealing. The artist must select for the design of his scene objects which have interesting and graceful qualities, and arrange these according to the rules of good composition.

A well-composed scene has, first, *unity.* All of its parts (the mass, line, and color of the larger units of scenery, the properties, the costumes, and the lighting) should appear to belong together; they should all create an environment particularly appropriate to the action. The environment desired for the first act of Philip Barry's *Holiday* (Section 5), for example, is that of a "handsome room, and quite a comfortable room, but very, very rich." The idea in a design for the first act of *You and I* by the same author, on the other hand, would be "a huge, uneven, motherly sort of room that pats your hand as you come into it, and tells you to sit down and be comfortable with the rest of us." Securing unity in a design involves, then, (*a*) the selection of only those elements which relate to one another and contribute to the specific environment desired; (*b*) the arrangement of the elements chosen into a plan that emphasizes that feature, or group of features (the "motifs"), which most clearly express the environment; and (*c*) the maintenance of a single style throughout the design. A unified scene may be said to be one that is *well focused.*

Also, a well-composed scene has *variety*. It avoids monotonous repetition. Identical shapes and colors should not appear everywhere. Forms with vertical lines are varied with forms with horizontal lines, round objects are varied with square objects, intense colors are varied with neutral colors, light colors with dark colors (Chapter 6, Sections 6 and 7), and so on. Contrast is introduced to make the design alive and interesting. If, for example, in designing a scene to represent a sitting room the doors and windows are made square, certain other details may be rounded; if one color, somewhat neutral, is selected for the walls, another quite dissimilar one, somewhat brighter than the first, may be chosen for the window hangings, table covers, certain pieces of pottery, lampshades, and other objects that stand in front of the walls. Variety cannot be demanded at the expense of unity. If, however, the primary motif is allowed to dominate at all times, there is little danger of losing unity through contrast and variety in the elements of the design. In fact, by their very difference from the main motif they will have a tendency to call attention to it.

A well-composed scene has *balance*. The prominent architectural features (such as the doors and windows), the larger pieces of furniture, and all the other objects of special pictorial or dramatic interest should be so distributed on the two sides of the stage that they weigh against each other more or less equally. Color, too, must conform to the principle of balance.

Finally, the well-composed scene has *harmony*. In it all of the different elements combine to make an attractive whole. This is the result of successfully applying the first three principles of good composition, namely, unity, variety, and balance.

11. MAKING THE SETTING CLEAR

Fourth, the stage setting should be *clear*. That is, it should be designed in such a way that it will be seen and understood at a distance. The majority of the members of the audience must view the stage picture from seats placed twenty to seventy-five or more feet away. Because the picture must be appreciated at a distance, it is clear that all parts of its design must be exaggerated. Line and color forms must be large. Fussy details that cannot be seen easily from a position in the audience, and hence tend to confuse the more important elements of the scene, should be omitted, and emphasis should be placed on the larger effects. A wallpaper pattern which in a real home would be composed of a dozen small figures on a dozen neutral colors, for example, might be reduced for use on the stage to three larger figures and three brighter colors. A body of foliage might be rendered in large masses of green, rather than in individual leaf forms. If a set of scenery is to project well across the footlights, it must possess the quality of "bigness" in all its parts.

12. MAKING THE SETTING SIMPLE

Fifth, the stage setting should be *simple.* Knowing that scenery cannot be fully locative, expressive, attractive, or clear if its plan is not readily grasped, the artist should endeavor to keep the design of scenery uncomplicated. He should select only those elements which will contribute to the development of the main idea, eliminate everything that is not related and essential, and then compose the elements he has retained into an orderly, unified, significant stage setting.

A point should be noted here, however: *a simple design need not be a bare one.* This fact very often is not appreciated. Simplicity is often—and quite incorrectly—associated with meagerness. It makes little difference whether a stage setting is composed of five lines and one color or fifty lines and ten colors; it is simple if its plan is uncomplicated—that is, if the spectator can grasp without effort the thought and emotion it has been designed to express.

The artist attempts to make his scenery simple, not only dramatically but also technically. He plans it so that it can be constructed, painted, and assembled with a minimum waste of time and materials.

13. MAKING THE SETTING UTILITARIAN

Sixth, the stage setting should be *utilitarian.* It should be planned so that it can be used efficiently and effectively by the actors. The artist must provide, in the places where they are most needed, the entrances, exits, platforms, steps, chairs, tables, and other means for walking, standing, sitting, and lying down demanded by the action. He must see that his scenery is not only effective for action, but also safe and strong enough for action. He should make certain that a platform that must bear the weight of a number of people is properly reinforced, that a wall or door against which an actor is to fall at some moment in the play is properly braced, and so on. All these points he must work out carefully with the director.

14. MAKING THE SETTING PRACTICABLE

Seventh, a set of scenery should be *practicable*. It must be capable of being efficiently constructed, assembled, and handled. In other words, it must fulfill the general technical requirements of scenery construction, and it must meet the specific technical demands of a particular stage (or class of stages, if the scenery is planned for touring).

To make the set of scenery fulfill the general construction requirements it must be designed so that it can be

a. easily and rapidly constructed,
b. economically constructed,
c. quickly and silently shifted,
d. protected against strain and wear,
e. well assembled,
f. packed or stored away after the performance.

This means that the artist must plan his scenery so that it can be constructed, as nearly as possible, in accordance with the standard methods outlined in Chapter 4.

To make the set of scenery meet the specific technical demands of a particular stage (or group of stages), the artist must consider the shape and amount of space (Chapter 2, Sections 2 and 10) and the shifting facilities (Chapter 7, Sections 5–12) available.

The set must be capable of being placed on a particular stage in such a way that

The sight lines are good (Chapter 2, Section 10).
The wings, the flies, and all other parts of the stage or scenery that are not supposed to be seen, are properly masked (Chapter 2, Section 10).

There is space for packing the scenery that is not in use in a given act. There is space for the manipulation of properties, lighting apparatus, and actors.

Before starting to design his set, then, the artist must thoroughly familiarize himself with the size and shape of the stage on which the scenery is to be set up, including:

The width of the stage.
The depth of the stage (from the curtain line).
The width and height of the proscenium opening (with the tormentors and teaser in positions for good sight lines).
The height of the gridiron (if units must be flied out of sight).
The height of the fly floor (if tall units must be placed under it).

The set must be capable of being shifted, on the particular stage, efficiently and safely. Before starting to design the scenery, therefore, the artist should become familiar with the character of the stage equipment, including:

The number of sets of lines.
The strength of the lines.
The strength of the loft and head blocks.
The strength of the grid supports.
The arrangement of any counterweighting devices.
The strength of the stage floor.
The arrangement of any special shifting devices.
The arrangement of storage spaces.

Chapter 2 outlines the usual plans for placing scenery on the stage, and Chapter 7 the standard methods of changing scenery.

15. MAKING THE SETTING ORGANIC

Eighth and finally, the stage setting should be *organic*. The design of the scenery, in character and purpose, should be carefully subordinated to the plan of the play presentation as a whole (Sections 1–3). If unity is required in the lesser, purely decorative phase of the design (Section 10), there certainly must be unity in its greater, over-all phase (Section 1). The scenic artist must therefore co-operate at all times with the director and other artists of the theatre in the mutual effort to produce that one unified impression which will best express to the audience the thought and spirit of the play and make possible its full enjoyment.

The fact that *environment*, vital as it is, can never rightfully occupy the place of first importance on the stage is a point which ambitious young designers frequently forget. So keenly do they become interested in the purely picturesque character of a stage setting that they lose sight of the living, human element (expressed through *action*) that must be placed within scenery to give it its real significance. An unusually brilliant background wall, a startlingly vivid expanse of sky, a peculiar arrangement of proportions and colors, or an odd handling of light may give scenery a striking appearance when viewed alone, but make it fail in its purpose when viewed with actors. In such a situation the attention of the audience is drawn to the surrounding scenery, away from the thing surrounded, and the *environment* loses its essential character. The implication here is not that good scenery should be undistinguished—forceful effects are often appropriate, and even necessary—but that in the organic design of a presentation one should recognize that scenery's position is always that of the servant, rather than the master, of the *action*. This point cannot be stressed too strongly.

16. NEW DIRECTIONS IN SCENIC DESIGN

The upheaval of political, social, and economic forces in any age is always accompanied by changes in aesthetic thinking. These changes are especially in evidence today. There is a constant shift of form in the arts, in literature, music, painting, and sculpture, as well as in playwriting, acting, directing, and stage design.

Although much of the scenery one sees on the stage today remains discreetly in the background, some of it behaves quite differently. Among the new directions which design is taking is one that puts scenic images in the midst of the dramatic movement, making the setting an integral part of the action of the play.

Other designers are moving in the opposite direction, trying to reduce the scenic forms to a minimum and to force the actor, with the aid of light, to depend more and more on his own resources. The player is made to use steps, platforms, and other simple shapes in such a way as to emphasize forcefully the contours and motions of his own body.

Some of the most experimental scenic forms are now being developed in our musical productions. These, together with other shapes derived from the films, are influencing our dramatic settings. A growing interest in psychological effects is pushing the artist into new fields of creativity. The evolving architecture of the playhouse, the use of open and multiple stages, the demand for epic outdoor presentations, and the availability of new materials are continually calling for a reappraisal of the artist's whole approach to theatrical design.

17. A SUMMARY

This chapter, which attempts to analyze the objectives of scenery in the theatre, has shown that the whole process of play presentation must be considered as a unit made up of such elements as acting, dancing, music, scenery, costumes, and lighting, all co-operating under the guidance of the director to produce a single emotional effect upon the audience. At the heart of the design is dramatic action. It is the purpose of scenery, one of the contributive arts, to place the action, to reinforce the action, and to dress the action. The artist who designs a set of scenery is successful when he makes it locative, expressive, attractive, clear, simple, utilitarian, practicable, and organic, in a style appropriate to the thought and feeling of the play.

To meet the varying demands of an ever-changing theatre, the designer and his scenic collaborators must be imaginative, resourceful, co-operative, and flexible. Much as they may be tempted to make their work central in the playhouse, they must remember that the dominant figure is the actor. Scenery exists not to give him competition, but to explain and support his performance.

Common Forms
in Scenery

1. INTRODUCTION

BEFORE THE scenic artist attempts to design or to construct scenery he must know its anatomy thoroughly. Shapes will change from setting to setting, of course, but the basic elements will remain the same.

This chapter examines briefly two things: the standard features of a conventional proscenium type stage, and the regular parts of the set of scenery which would be built for this stage. There will be some discussion of novel staging in Chapter 9. Scenic artists preparing to work with experimental factors would be wise to become thoroughly familiar with conventional staging, since in the theatre much of the new is derived from the old and constantly borrows from it—not only its forms but also its materials and dramatic devices.

2. THE TOPOGRAPHY OF A TYPICAL STAGE

The transverse wall dividing the auditorium from the stage is the *proscenium* (Figures 1 and 2). The opening in this wall, whether rounded or square at the top, through which one sees the stage, is called the *proscenium opening*. The architecture of the opening is the *proscenium arch*. Behind the proscenium wall, the spaces offstage to each side are the *wings*—that to the right. facing the audience, the *right wing*, that to the left, the *left wing*. Here are located the exit to dressing rooms, the loading door through which scenery is brought in and taken out, often a door to a special property room, the control board (usually in older theatres), the counterweight system—if the equipment includes

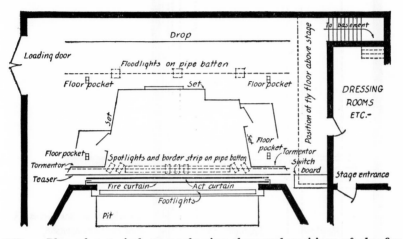

FIG. 1. Plan of a typical stage, showing the usual positions of the fire and act curtains, the teaser, tormentors, footlight trough, overhead lighting instruments, loading door, fly floor, and other features, and a set of scenery in place. This stage is 52 feet wide and 28 feet deep with a proscenium opening of 28 feet. Commonly the front of the stage extends out a little beyond the curtain line in the form of an apron. (See Fig. 2.)

this (Chapter 7, Section 8)—stacks of scenery, properties, lighting apparatus, safety devices, a clock, and the stage manager's prompt desk. The floor of the stage is of softwood boarding, usually tongue-and-groove fir or yellow pine, laid parallel to the proscenium from the front to the back wall. It is frequently pierced by *traps* that open into the basement to permit the use of sunken stairways, and so forth, and is usually covered during a performance by a large piece of heavy waterproof duck called a *ground cloth*. The *footlight trough* is located along the edge of the stage floor nearest the audience.

At the top of the space above the proscenium, known as the

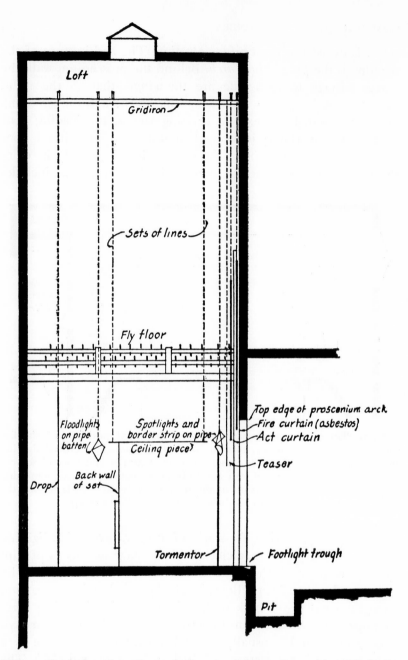

Loft

Gridiron

Sets of lines

Fly floor

Floodlights on pipe batten

Spotlights and border strip on pipe
Ceiling piece

Top edge of proscenium arch
Fire curtain (asbestos)
Act curtain

Teaser

Drop

Back wall of set

Tormentor

Footlight trough

Pit

FIG. 2. Vertical section of a typical stage, showing the positions of the fire and act curtains, teaser, one tormentor, footlight trough, overhead lighting units, fly floor, gridiron, and other features, and a set of scenery in place. This stage is 28 feet deep (from the curtain line), and the gridiron is 60 feet above the floor. (See Fig. 1.)

flies, is the *gridiron* or *grid,* a steel or wooden framework of open beams placed five to ten feet below the roof, forty to a hundred or more feet above the stage, and extending over the entire working area. From this frame is suspended all the hanging scenery such as drops, borders, and tree trunks, as well as certain lighting units. *Sets of lines* are attached to each hanging piece, passed over pulley blocks in the grid, brought down, and tied off on a double row of belaying pins, called the *pin rail,* on the *fly floor.* The fly floor is a shelf, or narrow gallery, extending along the wall of one of the wings some distance above the main floor. A more detailed description of the gridiron and the fly floor will be found in Chapter 7, Section 5. In many of the newer theatres the fly floor, with its pin rail, has been omitted and all hanging scenery is handled with a *counterweight system* operated from the floor. This method is described in Chapter 7, Section 8. Under the general subject of flies mention might be made also of the occasional *bridges* found in some theatres. These are light, narrow steel frames which, extending across the stage, may be fixed, moved on tracks, or suspended from the grid some distance above the floor, and are now used principally for mounting overhead lighting units.

We have just considered the stage and some of the permanent, built-in equipment. Now let us look at the principal adjustable "masking pieces." Returning to the proscenium opening—the two perpendicular and movable screens that mask from the audience the spaces on each side between the downstage edges of a set and the proscenium arch are the *tormentors.* These, together with the horizontal screen or mask known as the *teaser*—usually a simple, dark-colored border or piece of drapery suspended above, between the arch and the tormentors—form an adjustable inner frame for the stage picture. The *act curtain,* or *house curtain,* closes the proscenium opening between the arch and this inner frame. On most larger stages the curtain is of the *drop type* (Figure 3), suspended from the gridiron and rigged, balanced, and operated by an endless rope on the same general principle as a unit of the counterweight system (Chapter 7, Section 8 and Figure 66). Other common curtains, used more frequently on small stages, are the *draw* type (Figure 4), in which two sections, parting in the middle and tied to a number of wooden or fiber wheels, moving in a slotted track called a *traveller,* are pulled on and off without raising or lowering the curtain as a whole; and the *tableau* or *tab* type (Figure 6), in which the two sections are gathered up at the sides.

Fire regulations in most cities require that every theatre, com-

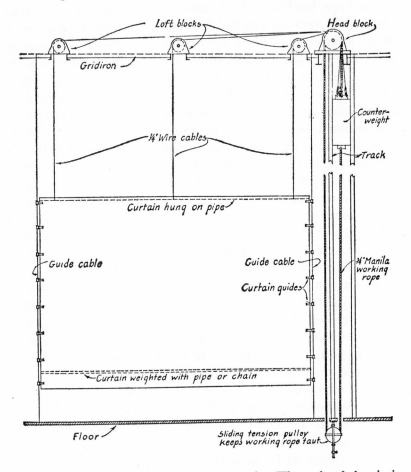

FIG. 3. Working principles of the drop curtain. (The scale of the rigging parts in relationship to the curtain in this picture has been exaggerated somewhat in order to make clear the way in which the parts work.)

mercial or otherwise, be equipped also with a steel or asbestos *fire curtain*. It hangs in front of the house curtain and, when dropped, completely seals the proscenium opening.

One should remember that in all references to positions on the stage floor, *downstage* means toward the audience and *upstage* means away from the audience. *Onstage* is toward the center of the stage, *offstage* is toward the wings or the rear wall. *Right* and *left* are determined from the point of view, not of the audience, but of the actor facing the audience.

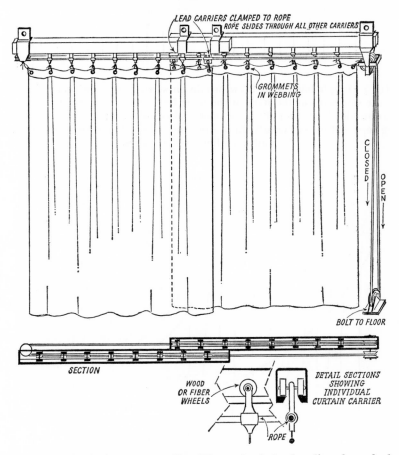

FIG. 4. Draw curtain on a traveller. The path of the drawline through the traveller is indicated in the diagram below the curtain.

3. UNIT SCENERY

After dramatic and decorative requirements have been considered, scenery must be designed for ease and rapidity of assembling and shifting on the stage (Chapter 1, Section 14). The interest of an audience can be held effectively during a performance only if

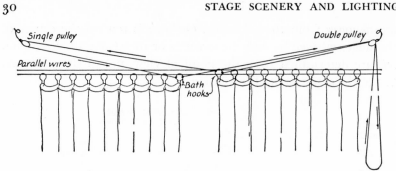

FIG. 5. Simple homemade draw curtain on wires. The two wires are fastened to the side walls of the stage at the same level and drawn taut by means of turnbuckles. The two pulleys are shown raised so that the path of the operating rope will be seen clearly. In practice the pulleys should be attached to the walls on a line with the wires.

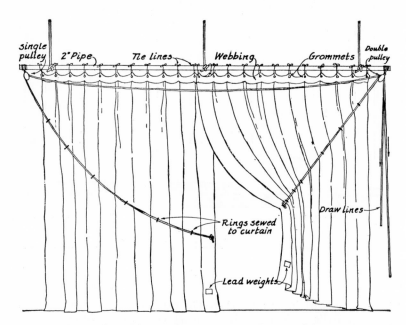

FIG. 6. Tab curtain. This curtain is not generally so satisfactory for closing the front of the stage as the drop or the draw curtain.

the time required for changing the scenery is reduced to a minimum. Because most modern stages are comparatively small and changes still have to be made by hand, the unit system in scenic construction is almost universally employed. Each set of scenery, whether simple or elaborate, is built up of a number of wood and canvas screens, platforms, and other light-frame pieces, which are so designed that they may be assembled or taken apart quickly and easily. Every unit of standard-built scenery has a maximum width of only 5′ 9″ when packed. This dimension (plus three inches allowed for clearance) is the exact size of the freight car door through which all units must pass when the play goes on tour. The maximum width of 5′ 9″ offers a number of other advantages in construction and handling—at home as well as on the road. For one thing, frames of this size are easy to cover (Chapter 4, Section 9), and for another, they are easy to assemble and shift, and to store away (Chapter 7, Section 13).

The most common forms of unit scenery may be grouped under five general headings:

A. **Standing Units:**

> *flat (plain)*—A tall screen made of wood and canvas, with a standard width of 5′ 9″, but no standard height, used as a section of a wall. (Figure 33)
>
> *door flat*—a flat with an opening for a door frame. (Figure 34)
>
> *window flat*—a flat with an opening for a window frame. (Figure 34)
>
> *fireplace flat*—a flat with an opening for a fireplace frame. (Figure 34)
>
> *jog*—a narrow flat. (Chapter 5, Section 4)
>
> *two-fold*—two flats hinged together to fold inward, face to face. (Chapter 5, Section 4)
>
> *three-fold*—three flats hinged in the same way. (Chapter 5, Section 4)
>
> *return*—two flats hinged together to fold outward, back to back. (Chapter 5, Section 4)
>
> *door frame unit*—a solid wood door frame made to fit in a flat designed for it. (Figure 35)
>
> *window frame unit*—a solid wood window frame made for a similar purpose. (Figure 38)
>
> *fireplace unit*—a fireplace frame, not always solid, made for a similar purpose. (Figure 40)
>
> *archway*—a flat with an arched opening, usually constructed with a detachable thickness. (Figure 41)

B. **Hanging Units:**

> *ceiling*—a large, horizontal, canvas-covered frame, suspended by a

set of lines from the grid, used to close the top of an interior
scene. (Figure 42)

drop—a large sheet of canvas, partly or fully framed, suspended
vertically on a set of lines from the grid—commonly used to
represent the sky. (Figure 44)

border—an abbreviated drop, occasionally used to represent foliage or to mask the flies. (Figure 44)

tab—a sheet of canvas or other material, framed or unframed,
smaller than a drop but suspended like it, used for a variety
of purposes. (Figure 44)

cyclorama—a large curtain of canvas, or other material, hung
from a horizontal U-shaped wood or metal frame suspended
by a set of lines from the grid—commonly used to represent
the sky in exterior scenes, as well as for a number of other purposes. (Figures 12 and 46)

C. Built Units:

platform—a collapsible and portable frame platform constructed
in unit sections. (Figure 48) Some small platforms are rigid.

steps—a light, portable run of steps constructed in unit sections.
(Figure 49)

column—a light frame or canvas column. (Figure 50)

tree—a light frame or canvas tree trunk. (Figure 50)

rock—a light, irregular frame-and-canvas imitation of a rock,
made in unit sections. (Figure 51)

built-up ground—a similar imitation of a bank of earth.

D. Set Units:

ground row—a flat profile of a bank of earth, or a distant mountain, painted on thin three-ply veneer board, cut out, framed
behind, and made to stand up independently on the floor.
(Figure 52)

fence or wall—a frame imitation of a fence or wall, designed to
stand up independent of other units on the floor. (Figure 53)

set house, etc.—various frame units, designed like the fence to
stand up independently. (Figure 54)

E. Draperies:

Under this head may be listed a variety of curtain units, largely
unframed.

These units might be called the "standard parts" of scenery.
Many non-standard forms must be designed to meet special demands, but the units listed are used exclusively in most plays.

The three principal methods by which the units may be fastened together—employing the lash-line, the loose-pin hinge, and the bolt—are described in Chapter 4, Section 10.

4. THE ARRANGEMENT OF SCENERY

In the preceding section are listed twenty-seven basic forms of unit scenery. The number of designs into which these standard parts may be assembled is almost limitless. Flats, door, window, and fireplace units, ceilings, drops, and frequently steps, columns and other units may be combined to represent descriptive indoor scenes in a wide variety of shapes and styles; while drops or cycloramas, trees, fences, ground rows, and frequently flats, columns, and other units may be put together to suggest realistic out-of-door scenes with equal variety. These or other units, again, may be combined to make suggestive, nonrealistic, or formal backgrounds.

There is no standard arrangement of standard parts. Certain general arrangements are, however, characteristic of some of the more common scenes. Five examples typical of their kind—two frame indoor settings, called *interiors,* two frame outdoor settings, called *exteriors,* and one drapery cyclorama setting—are described in the following three sections. When the reader studies the five settings he must bear in mind that they represent scenic environment stated in very simple terms. An intelligent artist who wishes to make use of the principles suggested here may adapt and elaborate as he pleases in his own designs.

5. TWO TYPICAL INTERIOR SETTINGS

The simplest form of interior that makes use of a full set of descriptive scenery is the *box set.* This represents any ordinary chamber—bedroom, sitting room, kitchen, or hall—with three walls and a ceiling. Figure 7 shows the front view and plan of a typical box set. The walls in this example are made up of seven flats placed edge to edge—two on each side and three at the back —which are laced together by means of lash lines thrown over lash cleats (Chapter 4, Section 10) and braced from the floor, where necessary, by stage braces (Chapter 7, Section 3). The flats up right, and down left and center back are pierced with holes to

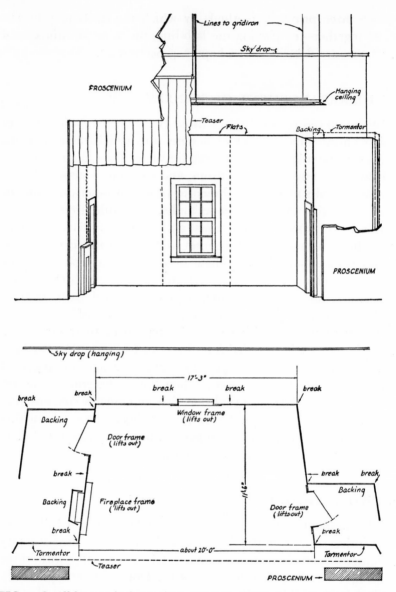

FIG. 7. Small box set in front view and plan, showing a typical arrangement of walls, door, window and fireplace units, ceiling, sky drop, backings and front masking pieces.

accommodate solid door and window frames, which are clamped in position when setting the scene and may be removed from the flats in "striking" (taking down) the scenery. A fireplace frame is placed in a similar way in the flat down right. A ceiling piece hung on two or three sets of lines closes in the room above. A sky drop acts as a background for the view through the window and two-fold backings, or spare flats lashed together, shield the views through the doors. The front edge of the set all the way around is framed in by means of the adjustable teaser and tormentors.

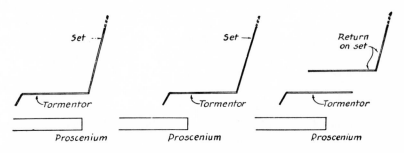

FIG. 8. The tormentor and the return. These diagrams show how the prosce-nium opening may be opened out or narrowed on each side by shifting the position of the tormentor, or by making use of an additional return. If side lighting units on standards are required on a set they are frequently placed between the tormentor and the return. In this case a 12-inch or 18-inch thick-ness is usually placed on the onstage edge of the tormentor to shield the light from the audience, and the return is pulled back to allow the lighting unit to be angled freely onto the set. A teaser (see Fig. 7) serves as an adjustable masking piece above.

Because the square box set is so plain in shape, it is seldom used now without some adapting. A turn is given to the walls, an alcove is added, or another room is made to open off the set in an un-usual way, in order to give the set a little new interest. In the floor plan in Figure 9, for instance, the right and rear wall have been set on a bias in order to give the impression that one is looking into the corner rather than into the flat side of the room. Also, a jog has been introduced into the back wall in order to keep it from being perfectly straight. Except for these features the room is quite conventional and would be suitable for a variety of settings.

There is, of course, no standard size or shape for interiors of the general type represented by the two settings described here. They may consist of any number of flats and be of any reasonable height,

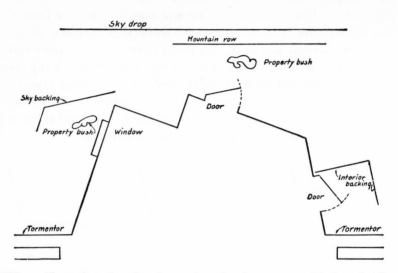

FIG. 9. Floor plan of an interior setting, showing a room with doors leading to the outside and to another part of the house.

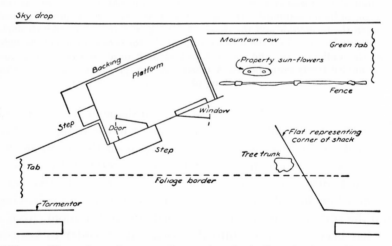

FIG. 10. Floor plan of an exterior setting, including the front of a small country store, and a view of distant mountains against the sky.

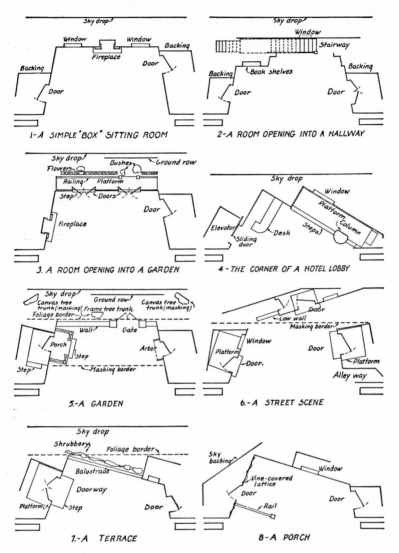

FIG. 11. Floor plans of several different types of interior and exterior settings.

depending only on stage conditions and the size of the proscenium opening. Four other typical arrangements of indoor scenery are diagramed in Figure 11.

6. TWO TYPICAL EXTERIOR SETTINGS

A simple arrangement of scenery to represent an out-of-door setting is shown in the country post office scene diagramed in the floor plan in Figure 10. The set consists of seven flats and two jogs arranged in the manner shown in the drawing. The store front is made up of three flats and one jog lashed together and braced (see preceding section); the backing is made up of three other flats and a jog; and the face of the shed at the left uses the other flat. A

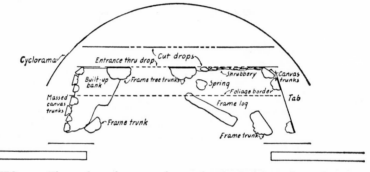

FIG. 12. Floor plan of an exterior setting backed by a sky cyclorama.

solid door and a solid window are placed in the flats cut for them. There are also a raised doorstep in front of the store, with a low platform inside to continue the raised level; a set fence and a set bed of sunflowers, at the side; a frame tree trunk down left; and a sky drop. A painted profile mountain row is placed at the foot of the sky drop both to mask the lower batten of the drop and to add pictorial interest to the background. Because no ceiling piece can be used in this exterior, the tops of the flats at the right are continued up far enough behind the teaser to be out of sight, and a cut-out foliage border—hung across the stage with its fullness at the left—is used to mask the view up into the flies at the left.

Another simple exterior arrangement, which in this case makes use of a sky cyclorama instead of a drop, is illustrated in the floor plan for the turpentine grove in Figure 12. It is made up simply of a few frame tree trunks and a built-up bank of earth set up in front of a couple of silhouetted cut-out foliage drops (Chapter 5, Section 16), all enclosed in a light blue sky cyclorama. Because no ceiling piece can be used in an outdoor scene, a cut foliage border is employed to mask the flies from the view of the audience.

Four other typical arrangements of exterior scenes are given in Figure 11.

7. CYCLORAMA SETTINGS

Certain formal and nonrealistic plays that do not require descriptive environments (Chapter 1, Section 4) are frequently presented using neutrally colored drapery cycloramas (Chapter 5, Section 12, and Figures 13 and 46). Sometimes this type of cyclorama (different in construction, appearance, and purpose from the sky cyclorama described in Section 11) is used alone. More frequently certain built or set units are combined with it, to relieve its rather bare simplicity. The drapery cyclorama is hung from a U-shaped wood or steel frame suspended by two or more sets of lines, while the additional units (if there are any) are secured in place in this setting independently, in exactly the same way as they are in a setting that uses flat and frame scenery alone. A border and two "legs" (Chapter 5, Section 12) of the same material as the cyclorama are generally required to mask the top and side edges of the cyclorama.

A word might be said here about the advisability of the general use of draperies in the setting for a play. There is an unfortunate tendency in many nonprofessional theatres to overwork this type of scenery. Soft, neutral draperies often form very effective backgrounds for poetical plays of the distinctly formal or classical kind which demand indefinite settings, but they are not suited for the more intimate and the more realistic type of play which demands definite characterization and atmosphere from its setting.

What is said here about draperies refers, of course, to the general use of this form of scenery in the set, not to its limited use. Draperies reasonably used may be combined with other forms of scenery to help express a wide range of environments.

8. NONCONVENTIONAL SCENERY

Descriptive interior and exterior frame sets and formal cyclorama sets of the types just explained may be said to be more or less conventional. Certain settings, however, which the artist may have to design from time to time for plays of a distinctly non-realistic nature (Chapter 1, Section 4), will be quite nonconventional. The planning of each new set usually presents problems of arrangement peculiarly its own. If the set is to be an interior, it

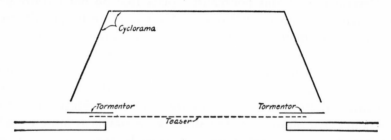

FIG. 13. Plan of a drapery cyclorama.

may or may not be designed to have surrounding walls and a ceiling. Place can be indicated by a grouping of the usual flats, door, window or fireplace frames, and ceiling piece, or simply by a free standing archway, window or balcony rail, or merely by a suggestive arrangement of furniture placed in front of a large neutral color panel, an unlighted sky cyclorama, or a black velvet curtain. If the set is an exterior, place may be indicated by an elaborate grouping of significant rock, foliage, or architectural shapes, or merely by a couple of suggestive platforms, tree trunks, or columns backed by the same type of cyclorama or draperies. A nonrealistic scene may be designed out of three-dimensional units or two-dimensional units. The whole scene may be done as a group of interrelated silhouettes or even painted quite flatly in the poster style on a single screen or drop. Each setting of this kind requires quite clearly, therefore, its own particular arrangement of scenic units.

It is important that a set of the type described here be adequately backed and have its top and sides properly masked off. In planning obviously nonrealistic scenes this requirement is generally met fairly easily. Because the scenery in such sets does not pretend to create an illusion of a particular locale, backings and maskings can be quite formal, and may be treated frankly as themselves, with no attempt at disguise.

If no side walls and ceilings are used in the set, it is commonly backed by a blue sky cyclorama or a black velvet (or duvetyn) cyclorama, while the sides and the top are masked (if the teaser and tormentors are not sufficient) by a set of plain or cut borders and a pair or more of returns, drapery legs (tabs), and so forth. Frequently the downstage edge of the set is framed by an inner proscenium made up of a border and two returns or plain flats. Often the masking elements for this type of set are cut and painted to lend interest to the principal design on the stage.

9. THE UNIT SET

Scenery, it has been stated, must be designed for easy and rapid shifting. This is an especially important consideration in setting plays with numerous scenes in which intra-act changes must be planned to cause the least possible interruption to the action. Some of the methods commonly employed to solve this problem are outlined in Chapter 4 on the general construction of scenery, and in Chapter 7 on the assembling and shifting of scenery. A word, however, might be said here about the use of the unit set.

A unit set is an arrangement of scenery in which some or all of the pieces of scenery employed in one scene are designed to be employed again (in other combinations) in other scenes of the play. In general, there are two kinds of unit set. A set of the first kind makes use of a permanent frame—representing, perhaps, certain sections of wall, banks of earth, rocks, or the like—which stands throughout the play, and in which insets (panels, alcoves, arch frames, window frames, and so on) are placed to mark the change of scene. Perhaps a large, permanent, architectural frame is erected on the stage, and the back and side walls of each succeeding scene, made into single panels by battening the unit flats together on the back, are set in and lifted out of this frame. Perhaps door and window frames are bolted into their openings so that time is not wasted in placing them.

In a unit set of the second kind, the unit pieces of scenery used to form the background for one scene are simply reassembled to form another. This method of handling scenery is used constantly in Shakespearean settings. An archway and a group of steps used on one side of the stage in one scene are moved to the other side in the next; a plain, flat wall at the back is changed by giving it a jog up or down, or by taking out a couple of flats and putting in their place a two-fold with two small windows; or an interior is transformed into an exterior by taking out a section of the wall at one corner—pushing out the back wall at an angle and introducing a balcony railing backed by trees—and so on.

For certain kinds of plays the advantages of the use of the unit set, wisely designed, is obvious. In addition to saving space and, at least to some extent, movement on the stage, it reduces the cost of constructing scenery, because certain parts are repeated. A warning must be given to nonprofessional artists, however, not to overwork this type of design. Unless one is very careful it is apt to degenerate into a plaything. The "community theatre unit set" has become something of a joke for this reason. It is never really successful when the attention of the audience is called to the tricks being practiced on it. The spectator who is given the opportunity to play the little game of "let's see where the tall, pointed arch and the three little windows appear next" is not going to pay much attention to the acting. The designer who decides to work his ideas of scenery into a unit set must also be sure that this arrangement promises a real economy in shifting. A unit set of a rather bulky type placed in a small house on Broadway some years ago took three times the normal number of stagehands to shift and cost the management far more in the end than a full set of scenery handled in the ordinary way would have done.

10. THE PROBLEM OF SIGHT LINES

One of the very first requirements of any arrangement of scenery is that it have good sight lines. A sight line is the line of vision from the spectator to the stage. A setting with good sight lines is one that is so shaped and so placed in relation to the proscenium opening that the vision is good from all positions in the audience. If not the whole set of scenery, at least every feature that is important dramatically or pictorially should be well in view from every seat—the seat in the first row, the last row, and at the extreme side in the orchestra, and the seat in the first row, the last row and at the extreme side (if the theatre is reasonably constructed) of the balcony, as well as the seat in the ideal center of the auditorium. This means that the setting must not be so wide or so tall that a part of it is hidden behind the edge of the proscenium; and it must not be so deep that the features at the back of the set are cut off from the view of the spectators at the sides or above. On the other hand, the setting must not be so narrow or so low that, in order to mask the downstage edges of the scenery, the two tormentors and the teaser have to be set in a position (Section 2) where they shield the view of the back parts of the setting from these same spectators.

When the artist works out the problems of good sight lines for various positions in the auditorium he considers not only how he may bring into view all that the audience should see, but also how he may hide all that they should not see—that is, the non-scenic part of backstage. When he is dealing with the conventional enclosed interior he seldom has much trouble with the latter phase of the problem; the side walls of the set mask the wings and the ceiling masks the flies quite naturally. All that he must see to is that the teaser and tormentors are trimmed to hide the downstage edge of the set all the way around, that the sky drop (if one is used), or other scenic pieces, are in a position to back up all exterior views of the scene itself, and that wall backings are in position to back up all interior views through doorways and other openings.

One point that the artist must never forget in the matter of arranging the downstage masking of the top edge of an interior is the necessity for taking into account room for the lighting instruments—borderlights and spotlights—hanging just behind the teaser. As these lights must be placed just below the edge of the ceiling, and the teaser, in turn, must be dropped down far enough to hide completely the lights from persons sitting in the first few rows of the orchestra, it is clear that the height of the

set must be 18 inches to 3 feet more than that of the final trimming of the teaser.

When the artist is dealing with an exterior scene he is likely
to run into considerably more difficulty than when he is dealing
with an interior one; he cannot use in the exterior set the natural
masking offered by interior walls and a ceiling. If the scene represents a street, a courtyard, or a garden set between houses, he
has at his disposal some exterior walls, and his problem may be
narrowed down to concealing the flies. In this case he will probably carry the walls and the sky (if one is used) so far up into
the flies that with the help of a plan of illumination which keeps
all light out of this part of the stage, the tops of the pieces of
scenery will not be visible even to people seated in the first row.
If this arrangement involves making the flats and drop too tall
for practical construction and handling, the artist may have to
hang a couple of black borders in the flies (as far as possible out
of the range of the lights)—frankly theatrical masking pieces.

If, on the other hand, the exterior scene represents an open
country landscape or a grove of trees, the artist may have to arrange his maskings without the help of walls at all. If there is
enough room on the floor of the stage and the gridiron is sufficiently high, the artist will probably back the hanging or set
pieces of his scene with a large sky cyclorama, or a plaster dome
(see following section), which extends all the way around and
downstage out of sight in the wings and away up out of sight in
the flies. In front of this he can set anything he pleases—trees,
fences, sides or corners of buildings, or distant mountains—with
the comforting knowledge that from whatever angle the spectator
may view the scene he will see sky beyond. If, because of limited
space, however, the artist cannot count on the use of a cyclorama
(or dome) and must limit himself to a flat sky drop, he must do
some ingenious designing to cover the view into the stage wings. If
he can possibly do so, he brings into his picture the side wall, or
walls, of buildings—sheds, cottages, and the like—and supplies
whatever deficiencies there still may be in maskings at the side by
using closely packed tree trunks, green gauze tabs, rocks, banks
of earth, or other scenic pieces. The flies he generally masks by
means of cut foliage borders (Chapter 5, Sections 11 and 16).

A typical arrangement of exterior maskings is illustrated in

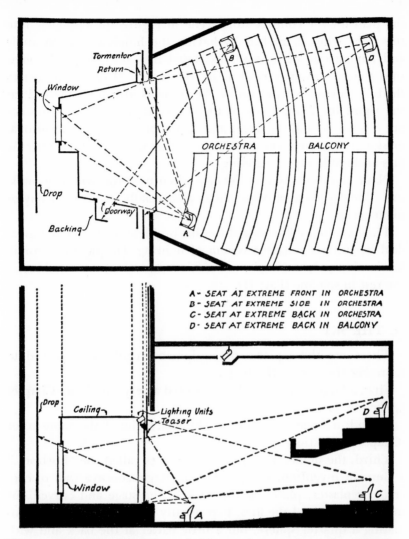

FIG. 14. Sight lines. Good lines of vision to the stage from the auditorium require (1) the full visibility of the acting area and the chief features of its setting, and (2) the adequate backing of door, window, and fireplace openings in the setting, and the complete masking of lighting units and stage machinery for every position in the house (except, occasionally, a few of the first row seats, if too close to the stage).

the plan for the country store scene in Figure 10. The view into the right wing is masked by having the house set on an angle and having one of its walls extended into the wing. The view into the left wing is masked by the side wall of an imaginary shed. The view at the top of the scene is also fully masked; at the right, the front walls of the store extend up some distance out of view behind the teaser and so do not require any additional masking; at the left, the cut foliage border masks the view into the flies at the side of the building.

Plain black duvetyn borders are often used for overhead masking. They are generally satisfactory, especially in shadowy day or night scenes.

The experienced artist reduces his problems of masking a great deal by using a selective system of lighting. He picks out for illumination only the important scenic (and acting) areas and leaves the rest in shadow (Part II).

11. THE SKY

There are three pieces of equipment regularly employed to represent the sky on the stage:

First, a large suspended drop, painted a very pale blue (Chapter 5, Section 11).

Second, a large suspended cyclorama, painted the same color (Chapter 5, Section 12).

Third, the dome. This piece, sometimes called the "horizont," a German invention, is a permanent, large, concave wall of concrete or plaster, placed at the back of the stage and curved out into the wings and the flies. It is usually made in a form approximating a quarter sphere, but a little flatter at the back and with a sharper curvature at the sides and top. The perfect quarter sphere has been found disadvantageous to the acoustics of the stage. The dome also is painted a pale blue.

The reader may wish to ask which form of sky is to be recommended. The answer depends upon the size and shape of the stage on which one of the three pieces of equipment is to be used. The dome gives by far the best effect. It is absolutely free from wrinkles, and its curved, granular surface takes light beautifully, much better than even the best of painted canvases. The dome occupies, however, a great deal of valuable space on the stage. The edges often extend out into the wings and the flies in such a way as to greatly handicap the shifting of scenery on the floor and limit the usefulness of the fly system (see Chapter 7, Section 5). A full dome should never be built on a stage unless there is plenty of room for both it and the more common equipment. Certain modifications of the dome, however, such as a very shallow, curved wall, may often be adopted for even limited stages (Chapter 7, Section 2).

The cyclorama, if properly painted, stretched, and lighted, produces an effect of open sky nearly as good as that of the plaster dome; and it has the advantage, from the point of view of stage mechanics, of being more flexible. If the gridiron is high enough, the cyclorama (or "cyc" as it is generally called) may be attached to two or more sets of lines, weighted with a U-shaped pipe at the bottom and, when it is not needed, flied up out of view. If the height of the grid does not permit flying such a tall piece of scenery, the cyc may be attached to lines at the top and fastened to floor hooks at the bottom in the manner described in Chapter 5, Section 12, so that as soon as it has served its purpose it may be dropped, untied, and folded up. This last method of taking down a cyc takes time, of course, which means certain disaster if it must happen in the middle of a performance. The cyclorama is really practicable only on a fairly large stage or for a setting which does not have to be changed on a small stage.

For the restricted stage the drop is generally the most practical. It cannot, it is true, give quite the same effect of depth of atmosphere that the dome (and, to a lesser degree, the cyc) can give; but if it is properly painted, hung, and lighted, it can be effective. The drop is by far the most flexible of the three sky units; it can be flied straight up with one set of lines, tripped with two, or rolled up in a very small space in no more than a few seconds. Also, the drop is the least expensive of the three units to build.

The methods of constructing the cyclorama and the sky drop are described in Chapter 5, Sections 11 and 12; the methods of painting these two units are described in Chapter 6, Section 20; and the methods of lighting the cyclorama, the drop, and the dome are described in Part II.

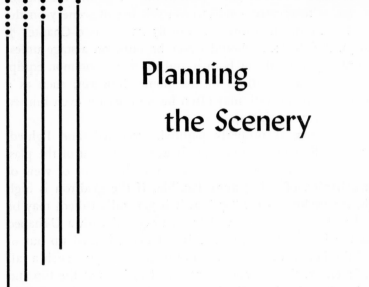

CHAPTER 3

Planning
the Scenery

1. INTRODUCTION

IF THE CONSTRUCTING, the painting, and the assembling of a group
of scenic units to form the visual environment of a play are to
be done effectively and efficiently, they must be carefully planned
in advance. The layout may be done in a variety of ways: by
making a pencil, ink, or color sketch, by drawing a floor plan, or
by building a small model of the proposed set. The process of
evolving a scenic idea in the professional studio more often than
not includes all three of these steps. The stage picture as seen
in elevation through the proscenium arch by the audience is first
visualized in a general way in a sketch; then the arrangement of
walls, entrances, steps, and other parts is worked out carefully in
a floor plan; and finally the complete setting is checked from a
three-dimensional point of view by constructing it in miniature
form as a scale model of wood or cardboard. The technique of developing scenery through these three steps, and the method of con-
verting the completed plan into working drawings for the carpenter
is outlined briefly in the following pages.

2. THE SKETCH

With the general design of his setting in mind, the artist usually attempts to visualize it first in the form of a sketch. Drawn in pencil or ink, and usually developed in water color, the sketch represents an ideal view of the projected scene as the latter would be seen from the front through the proscenium by a member of the audience. Offering, as it does, the best opportunity for the working out of the artist's ideas in line, mass, and color, it is in this step in the evolution of the setting that many designers expend their greatest effort.

FIG. 15. Pen and ink sketch for an interior scene.

One or two suggestions on the mechanical arrangement of the sketch are offered to those who are in doubt as to just what the drawing should include. Let the outside border of the sketch represent the proscenium opening. Draw the set within this boundary as one would assume it would be seen by a person sitting in about the center of the auditorium, downstairs. Suppose the set to represent a simple box interior. From this position one would see the whole back wall, a little of each side wall (in sharp perspective), a very narrow strip of the floor, and nothing of the ceiling.[1] As the teaser is always trimmed two or more feet below the edge of the ceiling to accommodate the border light and spotlights (Chapter 2, Section 10), the ceiling (unless it is made to slope down at the back) is never seen except by those sitting in the first few rows of

[1] If the relationship of parts in a design is quite clear without their being shown in perspective, the sketch may be drawn in simple elevation (Section 6), in which case the floor can be indicated by one straight line.

A design for Bernard Shaw's *Major Barbara* (the Salvation Army shelter), by Donald Oenslager.

the orchestra. This would obviously be a poor spot from which to design a scene. Figure 15 represents a rough pen-and-ink sketch for an interior scene. See, also, Robert Edmond Jones's and Donald Oenslager's water color sketches on pages 4 and 50.

One cannot emphasize too strongly the importance of keeping proportions accurate. If the maximum dimensions of the practical proscenium opening of the stage on which the scenery is to be set up are only 20′ x 12′, do not design a layout that would require an opening 50′ x 30′ to show the whole scene. Disappointment in the final staging of the scene, besides an endless amount of annoyance in the process of its creation, can be avoided only by strict honesty in the initial sketching. Never show in the drawing anything that cannot be made thoroughly real in production. Many of the so-called "Sketches for the Stage" published in abstract books and magazines on the theatre furnish illustrations of what not to do. Columns 100 feet high, gigantic screens, mountainous mechanical structures that would fill a whole city block if made of actual wood and steel, may give inspiration for certain magnificent productions in the distant future, but they are valueless as indications of what an artist may hope to re-create for an audience with the kind of equipment he has at his service today.

3. THE FLOOR PLAN

After the artist has worked out his inspiration first in the form of a general sketch, he develops his ideas further by making a diagram of them. The most valuable diagram he can use is the floor plan. The floor plan is a skeleton outline which shows the relationship of the walls, doors, windows, platforms, stairways, and other features that enter into the scheme of the scene, as these features would be seen from above, looking down onto the set. The diagraming can be done quite simply in a few lines. Floor plans of different scenes are shown in Figures 9–13.

If a floor plan is to be of practical value, it must be drawn carefully to scale throughout, and it must include the positions and dimensions of not only the main elements of the scene, but also the incidental units, such as backings for the doors, set pieces seen through the windows, and the larger properties, as well. The

size and position of the proscenium opening and the placement
of the tormentors in relation to the set should likewise be indicated. In this outline the arrangements for lighting the scene may
also be blocked in (Part II).

An artist frequently plots his first rough ideas, as well as his
later more matured ones, in the form of a floor plan. A simple
outline helps him to organize his ideas before he works them out
in his sketch.

4. THE MODEL

For those persons who possess a creative understanding of
scenery, but who cannot draw in perspective, an excellent medium of design is offered in the model. A model is a three-
dimensional miniature of a scene built carefully to scale out of
wood, cardboard, or other material (Figure 16). Many artists who
develop their ideas in sketch form make use of this miniature
also, either to check up on their plans before they lay them out
in the final working drawing for the carpenter, or to demon-
strate their plans to other members of the producing staff. The
model is especially valuable to the artist who is required to sub-
mit in advance the scheme of a proposed setting to a director for
his approval. A model usually presents a setting much more
clearly and definitely than does a sketch of the same scene.

The model is constructed most easily out of light cardboard.
Two-ply bristol board with a finished surface for painting is
excellent for this purpose. Matt board with an eggshell surface
makes a better model, but is more difficult to work with. The
model described below is of bristol board. The walls are first
drawn out carefully to some definite scale such as ¼ inch = 1 foot
or ½ inch = 1 foot. A scale of ½ inch = 1 foot indicates that
½ inch in the model represents 1 foot in the actual stage set. When
completely outlined, including door and window openings, the
walls are cut out. This is done in one piece, if possible, because
cardboard can be folded more easily than it can be fastened together. In cutting out the piece, or pieces, leave ¼-inch or
½-inch flaps along all edges which must be joined with glue to
other edges. Now, with the back of a knife or razor blade, score

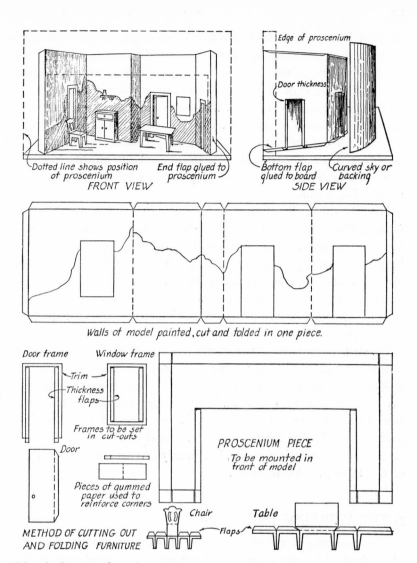

Edge of proscenium

Door thickness

Dotted line shows position of proscenium — End flap glued to proscenium
FRONT VIEW

Bottom flap glued to board — Curved sky or backing
SIDE VIEW

Walls of model painted, cut and folded in one piece.

Door frame   Window frame

Trim

Thickness flaps

Frames to be set in cut-outs

Door

Pieces of gummed paper used to reinforce corners

PROSCENIUM PIECE

To be mounted in front of model

Chair   Table

Flaps

METHOD OF CUTTING OUT AND FOLDING FURNITURE

FIG. 16. Construction of a cardboard model. The various pieces are cut out and folded forward on the dotted lines and backward on the heavy black lines.

all lines along which folds are to be made. In each case score the cardboard on the side opposite to that of the crease. Fold the wall up and mount it on edge, by means of the ¼-inch or ½-inch flaps, on a piece of heavy cardboard or a wooden panel. If the glue does not hold very well, the joints may be temporarily held in place by means of thumb tacks or paper clips. Rubber glue is superior to the ordinary forms of glue for model making. Pieces of gummed paper strips, such as those used for binding packages in stores, or Scotch or masking tape are excellent for making or reinforcing joints.

Usually the walls of the model are decorated before they are folded. Common water-color or show-card paints may be used for this purpose. Door and window openings can be made to look more real by inserting paper thicknesses (Chapter 5, Section 6) into them to represent their door and window frames, then fastening small door shutters or window sashes to the back edges of the thicknesses. Bits of furniture, folded out of paper and painted, add considerably to the effectiveness of the little set.

When the interior of the miniature has been finished, cut out a small proscenium to the same scale, paint it black or gray, and mount it in front of the set as a frame for it. Place a light blue sky piece at the back and add any foliage cutouts or mountain rows called for in the final plan. If the walls of the model are made a little higher than the proscenium opening, no ceiling need be used. In fact, it is a good plan in any case to leave at least part of the top open for lighting.

5. THE WORKING DRAWINGS

The working drawings of a set of scenery are the building plans drafted for the carpenter. Laid out to some selected scale—such as ¼ inch = 1 foot or 1 inch = 1 foot—they show the exact dimensions and construction of each unit, and include indications of materials to be used (if that is not apparent) and written explanations of all points that cannot be made clear by lines and figures alone. As the lines, however, are always more eloquent than the figures, words are employed very sparingly. If more than a dozen phrases are needed on any one sheet the plans may generally be considered poorly done. Details, such as the plan of a difficult joint, an arrangement of molding, or a special placing of hardware, are shown separately in enlarged detail drawings. Three-dimensional units, such as stairs and platforms, are laid

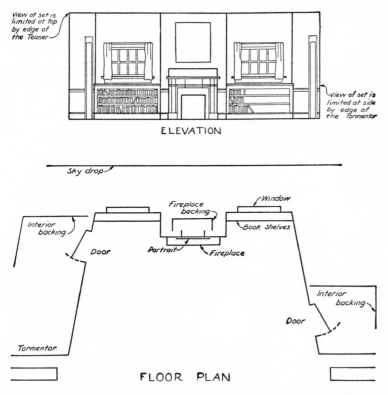

FIG. 17. Elevation and floor plan of an interior set. This drawing illustrates how standard scenery units are assembled to form a typical realistic interior setting. Included in this group are 2 plain flats, 2 door flats, 2 window flats, 2 jogs, 1 fireplace flat, 2 door frame units, 2 window frame units, 1 fireplace unit, 2 backing wings (behind the doorways), 1 fireplace backing, and 1 sky drop. The drawing also suggests how the designer may work out the elevation and the floor-plan of a set together. (See Ch. 3, Sects. 3, 6.) By placing the plan directly below the elevation he enables himself, as he draws, to visualize the whole and the parts of his setting in three dimensions, and to check carefully his arrangement of the different units.

out both in plan and elevation (Section 6). Cross sections of units are added wherever they are necessary for clarity. As building principles on the stage are seldom complicated, it is usually unnecessary to make drawings elaborate.

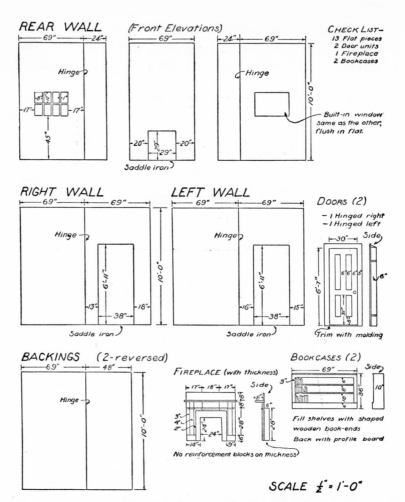

FIG. 18. Sheet of working drawings for the set of scenery pictured and diagramed on the preceding page. Each unit, or combination of units, is drawn separately. Because the two backings are similar (though reversed) only one is drawn. If the carpenter is familiar with standard building methods, simple front elevations are generally sufficient.

If the carpenter who is superintending the building of the scenery is a man of experience in the ways and means of the stage, it is, of course, a waste of effort to include in the working drawings all such details as the standard arrangement of parts in steps and parallels, of frame supports for columns and trees, or of joints and hardware on simple flats. Usually mere outlines of such units, with their widths and heights and the positions and sizes of any special features, like door or window openings, are all that are required.

A point in drawing flats should be noted. As the frames for these are constructed face downwards, the drawings are frequently done in reverse of the normal front view for the convenience of the carpenter. To save confusion it is wise to indicate which view of the flats is shown.

In general, make the complete drawing accurately to one scale. For this purpose the use of a scale ruler, such as that employed by architectural and mechanical draftsmen, is quite essential. By accuracy we mean that a line on the paper 6 inches long should not vary from 6 inches by more than $\frac{1}{32}$ inch. If an enlarged detail is shown, write the scale immediately under it. The scale for the whole drawing should be placed in the lower right hand corner of the page. Check dimensions carefully several times and be sure that the sum of the dimensions of parts equals the over-all dimensions. If there is a discrepancy, the carpenter will probably toss a coin to decide which is correct. Small errors of less than an inch in the completed set will make it very difficult or impossible to put the set together. Use a 2H pencil well sharpened on a sandpad for your light lines, and a 2B pencil for your heavier lines.

Do not overcrowd a drawing with repeated dimensions, or with a mass of notes that obscure the outlines. If the drawing is clearly and completely drawn with all of the views and dimensions which are necessary, few notes are needed. Such a drawing will be easy to read.

For the benefit of those who are unfamiliar with the conventions used in the mechanical drawing of frame structures a few of the terms and methods employed are discussed in the following section.

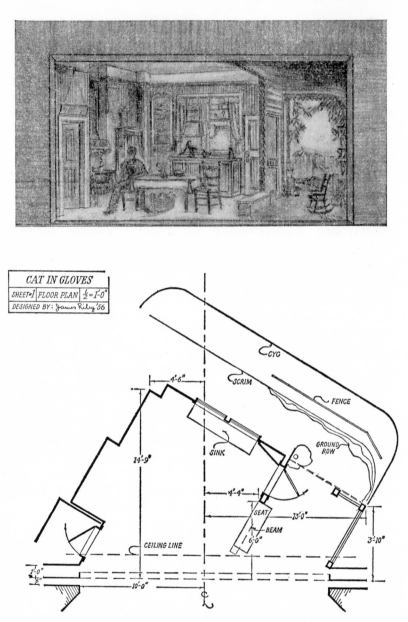

FIG. 19a. Drawings for *Cat in Gloves,* designed by James M. Riley. Pencil sketch, top; floor plan, below.

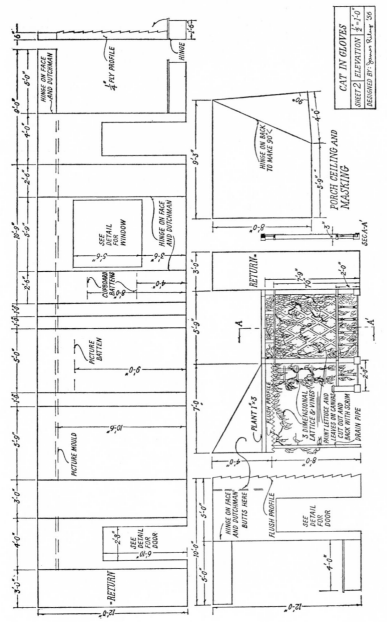

FIG. 19b. Working drawings for *Cat in Gloves*: the walls.

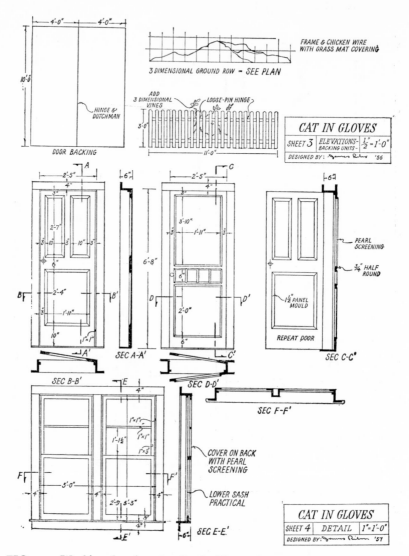

FIG. 19c. Working drawings for *Cat in Gloves:* doors, windows and a section of fence.

6. TERMS AND METHODS EMPLOYED IN DRAFTING CONSTRUCTION DRAWINGS

The shape and the construction of a frame structure (or any solid form) may be conveniently represented on paper by three types of conventional views, called *elevations, sections,* and *plans.* An *elevation* is a vertical view of the object of study, from the front, side, or rear, in which every element that is drawn is represented as being directly in front of the eye. No perspective whatsoever is used. The front elevation of a rectangular table would represent strictly the front face of it; one would see nothing at all of the top or the bottom of the table top. Nor would one glimpse anything of the rear legs (if they were of the same shape as, and were spaced equally with, the front legs), because they would be directly behind, and therefore hidden by, the front legs. The front elevation of a long avenue of trees planted on perfectly level ground, with all the trees of exactly the same shape and spaced equally from the center of the roadway (to take a conventional illustration) would show on each side only the first tree in each row. The house at the end of the avenue would be seen, not far away, but as though it were at the same distance from the observer as the nearest trees. In other words, in an elevation drawing the element of depth or thickness is omitted. The front, side, or rear elevations of the window sash in Figure 20, the window frames in Figure 38, and the fireplace in Figure 40 show the object (from the particular side from which the view is made) as though it were perfectly flat. The purpose of this type of drawing for the carpenter, or any other craftsman, is obvious. It enables him to take accurate measurements from any part of the drawing without having to take into account any effect of perspective or distance. Unless it is specifically labeled otherwise, the elevation of an object is understood to be its front elevation.

A *section* of an object is a cross-section view taken by passing an imaginary plane through the object vertically, horizontally, or longitudinally. The part, or parts, cut are outlined with a heavy black line and filled in with crosshatching. Everything beyond the plane of the section (the cut) is shown in light lines. A typical section is illustrated in the drawing in the upper-right-hand corner of Figure 20. Representing a slice taken down through the center of the window sash, it shows the cut ends of the top and bottom rails and the horizontal muntin, outlined and crosshatched, and the side of one of the vertical muntins beyond, in lighter lines. Other typical section drawings may be seen in Figures 35, 38, and 53. When lines showing the positions of parts beyond the plane of the section—especially in section drawings of enlarged details (see section of ledge in Figure 22 and sections of door and window

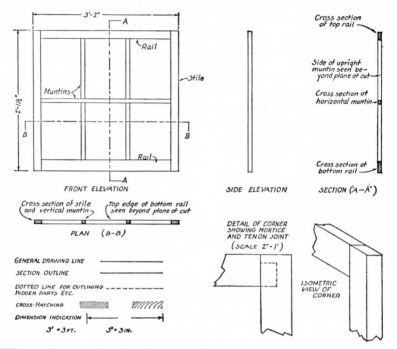

FIG. 20. Construction drawing of a window sash, showing the methods of drawing front and side elevations, a vertical section and plan, an enlarged detail, an isometric projection, section outlines, cross hatching of sections, and dimension indications. Scale ½″ = 1′. This sash fits the double hung window shown in Fig. 38.

casings in Figure 39)—add nothing to the understanding of the drawing, they may be omitted. This is done frequently in the sketches in this book. Unless it is specifically labeled otherwise, the section of an object is understood to be its vertical section.

A *plan* of an object is either an outside view of the object looking directly down on the top of it (see plan of template in Figure 22) or it is a horizontal section of the object (see plan of sash in

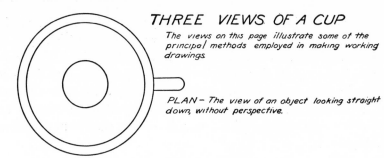

THREE VIEWS OF A CUP

The views on this page illustrate some of the principal methods employed in making working drawings.

PLAN – The view of an object looking straight down, without perspective.

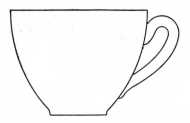

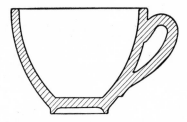

ELEVATION – The view of an object looking directly from the front, side, or rear, without perspective.

SECTION – The interior view (without perspective) of an object cut open. The cut part is cross-hatched and surrounded by a heavy section outline.

LINE STRENGTHS USED IN DRAWING

SECTION OUTLINE ———————————— Heavy
DRAWING LINE ———————————— Medium
DIMENSION LINE ———————————— Light
HIDDEN LINE -------------------- Dotted

DIMENSIONS

5'– 0" means 5 feet
   3" means 3 inches
5'–3" means 5 feet 3 inches

├——————— 5'–3" ———————┤
The arrows touch the lines limiting a measurement.

FIG. 21. Methods and symbols employed in the drafting of working drawings, illustrated in the drawing of a coffee cup.

Figure 20, of door frame in Figure 35, of window frames in Figure 38). One must be able to tell at a glance which type of plan is indicated in the drawing. In a horizontal section there should be heavy section outlines and crosshatching (to show cut parts); in the plan representing an external view, section outlines and crosshatching would, of course, be absent. The plan of an object is most frequently understood to be its horizontal section looking down.

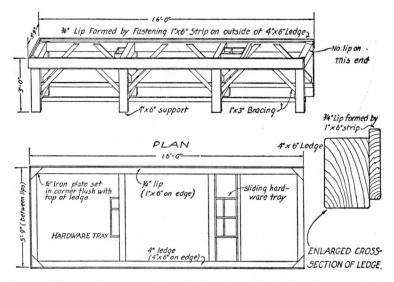

FIG. 22. The template. A work bench for the construction of flats and other scenic frames. Sometimes the top is covered.

The approximate position at which the imaginary plane is assumed to be passed through an object to give a section or plan view is generally clear enough when one compares the section or plan drawing with the elevation. If there is any danger of doubt, a light, broken line may be drawn across the elevation to show exactly where the cut of a section is made, turned at the ends to indicate the direction in which the section is to be viewed, and lettered in some way to make clear what section drawing it explains. In Figure 20, for instance, the broken line A-A across the elevation explains the fact that "Section A-A" represents a vertical cross-section view through the middle of the sash, looking to the right. The broken line B-B explains the fact that "Plan B-B" represents a horizontal cross-section view taken between the horizontal muntin and the bottom rail, looking down.

Objects, or parts of objects, which can be explained more clearly in three planes than in one may be drawn in isometric projection. The difference between an isometric and a true perspective drawing is that in the former all parallel lines are placed on paper actually parallel to each other, without making them converge toward common vanishing points, as is done in the latter. Probably the most obvious example of isometric projection in this book may be seen in the three-plane view of a wagon unit in Figure 71. Another example of isometric projection may be seen in Figure 22. If, in drafting, use is made of 30, 45, 60, and 90 degree angles as standards, isometric drawings may be done much more rapidly and accurately (from the point of view of the person who must read the drawings) than true perspective drawings.

The position of concealed parts, when they must be shown, are commonly indicated by dotted lines (Figure 20). Dotted lines are also used occasionally (though not often) to represent the position of some part above or forward, or even sometimes back, of the plane of a section.

Dimensions are conveniently represented by double-headed arrows with the figures placed in the center of the shaft.

In general, the drawings in this book conform to the conventions in drafting set down in these pages. In one or two instances the sketches have been made a little unorthodox in an effort to simplify them.

For a more extensive discussion of the correct methods employed in making layouts, and the efficient use of drafting instruments the reader is referred to any standard book on architectural or mechanical drawing. (See Bibliography.)

7. PERSPECTIVE DRAWING

It is quite possible that the designer will feel that he needs to work out at least one step of his planning in the form of a perspective drawing. If he goes to a regular architectural manual for guidance in preparing such a drawing, however, he will find that the standard methods recommended there are elaborate, complicated, and require the use of more space than he probably has available

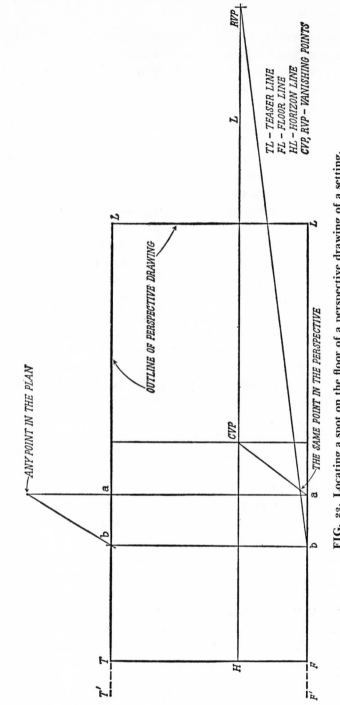

ANY POINT IN THE PLAN

OUTLINE OF PERSPECTIVE DRAWING

CVP

THE SAME POINT IN THE PERSPECTIVE

RVP

TL – TEASER LINE
FL – FLOOR LINE
HL – HORIZON LINE
CVP, RVP – VANISHING POINTS

FIG. 23. Locating a spot on the floor of a perspective drawing of a setting.

on his single drafting board. Since, generally speaking, the precise details of a stage setting are fixed in the plan and elevation drawings, the perspective can usually be reserved for just checking the effects. Hence the perspective drawing for the stage does not have to be quite so exact in all its parts as does its architectural counterpart. The theatre man can take a few judicious short cuts.

The method of making a perspective proposed here has three advantages over the regular architectural methods referred to: it does not require a station point, it employs only two vanishing points, and its rules of work are very simple. This is the way the linear apparatus is set up and the method is put into action:

Draft the rectangular outline for your perspective drawing down far enough on your sheet to allow you to place a plan of your set just above it. The rectangle, drawn to some convenient scale (usually $\frac{1}{2} = 1$ foot), is presumably of the same shape and size as the proscenium opening of the stage on which your scenery will be mounted; the side lines represent the edges of the proscenium arch, or of the tormentors; the top line marks the position of the teaser; and the bottom line the floor.

In Figure 23 the teaser line is designated by TL and the floor line by FL. Extend the first line a little to the left to T' and the second line in the same direction to F'. Now drop a center line. Find a point on this line about 5 feet from the bottom and draw a horizontal line, carrying it from the left border of your perspective drawing well over to the right. Since this is the horizon line for your perspective, it is marked HL.

Find a point on HL to the right of the center line which has a distance from the center line equal to the width of the proscenium opening. That is, if the width of your opening is 25 feet (according to your scale), put the point on HL to the right 25 feet from the center line; if the width of the opening is 30 feet, place the point on HL 30 feet from the center line. The intersection of the center line and horizon line will be recognized as the center vanishing point (CVP) of the drawing, and the mark to the right, the right vanishing point (RVP).

Above TL will now be the area which will be occupied with reference details of your plan. You are looking straight ahead at the perspective, but down from above at your plan. In the plan,

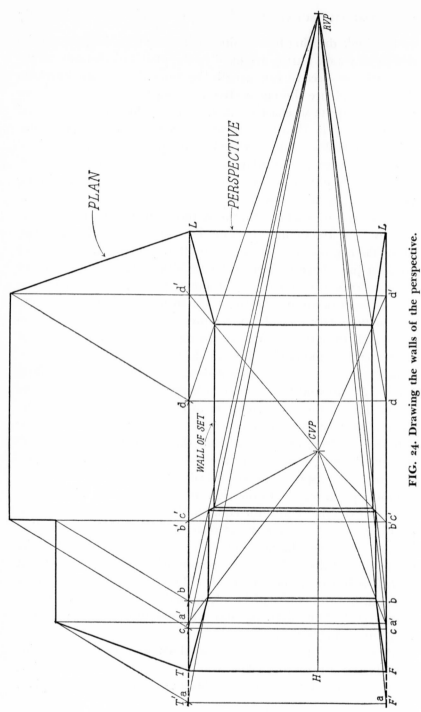

FIG. 24. Drawing the walls of the perspective.

TL will represent the downstage curtain line, and the points T and L the right and left edges of the proscenium opening.

To establish on the floor of the perspective drawing a spot which corresponds to a point in the plan above, plot two sets of lines (Figure 23). From the point in the plan drop a vertical line, a, across TL to meet FL, and from here draw another line to the center vanishing point (CVP). Now from the point in the plan draw a second line, b, this time to the left at a 30-degree angle to the vertical (use your 30°–60° drafting triangle). From the point where this crosses TL, drop a vertical to FL; and from the meeting of these two draw a line to the right vanishing point (RVP). The point where the lines to CVP and RVP intersect each other is the one desired.

Figure 24 shows how the method for finding one spot on the floor of the perspective can be applied to the plotting of all the bottom corners of a set of scenery. The upper corners of the various planes also can be found by drawing a second set of diagonals to the two vanishing points (from the intersections of the vertical lines with TL to CVP, and from the intersections of the 30-degree lines with TL to RVP). The point where, in each case, the lines to the two vanishing points cross in the space above HL is the upper corner of a piece of scenery (just as each corresponding intersection below marks the lower corner). By drawing a line from the upper corner to the one under it you are marking the line along which two sections of the wall are meeting. Now connect all the floor points and all the ceiling points together and you have the perspective of the walls of your set.

Figure 25 illustrates a way to mark off a grid on the floor of the perspective.

The wall and the grid should serve as sufficient guides to the approximate location and scaling of other objects in the setting to make the drafting of additional plot lines unnecessary. If, however, you wish to be a little more exact about these objects you can follow the plotting diagramed in Figure 26. To determine precisely the place and size of a perspective window, for example, begin by extending the sides of the window in the plan straight down to FL by means of the lines a and b. All points on a plane parallel to FL, if the plane is moved toward the rear, finally vanish

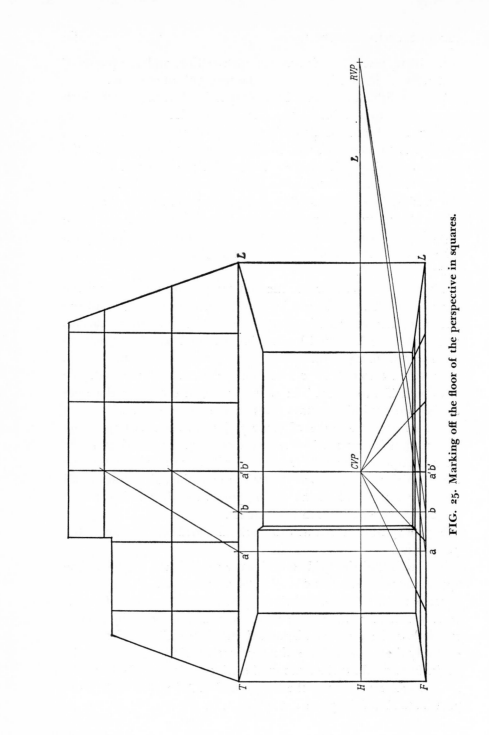

FIG. 25. Marking off the floor of the perspective in squares.

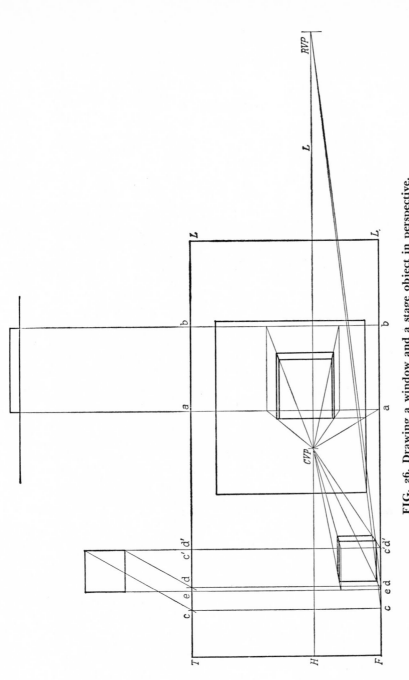

FIG. 26. Drawing a window and a stage object in perspective.

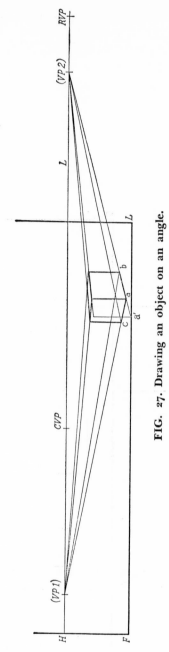

FIG. 27. Drawing an object on an angle.

at *CVP*. You know now that the window in the flat would have the same proportions if it were drawn down front at *FL* as it would have upstage in its desired position. So construct on *FL*, to the established scale, an outline of your window, putting it at the right height from the floor. Draw four lines from the corners of the window outline back to *CVP*. Now, from the point where line *a* intersects *FL*, draw a line back to *CVP;* where this line crosses the bottom of the perspective wall erect a vertical. The segment of this line which occupies the space between the two lines on the left to *CVP* is the left edge of the perspective window. All you have to do now is to connect the ends of this segment of vertical line to the other two lines going back to *CVP*, add another short vertical on the right, and you have your completed outline for your perspective window.

To ascertain the size and place of an object which does not happen to be touching the back wall, use the same method as that suggested for the window, but start with two corner points on the floor (one downstage, one upstage) so that you will know just where to erect the object's front and back edges.

Other vanishing points can be added if they should be desired for objects set on lines not parallel to *FL* (Figure 27). All one has to do to diminish a rectangular object set on any angle is to establish three corner points on the floor of the perspective (here designated as *a*, *b*, and *c*), then draw lines in turn from the front point to the two rear points. These two lines will point directly to the special vanishing points (VP 1 and VP 2 on *HL*) for the two upstage planes of the object. Now the draftsman will extend one of the lines down to *FL* and there (*a'*) construct the true elevation of one corner, then draw a line from the top of this, back to the same vanishing point as that to which the line below leads. With these lines, plus the three original dots, one has enough guides for the completion of the object. (If one of these supplementary vanishing points threatens to go off the edge of the board, don't hesitate to bring it back. A little forcing of perspective in the drawing of details will do no serious harm.)

The positions of the two vanishing points, *CVP* and *RVP*, illustrated in this section, are not fixed by any rule. If one wants to show more or less of the floor in the perspective he can raise or lower the line HL with *CVP* and *RVP*. If one wishes to sharpen the pitch of the perspective's angles he can move *RVP* toward the center line; if one wants to soften the angles he will move the point farther out to the right.

CHAPTER **4**

Constructing

the Scenery:

General Practice

1. INTRODUCTION

THIS CHAPTER, which deals with the general practice of scenery construction, is an introduction to the study of specific problems in the following chapter. Opening with a discussion of the practical demands of scenery construction, the following sections will consider, in turn, the choice of tools, the selection of building materials, procedures in construction, some methods of joining frames, the general method of covering frames, three systems employed to fasten units of scenery together, and the flameproofing of scenery.

2. PRACTICAL DEMANDS OF SCENERY CONSTRUCTION

Scenery constructed for the stage must fulfill a number of practical requirements.

First, scenery must be designed for easy and rapid construction. The plan of production most frequently adopted by both professional and nonprofessional producing groups allows from three to five weeks only for the complete preparation of a play. Within this brief period the stage designer, the technical director, and his staff and crew, must design, draft, build, paint, and fit to the stage usually two or three—frequently more—complete sets of scenery. It is absolutely necessary, therefore, that this scenery be planned for the simplest and quickest possible methods of construction.

Second, scenery must be designed for economical construction. Unless great care is exercised, the item of scenery on the final expense sheet of a production is apt to be a large one. It should be the purpose of the designer and his technical colleagues, therefore, to keep down costs by choosing materials wisely, by adopting efficient methods of building and, above all, by avoiding waste.

Third, scenery must be designed for quick and silent shifting. That is, it must be constructed in light, well-shaped units which can be handled efficiently by a minimum number of stagehands.

Fourth, scenery must be strong. It must be able to resist considerable strain in the course of being handled by stagehands and actors, especially when it is to be placed in service for performances night after night. It must be firmly put together and well joined.

Fifth, scenery must be well assembled. The methods of fastening together the various units must be such that it will be unnecessary to drive a nail during the performance. Nothing sounds more amateurish to the audience during a scene shift than hammering on the stage. The assembling and taking apart of the units should be handled during the shifts quickly and silently.

Sixth, scenery must be designed for easy storage. It must be so planned and constructed that when it is not in use it may be packed away on the stage or in a storeroom in a minimum amount of space. That is, large flat units, like drops, flats over 5′ 9″ wide (Chapter 5, Section 2), and ceilings must be able to be rolled or folded; three-dimensional frame units, like platforms, must be collapsible; wide thicknesses on archways and other flats must be removable; and other bulky, awkward units, must be made either to be folded or to be taken apart in sections. Scenery which is to be sent on tour and must be planned for storage in a crowded boxcar or truck must be planned to fulfill these requirements especially.

3. WORKSHOP EQUIPMENT

The following hand tools are the minimum necessary for construction work:

Hammers
  12-ounce hammer
  Tack hammer
  Hand-operated compression stapler (with staples)
Saws
  Cross cut saw (for cutting across the grain)
  Rip saw (for cutting with the grain)
  Compass or key hole saw (for cutting curves)
Plane
  2″ plane
Screw Drivers
  Ordinary solid screw driver
  Spiral ratchet screw driver
Chisels
  Several sizes
Brace and Bits
  Most useful bits: $\frac{3}{8}$-inch, $\frac{1}{2}$-inch, and 1-inch
Hand Drill
  With $\frac{1}{8}$-inch and $\frac{3}{16}$-inch bits
Draw Knife
Files
Rasp
Clinching Iron
  A flat piece of iron for clinching or "bradding" nails
Squares
  Steel square
  Try square
Rule
  6-foot folding rule
Mitre Box
  Steel or wood
Carpenter's Marking Pencil

These hand tools represent a construction carpenter's minimum equipment. Where quantity production must be provided for, certain power tools, such as a band saw, power rip and cross-cut saws, jointer, electric hand drills, and a motor-driven bench grinder are helpful. A work bench fitted with at least one vise is an absolute necessity.

Also, for securing accuracy and speed, and for saving many tired backs in assembling frames, the service of a *template* (Figure 22) is a great help. A template is a stout, open-frame bench, built waist high, the width of a standard flat (5′ 9″), and 12 feet or 16 feet long, depending upon the average height of scenery to be made on it. The working part of the bench is a flat, narrow ledge of 4″ x 6″ lumber on edge, extending the length of both sides and the width of each end. Three 1″ x 6″ strips are fastened to the outside of the ledge on three sides to form a lip which will stand ¾ inch above the surface of the ledge. In order to allow frames with a greater length than that of the bench to lie flat on the ledge, the lip is not fastened to one end of the bench. If the whole bench is made absolutely level and square, scenery may be built on it without having to sight straight sides or test right angles. If the constructed frame lies well on the ledge and fits snugly against the lip all the way around, the carpenter is assured that it is true. Some templates are made with solid tops.

Workshop equipment should also include, for gluing and covering purposes, a small gas, electric, or kerosene stove with at least two burners, several galvanized pails, and a couple of cheap 3-inch or 4-inch paint brushes.

In the following sections are listed the most useful materials for building scenery.

4. LUMBER MATERIALS

Because all frames must be light and strong, only particular grades of lumber may be used. Requirements of shop and stage demand that the lumber be soft enough for easy working, light enough for easy handling, yet tough enough to stand considerable strain and wear. It must not splinter readily, it must not warp, it must be straight-grained and free from any large blemishes, and it must be well seasoned. By far the best wood for general scenic construction is good grade Northern or Idaho *white pine*. It is the standard. Sugar pine is the best substitute. Douglas fir, yellow pine, and certain other soft woods also may be substituted; but none of these can approach the efficiency of white pine. (The choice of lumber will depend to a great extent on the section of the country in which the shop is located.)

For ordinary purposes, the lumber should be ordered in strips 1″ x 2″, 1″ x 3″, and 1″ x 4″, by 12 feet to 20 feet long, dressed and surfaced. The first two widths are used in building flats, the last in building ceilings, door frames, and so forth. In surfacing a strip at the yard, about ⅛ inch is planed off the thickness and about ¼ inch off the width, making a so-called 1″ x 2″ strip actually ⅞″ x 1¾″, and so on. This makes no difference except that proper allowances must be made in measurements during construction.[1] If the lumberman is obliging, he will prepare the strips with a thickness of ⅞ inch to accommodate theatrical hardware designed for it and, at the same time, with widths in even inches, to facilitate the work of the carpenter.

To prevent waste one should choose the standards lengths in lumber which best suit the scenery to be built. If 14-foot scenery is to be built, for instance, strips should be ordered either in 14-foot or 20-foot lengths—neither 16-foot nor 18-foot would in this case be as economical. Each 6-foot piece cut out from a 20-foot length may be used as a top, bottom, or toggle rail in the frame of a flat, where a piece 2 feet or 4 feet long would be useless.[2]

Above all things, when ordering, a carpenter must see that his lumber is absolutely straight. Flats with warped or crooked edges cannot be lashed together closely and may cause an endless amount of annoyance.

Another useful wood material is veneer board of fir, basswood, or whitewood (or other wood, preferably soft) in three or more plies, called *plywood* or *plyboard* or, sometimes in stage work, *profile board*. It comes in 4′ x 8′ sheets in several thicknesses (the most practicable of which are the ¼ inch and ¾ inch), and is useful for all semi-rigid parts requiring lightness and toughness combined with flexibility. A strip of plywood can be bent into a fairly small circle without cracking. It is employed to advantage in various kinds of light facings, such as risers for steps, curved backs of benches, ground rows, silhouettes, cutouts, and so forth.

A good substitute for plywood where strength is not of primary

[1] Because mills vary a little in the amount of wood they remove in dressing a strip of lumber, this loss in width and thickness will not be taken into account at all (unless it is specifically stated otherwise) in the discussion of cutting lengths of lumber in this and the following chapter. That is, a 1″ x 3″ batten will be assumed, in the specifications, to be actually 1 inch thick and 3 inches wide. Each building carpenter, with the dressed size of his own lumber in mind, can make allowances wherever necessary.

[2] In the following chapters the common term *batten* will be used as a synonym for *strip*.

importance is Upson board or Teakwood, which is considerably cheaper than plywood.

5. COVERING MATERIALS

Scenery is usually covered with either *canvas* or *muslin*. Flame-proofed linen canvas is the best, but it is now too expensive for general use. Duck canvas is very serviceable, while muslin is cheaper and comes in various weights. Heavyweight muslin should be picked for covering large frames. Lightweight cloth can be used to advantage on small frames only. If necessary, two 36-inch strips may be seamed together to make a 72-inch width. Drill, also, is a good covering material.

Other necessary covering materials are:

Chicken wire (for frame trees, built-up ground, and so on)
Fish netting (for backing cut-out drops and borders)
Ground or flake glue
Cold water theatrical paste
Rosine (for attaching scrim or netting to drops and borders). Rosine must be ordered from a theatrical supply house
Bolted whiting

6. HARDWARE MATERIALS

The following hardware must be ordered from some theatrical supply house:

Lash cleats—small hooks on the frame of a flat over which a lash line is thrown to bind one flat to another
Lash-line eyes—metal eyes to which the lash line is attached
Brace cleats—small plates into which stage braces are hooked to prop flats
Ceiling plates—plates for bolting together and hanging ceiling frames
Hanging irons—hardware for hanging scenery
Foot irons—hardware for securing scenery to the floor
Stage picture-frame hooks and sockets—hardware for hanging or otherwise attaching light scenery units to other units
Corner blocks and keystones—small triangular and keystone-shaped pieces of ¼-inch plywood used to reinforce joints

The following hardware may be secured from a local dealer:

Screws—No. 9 wood screws (¾-inch and 1½ inches)
        No. 8 wood screws (¾-inch, 1½ inches and 2 inches)
Corrugated fasteners—No. 5 (¾-inch)
Nails—Cement coated wire nails (4, 6, and 10 penny)
        Finishing nails (assorted)
        1¼-inch lath nails
        1¼-inch clout nails
Tacks—No. 4, No. 6, and No. 8 carpet tacks
Hinges—2-inch tight-pin back flaps (each flap 2 inches)
        2-inch loose-pin back flaps (each flap 2 inches)
        6-inch strap hinges (each flap 6 inches)
Butt hinges—(for lightweight doors)
Bolts—³⁄₁₆″ x 2″ stove bolts
        ⅜″ x 2″ carriage bolts with wing nuts
Door knobs and rim locks
Angle irons and flat corner braces—assorted sizes
Pulleys—assorted sizes
Sash cord—No. 8 (used for lash lines)
Strap iron—³⁄₁₆″ x ⅞″ strips to be made into saddle irons

There are some materials which the stage carpenter will not use so often but with which he should be familiar.

Burlap, rep, and monkscloth—coarse-textured fabrics which are useful for hangings, tapestries, and curtains
Plasterer's burlap—a loosely woven material which can be used for surfacing rocks, mounds, and tree trunks
Bobbinet and linen scrim—fine gauzes used for creating hazy effects and transformations ("vision" scenes)
Netting—for holding together painted flat foliage sections
Hansen gauze—a durable, heavy gauze with a smooth side and a ribbed side, suitable for painting when transparent or semi-transparent effects are desired
Velour—a heavy fabric resembling velvet, used in the making of drapery cycloramas, and occasionally for covering scenery when a surface with a nap is required
Duvetyn—similar to velour, but cheaper
Felt—somewhat similar to duvetyn in surface, obtainable in a number of bright colors, useful for cut-out leaves and other details
Satin, sateen, and taffeta—useful in small or larger amounts where a high sheen is required
Pearl screening—used in place of glass in windows

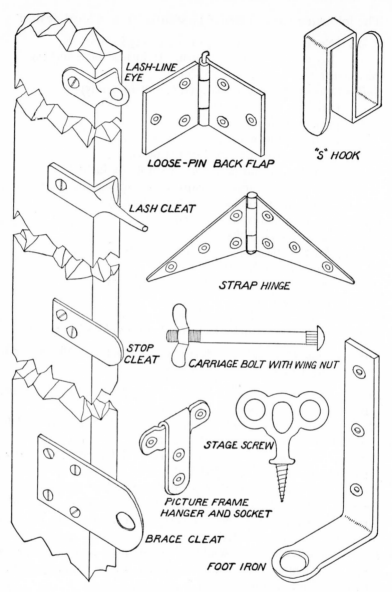

LASH-LINE EYE

LOOSE-PIN BACK FLAP

"S" HOOK

LASH CLEAT

STRAP HINGE

STOP CLEAT

CARRIAGE BOLT WITH WING NUT

STAGE SCREW

PICTURE FRAME HANGER AND SOCKET

BRACE CLEAT

FOOT IRON

FIG. 28. Common pieces of hardware.

Translucent plastic sheets—good for the representation of glass in units, such as windows, through which light but not shapes must be transmitted

7. CONSTRUCTION PROCEDURE

Before starting even the first steps in building, the whole plan of a set of scenery should be carefully drafted on paper. This plan is made up of what are called the "working drawings" (Chapter 3, Section 5) and is usually supplied to the carpenter by the artist who designs the set. It includes complete diagrams—plan, elevation, and, where necessary, cross sections and details—of each unit to show beyond any question the exact construction of every part. In order to prevent any possible waste of materials and time (not to mention patience) caused by the finished product's failure to check with the artist's original idea, a good carpenter demands to know in advance, to the fraction of an inch, just what he is supposed to do. If the carpenter is a man of experience, certain standard arrangements of joints, braces, and hardware may be omitted from the drawings, but enough detail must be included to make the plans clear.

1. With the working drawings before him, the carpenter is ready to start. He checks them over and decides what materials are required. From stock he selects lumber of the right widths and thicknesses in lengths that will leave the least waste. He examines each piece for straightness and absence of flaws. He sets the best pieces aside for use in parts that require the greatest strength and trueness, such as the stiles of a flat, while he places any slightly blemished pieces in another pile for making toggle rails, cross braces, and so on. Before cutting the lumber, he removes the raw edges (the sharp corners, called appropriately by stagehands the "curse") from each strip with a plane. This eliminates the hazard of splinters. A sixteenth of an inch is all that needs to be shaved off. This is done by running the plane the length of each edge once, with the grain.

2. The lumber is now carefully measured, marked, and cut. When several pieces of equal length are to be used, such as the stiles, rails, and corner braces of a series of flats, time as well as accuracy may be gained by cutting one piece for each dimension and using

this piece as a model for marking off the rest. After all of one kind have been cut they may be piled together, as a last check, to make certain that all of the pieces are of exactly the same length. This is most important. It is difficult to think of anything more aggravating than the discovery that a handsomely completed flat is just $3\frac{1}{2}$ inches taller or shorter than its fellows.

If pieces of various dimensions must be cut and heaped together, penciled notations should be placed on each to provide ready identification later.

3. The next step is the assembling. Each unit, such as the side of a parallel or a window frame, is considered by itself. The various battens that are to compose the frame are laid together in the proper arrangement on either a level floor or the template, the corners of the assemblage are carefully squared, and the parts are secured.

8. JOINTING

The joint most commonly used on the stage—at least, in non-professional construction work—is the simple butt or right-angle joint, reinforced with a corner block or keystone (Figures 29 and 30). The two pieces to be joined are placed squarely together, one at right angles to the other, and two $\frac{3}{4}$-inch No. 5 corrugated fasteners (if these are used) are driven in edgewise (teeth down), flush with the wood, across the seam. The corner block or keystone (small triangular or keystone-shaped piece of $\frac{1}{4}$-inch plywood (see Figures 30 and 33) is laid above this and secured by a number of $1\frac{1}{4}$-inch lath or clout nails. (When clout nails are used they should be inserted with their flat edge at right angles to the grain so that they will not split the wood.) Since the combined thickness of the $\frac{7}{8}$-inch batten and the $\frac{1}{4}$-inch block is $1\frac{1}{8}$ inches, the $\frac{1}{8}$ inch of the point of the nail which protrudes must be turned by holding a flat, heavy piece of iron, called a *clinching iron,* against the under side of the batten while driving the point of the nail. The easiest method is to drive all the nails part way in at first, while the frame is flat on the template, to keep the parts from slipping; then to lift the corner, place the iron underneath, and drive the nails in the rest of the way. If iron plates are built into the corners

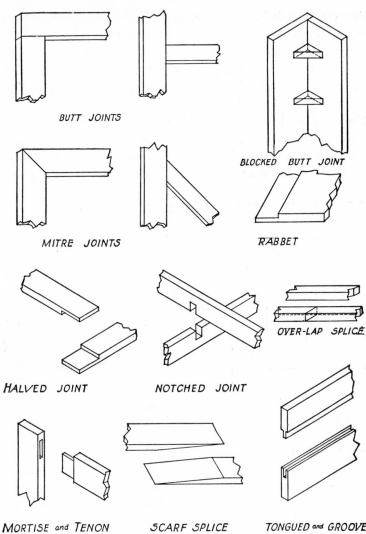

BUTT JOINTS

BLOCKED BUTT JOINT

MITRE JOINTS

RABBET

HALVED JOINT

NOTCHED JOINT

OVER-LAP SPLICE

MORTISE and TENON
JOINT

SCARF SPLICE

TONGUED and GROOVED
BOARDING

FIG. 29. Joints commonly used in scenery construction.

of the template, it is, of course, unnecessary to use an additional plate. The clinching helps to hold the joint rigid (Figure 30).

Corner blocks and keystones should be set in ¾ inch from the outer edge of the piece of scenery to which they are attached in order to make them fit the edges of other flats which may be butted up against them from behind.

The reinforced butt joint makes a firm fastening, strong enough for most purposes on the stage. Some professional studios favor a mortise-and-tenon joint, in which a tongue (tenon), cut on one of the two pieces to be united, is fitted into a slot (mortise) in the

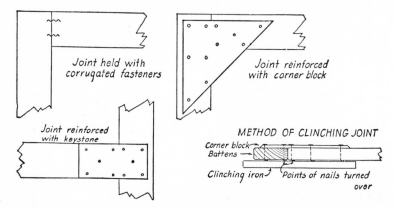

FIG. 30. Corner block and keystone reinforcements. The plyboard plates shown here are of the smaller, homemade, type. (See Sect. 8 and Fig. 33.)

other. A nail is driven through to hold the parts and a corner block or keystone added for reinforcement in the usual manner. As the strength of this joint depends on good fitting it should not be attempted without proper tools. Under most circumstances a simpler method is preferable. A loose mortise-and-tenon combination is useless.

When special strength is required of certain types of joints, use may be made of a bolt, a small block of wood, an angle iron, a mending plate, or a steel corner brace. Special fastenings and reinforcements will be taken up in their proper places in later sections.

The regular corner blocks and keystones mentioned above are rather expensive when secured from theatrical firms. Substitutes can be made easily at home from ¼-inch plywood. Corner blocks should be cut in triangles about 8″ x 8″ and keystones in rectangles 6″ x 3″. Sizes may be varied to suit needs. Composition board, such as beaver board, however, because it is not very tough, is of little use for reinforcing joints.

Screws hold more firmly than nails. Where real strength is required in joints which cannot be reinforced by corner blocks and keystones, such as those used to put door and window frames together, only screws should be used.

During the process of construction it is important to keep the frame absolutely square at all times. Corners should be tested frequently with the steel square. A flat that is even half an inch out of line will cause trouble when placed in the set.

4. After the jointing is completed, the frame is ready for covering and the application of the lashing hardware. It does not make much difference which is done first, although the usual practice is to apply the hardware before covering (Sections 9 and 10 and Figures 31 and 32).

9. COVERING

Covering is the term applied to the process of attaching a canvas face or surface to a frame. The method of covering a flat will be used to illustrate the steps in this process.

a. Turn the frame over on its back so that the smooth side—the side without corner blocks and hardware—is facing up. Lay the canvas or muslin, which has been cut the proper length plus 2 inches or 3 inches, over this. The frame is presumably 69 inches (5′ 9″) wide while the cloth is 72 inches wide. Divide the difference, so that about 1½ inches extends over the frame all around. Stretch the canvas and fasten each corner with a No. 8 carpet tack, driven in part way only.

b. Now tack the canvas to the wood a half an inch from the inner edge of the frame all the way around. Keep the cloth pulled evenly. A good plan is to tack one end first, and to walk to the other end and stretch the canvas from the first row of tacks while driving in the second row. Repeat this process on the sides. It is unnecessary to draw the cloth extremely tight in covering because the first coat of paint will shrink it somewhat. Do not fasten the cloth to the toggle rail and the braces. Space the tacks about 6 inches apart.[3]

  c. Remove the four temporary tacks in the corners and lay back the loose cloth. If the canvas has been properly secured to the wood, there should be a free flap about 4 inches wide all the way around. Two and one-half inches of this are pasted to the frame. To prepare an adhesive agent for this purpose mix 1 pound of flake or ground glue in 2 quarts of water in a pail, and cook this on a stove until it is thoroughly dissolved. Be careful that it does not

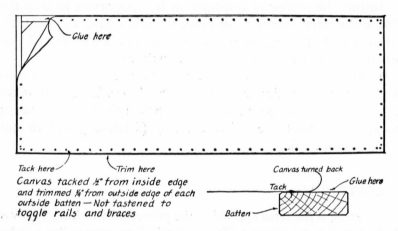

FIG. 31. Covering the frame. The canvas is stretched, tacked, and glued on the face of the frame, the other side from that on which the plywood reinforcement and hardware are placed.

burn. When glue burns, anyone two blocks away is aware of it. For safety's sake, it is well to put the vessel inside another containing a little water, in the double boiler manner, with a small block at the bottom of the larger vessel to prevent the inside pail from touching bottom. When the glue has completely dissolved, stir 1 pound of whiting into it.[4] Turn back the flap of muslin on the frame and apply the mixture, while it is still hot, evenly and generously to the wood with an old brush. Do not place any over the edge; apply to one surface only. If the paste seems thin, let it dry for a moment before applying the cloth to it. Use the edge of a keystone, covered

  [3] Some stage carpenters prefer to use, in place of hammer and tacks, the hand-operated compression stapler.

  [4] An alternate mixture is made of flour (wallpaper) paste, sometimes reinforced with a little glue.

with a rag dipped into warm water and wrung out, to rub over the glued area in order to make sure that the canvas sticks smoothly everywhere. Drive a couple of tacks into each corner, and trim the excess canvas with a sharp knife ¼ inch from the outer edge of the flat. This forces the cut edge into the wood, and prevents fraying when the set is handled.

Because wood does not take scene paint as well as cloth, all large wood surfaces, such as those on columns and steps, should likewise be covered with canvas. Brush the hot glue and whiting preparation over the surface to be covered and spread the canvas over it carefully; then pull the canvas tight, rub it down and tack it, trim the edges, and allow the glue to harden before painting.

10. FASTENING THE UNITS TOGETHER

There are three principal ways by which one unit may be fastened to another: (1) by a lash line, (2) by a loose-pin hinge, and (3) by a carriage bolt (Figure 32).

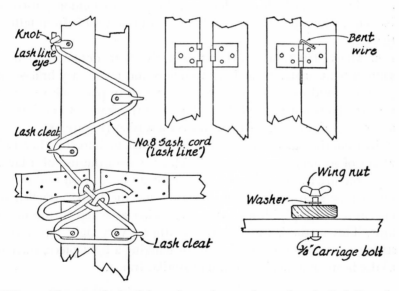

FIG. 32. Three methods of fastening units together, using the lash line, the loose-pin hinge, and the ⅜-inch carriage bolt with wing nut.

1. Flat, standing scenery, and occasionally tall built pieces, are tied together by the lash line method. This method uses a piece

of No. 8 sash cord, called the lash line, and a series of small metal plates or hooks, called lash cleats, placed parallel to each other near two adjacent edges. The lash line, attached to the upper-right-hand corner of one frame, is tossed over the lash cleat placed a little below it on the other frame, carried over a second cleat lower on the first frame, and so on down to be tied off on two parallel cleats about 3′ 6″ from the floor (Figure 59). If the knot is a bow, it may be quickly untied when the scene is struck (Chapter 7, Section 3). This method of lacing two flats or other large units together works very efficiently.

2. Certain small pieces, as well as most of the heavier units, such as platforms and stairs, are fastened to each other by what is commonly called the *pin-hinge*. The full title of this humble piece of hardware, however, is a "2-inch loose-pin back flap." One half of the hinge is screwed to the edge of each unit and fastenings and unfastenings are made simply by inserting or removing the pin (Figure 32). As the regular pin fits so snugly that it is sometimes difficult to put it in and take it out quickly, a short piece of heavy annealed wire (a little smaller than the pin) is commonly used in its place. The top of the wire is bent over to prevent it from falling through.

3. Many structural units, particularly those designed to bear some weight or strain, such as stretchers and temporary braces for platforms and imitation beams, are fastened in place with $\frac{3}{8}$-inch carriage bolts put through holes bored in the frames to be joined, and drawn tight with a wing nut over a washer (Figure 32).

Still another method is occasionally used to join together two pieces of scenery (see Figure 54). This involves the use of a large stage picture-frame hook and socket (or an angle iron and a flattened pipe strap). To make the fastening, the hook, attached to one unit, is simply slipped into the socket attached to the other unit. This method, which makes neither a very tight nor a very strong joint, is really only useful for hanging a light piece, such as a false beam or a shelf, on a wall or similar frame.

11. FLAMEPROOFING

Fire regulations in many communities make flameproof scenery necessary. This may be done by painting all frames before they are covered with chemicals secured from the Anti-pyros Company in New York, and using canvas already treated. If this is found inconvenient or expensive, scenery may be flameproofed at home by painting both cloth and wood with a 40 per cent solution of sodium silicate or a wash made up of the following, stirred well until thoroughly dissolved:

1 lb. borax (sodium tetraborate)
1 lb. sal ammoniac (ammonium chloride)
3 qts. water

All these chemicals may be secured from a local drugstore. So-called flameproof scenery does not have to be actually 100 per cent fireproof. The inspector is usually satisfied if a sample to which a match is applied for a second chars but does not blaze. There should be no live coals.

12. THE USE OF PAPIER-MÂCHÉ AND IMPREGNATED FABRICS

Sometimes in making details of scenery (such as simulated carvings), but more often in the construction of properties (such as statues, urns, ornamented platters, and masks) the shop worker will wish to do some molding which cannot be done with either wood or canvas. In these cases he will find papier-mâché very useful.

Papier-mâché is prepared by cutting or tearing long strips of newspaper from ½ inch to 2 inches wide (depending on the fineness of the molding desired) and soaking these in a mixture of thick *size water* and a little whiting. This mixture is similar to the dope used for gluing down the canvas edges of flats, except that it is a little thinner. In place of this mixture one can use flour paste. The paper strips are torn into easily manageable lengths and pasted on the object to be shaped, one strip crossing the one beneath it to insure strength. Commonly, three or four layers of paper are required. It will take at least twenty-four hours for the papier-mâché to dry, and it may take several days.

If the object to be molded is of any considerable size it should have an armature (interior framework) of wood and chicken wire, worked into a shape approximating the form desired. Unwanted hollows can be filled and desired bulges and projections can be created with twists or clumps of newspaper tied into place. The paper strips are then pasted over all of this.

Such forms as masks cannot have, of course, any underlying framework. They may be made directly on a preliminary molding made of modeling clay (coated with a little Vaseline), allowed to dry, then lifted off. Since the clay itself is moist, however, the coating of paper strips may take a long time to dry. Sometimes it is better first to make a plaster cast of the clay form, to allow this to set and dry, then to cover the inside of it with a thin coating of Vaseline, and to paste the papier-mâché strips in the mold.

Papier-mâché has the advantages of being cheap and easy to work with. It has also certain disadvantages. It is not too strong, it is not waterproof, and when it is stored it is tempting food for rats. A new medium which has none of these disadvantages is an impregnated fabric now being manufactured under several trade names. The best of the products on the market is Celastic, which is extremely rugged, sheds water, and lasts like iron. Celastic may be purchased in sheets of various sizes and various widths. That which is needed is cut off, soaked in a liquid called Box Toe Softener, then applied to the mold and allowed to dry, like papier-mâché. Since Celastic is much stronger than paper, it does not need to be cut into strips pasted one over the other, but it should be applied in small enough pieces to make wrinkling unnecessary. To prevent the Celastic from sticking to the mold, one must coat the mold with Parting Agent before the pieces of the impregnated cloth are put on.

CHAPTER 5

Constructing
the Scenery:
Specific Practice

1. INTRODUCTION

THE NUMBER of possible scenic units employed in building up stage settings is, as we have said, very large. No attempt will be made in this chapter to describe the construction of all of them. The building plans of the several pieces outlined in the following pages are, however, characteristic of whole groups of others similar in purpose and general structure. Consequently, an understanding of the principles involved in making the units laid out in this chapter should make fairly easy the solution of most of the common problems of construction not specifically analyzed here.

2. A PLAIN FLAT

The height of a flat (Figure 33), which depends upon the size of the stage and the demands of the set for which it is designed, may be of practically any size (though seldom over 20 feet), but its width is usually not more than the standard 5′ 9″. This width is generally found to be the most satisfactory. It makes the flat easy to construct and cover, easy to handle, and easy to store (see Chapter 2, Section 3 and Chapter 4, Section 2).

93

For a flat 12 feet high, one should cut from white pine or other softwood stock (Chapter 4, Section 4) the following:

2 battens 1″ x 3″ by 11′ 6″ with square ends (stiles) [1]
2   "   1″ x 3″ by 5′ 9″   "   "   "   (top and bottom rails)
1   "   1″ x 3″ by 5′ 3″   "   "   "   (toggle rail)
2   "   1″ x 2″ by 3′ 6″ with mitred ends (corner braces)

Place the first four pieces on the template or the floor and put them together in the form of a rectangle, with the two 5′ 9″ rails lapping the two 11′ 6″ stiles, as illustrated in Figure 33. Making sure that the corners are absolutely square, first secure each joint by driving a couple of corrugated fasteners [2] across the seam, then reinforce it with a corner block in the manner described in Chapter 4, Section 8. Place the 1″ x 3″ by 5′ 3″ piece (the toggle rail) between the stiles 6′ from the bottom, and the two mitred 1″ x 2″ by 3′ 6″ pieces (corner braces) in the upper- and lower-right-hand corners. Secure the corner braces with corrugated fasteners but reinforce the joints with keystones (which fit better here) instead of with corner blocks. If one wishes to take the time, the edges of the blocks and keystones may be beveled off with a plane. If one flat is to be butted up against the back of another, to make a corner, the corner blocks and keystones along one edge of one of the flats should be set back ⅞ inch (the thickness of a batten) in order to permit making a snug joint (Chapter 4, Section 8). If the flat is over 12 feet high, one or more additional toggle rails will be necessary. Toggles in the frame should not be more than 6 feet apart. They may be less.

Apply the hardware. Place a lash-line eye, or a screw eye with a ½-inch hole, in the upper-right-hand corner,[3] a lash cleat just above the toggle rail on the same side, another one on the left side opposite a point halfway between the first two plates, and two

[1] See footnotes at bottom of page 79

[2] There is a growing tendency in school and community theatre shops to omit the use of corrugated fasteners in the construction of flats, since they are very likely to split the lumber unless they are handled just right, and they are in the way if one wishes to take apart one flat to make another. If the joint must be held rigid before the clout nails are driven in, two or three thin wire nails can be used. Screws may be substituted for the clout nails.

[3] When hardware is not readily available, the lash can be fastened to the top of the stile with one or two large staples.

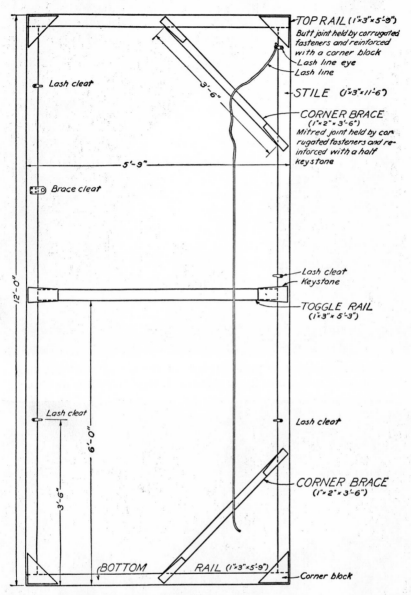

TOP RAIL (1"×3"×5'-9")
Butt joint held by corrugated
fasteners and reinforced
with a corner block
Lash line eye
Lash line

STILE (1"×3"×11'-6")

CORNER BRACE
(1"×2"×3'-6")
Mitred joint held by cor-
rugated fasteners and re-
inforced with a half
keystone

Lash cleat

Brace cleat

5'-9"

Lash cleat

Lash cleat
Keystone

TOGGLE RAIL
(1"×3"×5'-3")

6'-0"

Lash cleat

3'-6"

12'-0"

3'-6"

CORNER BRACE
(1"×2"×3'-6")

(BOTTOM   RAIL (1"×3"×5'-9")

Corner block

FIG. 33. Plain flat, rear elevation. The plywood reinforcements shown here
are of the larger professional size. (See Chap. 4, Sect. 8). Scale ½" = 1'.

Above: *Blood Wedding*, designed by James M. Riley, University of North Carolina.
Below: *Romeo and Juliet*, designed by Roger Sherman, College of William and Mary.

more, one on each side, 3′ 6″ from the bottom of the bottom rail. If the frame is over 12 or 14 feet, of course additional lash cleats are required. Attach brace cleats only to flats which need special propping up by stage braces, such as those occupying a position in the center of a long straight wall, or those holding door frames. In an emergency, 6-penny finishing nails may be substituted for lash cleats, and screw eyes with 1-inch holes for brace cleats. It should be understood, however, that the use of this emergency hardware is distinctly makeshift.

Cut a length of No. 8 sash cord long enough to reach from the lash-line eye to within 3 inches of the floor, put one end through the hole in the hardware, and knot it to prevent it from pulling through. The method of lashing two flats together is described in Chapter 7, Section 3.

When the hardware has been applied, turn the frame over and cover it with canvas on the smooth side, that is, the side without corner blocks and keystones (see Chapter 4, Section 9).

3. A PANELED FLAT

If a wall is to be paneled, a light skeleton is made into the back of each flat to give a footing to the molding strips nailed to the face. Two toggle rails may be spaced to catch the upper and lower edges of a panel, while two upright 1″ x 2″ battens are set between these to catch the sides. If the panels are small and the molding light, the vertical battens can be omitted and the molding strips held snugly against the canvas by having them tacked in place through the canvas from behind. If a cornice of any size is to be used, it must be built separately and hung on, or bolted to, the flat or set of flats.

Incidentally, if a picture or mirror is to be hung on a wall, a similar arrangement of batten support may be used. A 2-inch toggle rail is set in the back of the flat high enough to catch the top of the picture. The latter is hung by fastening to it one or two stage picture-frame hooks (which may be secured from any theatrical hardware company) and slipping these into one or two corresponding sockets attached on the face of the flat to the supporting batten. If the bottom edge of the picture leans heavily against the canvas, a second horizontal batten may be used to brace it.

4. A JOG, A TWO-FOLD, AND A RETURN

A jog, a narrow flat, is constructed in the same general way as the larger unit.

A two-fold, a combination of two flats, is hinged so that the members fold face to face. Three or more 2-inch tight-pin back flaps are used to fasten the two frames together; and a 5-inch strip of canvas is glued and tacked carefully over the crack to prevent light from shining between the flats when the two-fold is set up. A three-fold is built in the same way, except that an extra 2-inch batten, called a *tumbler,* must be hinged between No. 2 and No. 3 flats to allow the latter to fold over the edge of No. 1 when the combination is closed and packed away. In this way whole walls are often constructed in one piece.

The return is a two-fold in reverse. It may, if necessary, be made so that it can fold both frontward and backward by using two-way screen hinges.

5. FLATS FOR A DOOR, A WINDOW, AND A FIREPLACE

One method of treating doors and windows is to construct them of canvas and hinge them to flats. A second method is to build them separately of solid wood, like those found in any real home, and to clamp them, with their frames, into flats when setting the scene. Canvas doors and windows are less expensive, but solid frames are obviously more convincing in appearance. The latter not only give a reassuring impression of substantiality but also add interesting bits of modeling to otherwise flat wall surfaces. By reason of their being set back into the walls 4 or 6 inches they help to suggest that these, too, have thickness—a valuable aid to illusion. The flats illustrated in Figure 34 will accommodate either canvas or solid doors and windows.

The construction of these units is almost the same as that of plain flats, except that an inner frame is added. In the flat for the door, the toggle is raised to form the top of the opening and two extra uprights are placed between this and the bottom rail. The part of the bottom rail between the uprights is cut away. In order to prevent the two legs from racking, a 5′ 9″ piece of $7/8''$ x $3/16''$

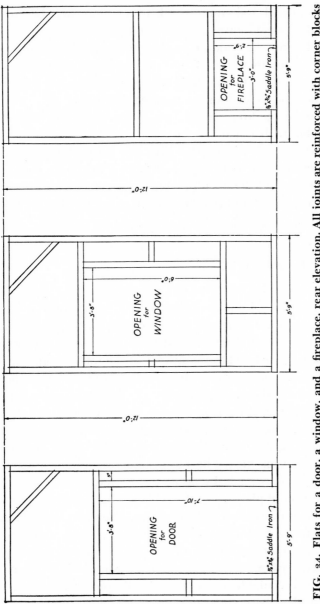

OPENING
for
FIREPLACE

2'-9"

3'-0"

⅛"x¾"Saddle Iron

5'-9"

12'-0"

OPENING
for
WINDOW

3'-6"

6'-0"

5'-9"

12'-0"

OPENING
for
DOOR

3'-8"

7'-10"

¾"x¾" Saddle Iron

5'-9"

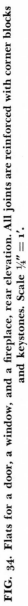

FIG. 34. Flats for a door, a window, and a fireplace, rear elevation. All joints are reinforced with corner blocks and keystones. Scale ¼″ = 1′.

soft steel, drilled and countersunk to accommodate No. 9 wood screws, called a saddle iron, is fastened to the bottom edge.

In the flat for the window one toggle rail forms the top of the opening, and another one, the bottom. Corner blocks and keystones have been omitted in the diagram (cf. Figure 34) to permit the arrangement of the various joints being shown.

The flat for the fireplace (Section 8) is constructed like that for the door, but with a smaller opening.

In covering each of the three flats described above, the canvas is stretched over the entire flat and tacked, first around the outer edge, then around the opening. The center is finally cut out, and the flaps are pasted and trimmed in the way described in Chapter 4, Section 9.

6. A DOOR FRAME UNIT

A door frame unit (Figure 35) consists of a solid *shutter* hung in a frame *casing*, built usually of 1″ x 4″ to 6″ white pine stock and ¼″ plywood. A section of the casing itself (Figure 39) includes a box, or *thickness,* the part that fits into the wall; and a facing, or *trim,* parallel to the surface of the wall at right angles to the thickness. The door is set back in the casing, so that when the door is closed it shows the thickness; the door is commonly hinged in such a way that when it is opened it swings off and upstage.

Because the casing can be constructed to fit the shutter more easily than the shutter can be made to fit the casing, it is wise to build the shutter first. The most common form of door is the paneled one. It is made by fastening (by means of ⅞-inch No. 9 screws) a sheet of plywood to the back of a light skeleton of 1″ x 4″ to 6″ stock, as illustrated in the drawing. The skeleton which represents the raised framework of the paneling should, if possible, be fastened together by means of mortise-and-tenon joints (glued and nailed without keystones). If tools for making this type of joint are not available, the 1″ x 4″ (to 6″) pieces may be attached directly to the plywood. Fasten each piece of the heavier wood to this board with a couple of nails, then turn the door over and secure all the pieces with screws. If the latter method of building a shutter is employed, be certain that the sheet of plywood selected for the back is absolutely flat, and heavy enough to keep the shutter

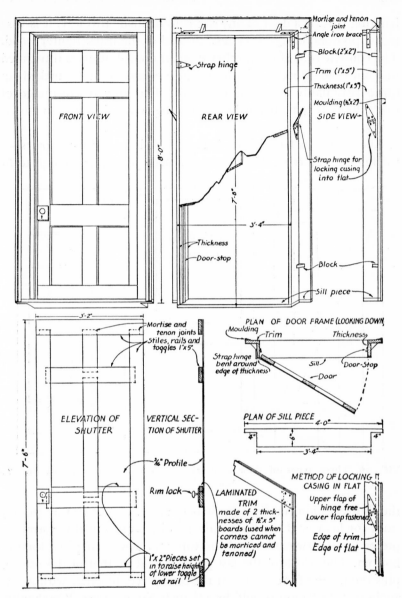

FIG. 35. Door frame unit, front, rear, and side views. Section and plan of the casing and shutter. Scale ⅜″ = 1′.

hanging true. If a door of any size is to be made this way, it is wise to use plywood of ½″ thickness, instead of the usual lighter wood. The construction of three other types of door shutters is illustrated in Figure 36. Good ready-built shutters can often be picked up quite reasonably at the lumberyard. The only disadvantage of stock doors is that, being built for long wear, they are apt to be heavy.

The casing, as has already been stated, is built in two parts—a thickness and a trim. The thickness, made just large enough to fit

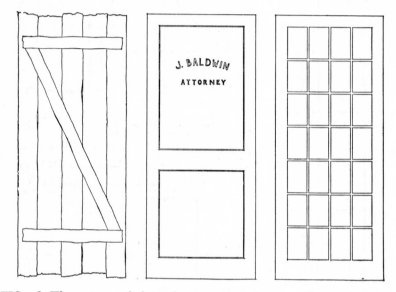

J. BALDWIN
ATTORNEY

FIG. 36. Three types of door shutters, rough batten, office, and French. Scale ⅜″ = 1′.

the shutter comfortably, is constructed first. Out of 1″ x 4″ (to 6″) stock (or heavier if the door unit is to be large) cut three straight pieces for the two sides and the top, and a winged piece for the bottom. The width of the last piece should be that of the others, plus the width of the trim. Put the four pieces together with right-angle box (butt) joints held by 1½-inch No. 9 screws. Wood splits very easily when long screws are driven into it. To prevent this from happening, first make a hole by using a hand drill with a ⅛-inch bit or by driving in and drawing out a 6-penny nail, and then inserting the screw. The head and the sill should lap the edges of the jambs. The sill is attached in such a way that its extra width extends to the front. The trim is fastened with screws to the thickness, at right angles to the latter, all the way around except across the bottom. Its lower edges meet the two narrow wings on the sill. The latter is secured to the former by means of 1¾-inch No. 9 screws put through from below. The sill piece (sometimes called the *saddle*) will sit more steadily on the saddle iron of the flat into which the door frame is placed if a shallow groove is cut in the bottom of the sill.

Use mortise-and-tenon joints, if possible, for fastening together the three members composing the trim. If this cannot be done, build the trim out of two layers of ½-inch stock and lap the corners. That is, cut the three pieces for the first layer so that the two side pieces will extend the full height of the trim and the top piece will fit between them, and cut the three pieces for the second layer so that the top piece will extend the full width, and the side pieces will fit below it. Firm corner joints will be obtained if the second layer is bound to the first by a number of screws, or by 1¼″ lath nails driven through and clinched on the under side (Chapter 4, Section 8 and Figure 30). For further strengthening, a few 2″ x 2″, or larger, rectangular or triangular blocks may be placed in the angle formed by the meeting of the thickness and the trim.

The shutter is hung in the casing by means of two 6-inch strap hinges usually placed on the outside. One flap of each hinge is fastened to the shutter, and the other flap is carried over the edge of the thickness, bent, and attached to the side of the latter. Small strips of ¾″ x ⅜″ wood, called door stops, are nailed around the inside of the casing to prevent the door from swinging the wrong way.

The appearance of a door unit is usually very much improved by the addition of a little molding.

Both door and window units are contrived to lock into their respective flats. To make this possible the 6-inch strap hinge is again brought into use. One of these hinges is fastened to the thickness, part way up, on each side (Figures 35 and 37). It is set at an angle, as illustrated, and only the lower flap is screwed to the wood, the upper flap remaining free. In setting the scene the free flaps are raised, the thickness part of the frame is put through the opening in the flat, and the free flaps of the hinges are lowered to bind the door and casing against the 1″ x 3″ upright battens of the flat that form the sides of the opening. The trim, resting against the surface of the flat on the inside, prevents the frame from falling out.

In order to permit room for the strap hinges and the little rectangular reinforcement blocks in the angle of the trim and thickness on the casing, and to make it possible to lift door and window frames out and in easily, the openings in the flats should be a little larger than the height and width of the thicknesses. Allow about 2½ inches clearance all the way around. That is, if the over-all measurement of the part of the door frame that comes

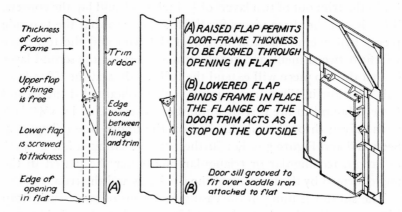

FIG. 37. Strap hinge method of locking door, window, and fireplace frames into their flats.

through it is 7' 8" x 3' 4", the opening in the flat should be 7' 10½" x 3' 9". If the little rectangular reinforcement blocks are not used on the casing, a clearance of 1 inch all the way around will be ample.

If a door unit is to be left in a flat through the whole of a performance and set or flied with the flat (as is often done), the door unit may be fastened in place by means of two or four ⅜-inch bolts (put through the trim of the door unit and the frame of the flat), instead of the strap hinges.

A door unit should be well made. If it is loosely put together, it will sag after a little use, and the shutter will bind against the casing. A firmly constructed unit, on the other hand, will last for years.

7. A WINDOW FRAME UNIT

A typical double-hung window unit (Figure 38) consists of two sash frames sliding between ¼″ x ¾″ and ¼″ x ¼″ strips of wood (called a window stop and a parting strip) in a casing similar to that used with the door (see Figures 35 and 39). The general plan of construction for both units is the same. Sash weights and other

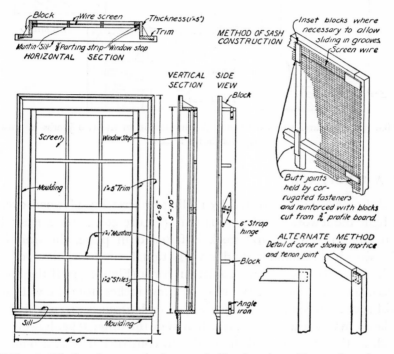

FIG. 38. Window frame unit, front and side elevations. Plan and section of a double-hung window. Scale ⅜″ = 1′.

hardware are seldom used on windows. If one sash must be raised, it can be held in place temporarily by means of a nail, or some other simple fastening. Because real glass is shattered so easily, it is desirable to use in its place galvanized wire screening (or pearl screening, or translucent plastic sheet) tacked to the back of each sash.

The unit is said to be *practical* if it can be opened, *impractical* if it is permanently closed. The window casing is fastened into its flat by either the strap-hinges or the bolt method described in the preceding section.

Another type of window is the casement window which hinges at the side. The flat which holds the double-hung type of window is illustrated in Figure 34.

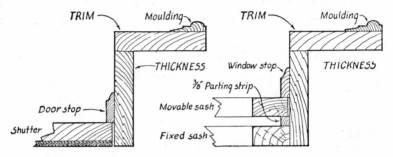

FIG. 39. Door and window casings. A comparison of the two jambs in cross section. Scale 2″ = 1′.

8. A FIREPLACE

A fireplace is constructed by nailing or screwing plywood over a light framework of 1″ x 3″ battens (Figure 40). After a mantel cut from 1″ x 8″ or 10″ stock is fastened in place, the unit is dressed up with molding and any additional woodwork desired.

The fireplace is used with a flat cut for it (Figure 34). If the fireplace is of the type that extends out a few inches from the wall, it will stand safely by itself, especially if its bottom is given a slight rake so that it leans backwards. If it is of the other type, however, such as the one pictured, it is safer to construct it with a 6-inch permanent thickness, and to mount on the outer sides of this two 6-inch strap hinges, to clamp the frame into the flat in the same manner as door and window frames.

A small three-fold screen daubed with gray and black serves as a backing for the opening. If the thickness described above is used, it must be painted to match this.

9. AN ARCHWAY

An archway is made in four parts—a flat, a curved thickness-piece, and two side thickness-pieces. To build the first, two ele-

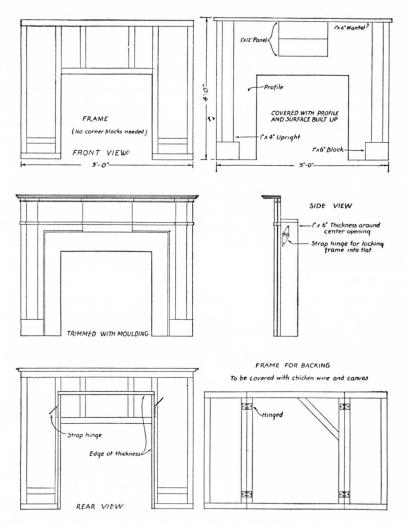

FRAME
(No corner blocks needed)

FRONT VIEW

5'-0"

4'-0"

1"x12" Panel

1"x6" Mantel

Profile

COVERED WITH PROFILE
AND SURFACE BUILT UP

1"x4" Upright

1"x6" Block

5'-0"

TRIMMED WITH MOULDING

SIDE VIEW

1"x 6" Thickness around
center opening

Strap hinge for locking
frame into flat

FRAME FOR BACKING
To be covered with chicken wire and canvas

Strap hinge

Edge of thickness

REAR VIEW

Hinged

FIG. 40. Fireplace unit, showing the method of building it up from a flat frame. Also a hinged backing. (The "profile" indicated in the second drawing at the top is plywood. Scale ⅜" = 1'.)

ments, called *sweeps*, which together form a semicircle, are cut from a wide plank and inserted into the frame of a regular door flat as illustrated in Figure 41. The curved thickness-piece (often made in two parts as illustrated) is made up of two semicircles (or four quarter circles) held apart by light perpendicular blocks of wood. A strip of plywood nailed to the sweeps underneath gives the upper face to the archway. Two 3-inch battens, or wider boards, on edge, make the vertical sides of the opening. To assemble the archway the curved thickness-piece is fastened to the flat with ⅜-inch carriage bolts, and the side thickness-pieces to both the arched piece and the flat by loose-pin hinges.

A wider arch may be built in a two-fold. In this arrangement the saddle iron, holding the legs of the two flats, should be made to hinge in the middle. If the curved thickness-piece is too long for convenient construction or handling, it may be constructed in two or more parts and bolted together.

Without the service of a band saw, cutting accurate sweeps is rather difficult work. A simpler, less "official" arch is illustrated in the lower-right-hand corner of Figure 41. A square box-thickness is fastened to the back of a rectangular opening in the flat, and the curve is created by merely bending and nailing in place a plywood strip (indicated as "profile" in the drawing) of appropriate width. A piece of canvas, on the face of the flat, is tacked to the toggle rail, brought down, cut and pasted over the edge of the profile. This archway is not always very true, and its thickness cannot be removed in striking, a disadvantage when the scenery must be packed; but where accuracy and portability are not so essential, it does well enough.

All solid wood pieces which are to be painted should first be covered with canvas (Chapter 4, Section 9). In covering a sweep, the canvas should be split along the edge and each strip glued down separately, in order that the canvas may hug the curve.

10. THE CEILING

In old-fashioned interiors the space above the wings or flats was masked by a series of vertical cloth strips called *borders*. Modern practice, however, uses the more realistic ceiling piece to close in

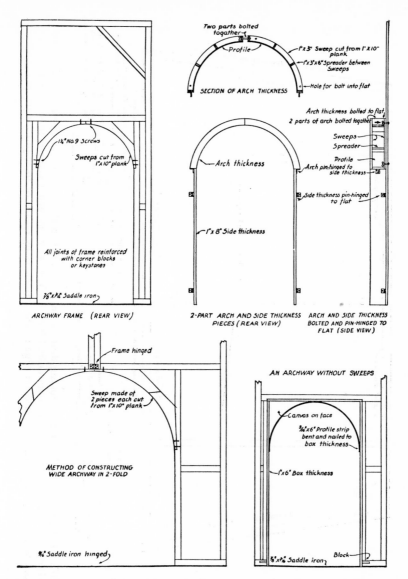

Two parts bolted together

Profile

SECTION OF ARCH THICKNESS

1"x 3" Sweep cut from 1"x 10" plank

1"x 3"x 6" Spreader between Sweeps

Hole for bolt into flat

1¼" No 9 Screws

Sweeps cut from 1"x 10" plank

Arch thickness

1"x 8" Side thickness

All joints of frame reinforced with corner blocks or keystones

⅞"x 1½" Saddle iron

ARCHWAY FRAME (REAR VIEW)

2-PART ARCH AND SIDE THICKNESS PIECES (REAR VIEW)

Arch thickness bolted to flat
2 parts of arch bolted together

Sweeps
Spreader
Profile
Arch pin-hinged to side thickness
Side thickness pin-hinged to flat

ARCH AND SIDE THICKNESS BOLTED AND PIN-HINGED TO FLAT (SIDE VIEW)

Frame hinged

Sweep made of 2 pieces each cut from 1"x 10" plank

METHOD OF CONSTRUCTING WIDE ARCHWAY IN 2-FOLD

⅞" Saddle iron hinged

AN ARCHWAY WITHOUT SWEEPS

Canvas on face

¾₁₆"x 6" Profile strip bent and nailed to box thickness

1"x 6" Box thickness

⅝"x 1½" Saddle iron

Block

FIG. 41. A narrow and a wide professional-type arch with a detachable thickness, and a homemade arch with a permanent thickness. Scale ¼″ = 1′.

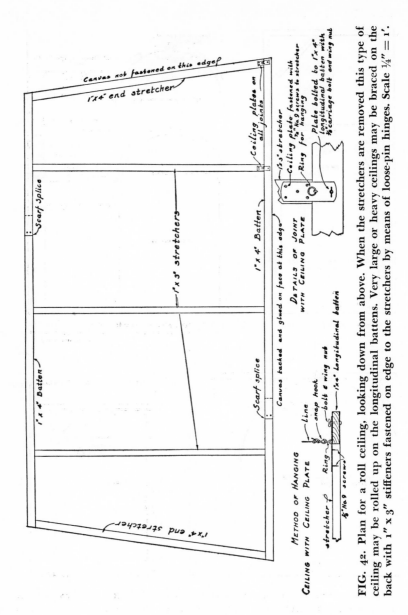

Canvas not fastened on this edge

1"x4" end stretcher

Scarf Splice

Ceiling plates on all joints

1"x 4" Batten

1"x 3" stretchers

1"x 4" Batten

1"x 4" Batten

Scarf splice

Canvas tacked and glued on face at this edge

1"x3" stretcher

Ceiling plate fastened with ⁷⁄₈" No. 9 screws to stretcher

Ring for hanging

DETAILS OF JOINT WITH CEILING PLATE

Plate bolted to 1"x 4" longitudinal batten with ³⁄₈" carriage bolt and wing nut

1"x4" end stretcher

METHOD OF HANGING CEILING WITH CEILING PLATE

Line

snap hook

bolt & wing nut

1"x4" longitudinal batten

stretcher

Ring

⁷⁄₈" No. 9 screws

FIG. 42. Plan for a roll ceiling, looking down from above. When the stretchers are removed this type of ceiling may be rolled up on the longitudinal battens. Very large or heavy ceilings may be braced on the back with 1″ x 3″ stiffeners fastened on edge to the stretchers by means of loose-pin hinges. Scale ¼″ = 1′.

the set above. Attached to two or three sets of lines, it is raised and lowered horizontally.

The more common type for small stages is the *roll ceiling* (Figure 42). Its construction is simple. A large sheet of canvas, made by sewing together several widths, with seams running lengthwise, is tacked and glued to two long 1" x 4" battens, one at the upstage edge and one at the down. If the ceiling is to be of any length— over 20 or 22 feet, for instance—each of these battens may be made of two shorter lengths spliced together with a scarf splice (Figure 29). Three or more 1" x 3" battens, called *stretchers,* cut the width of the ceiling minus 8 inches (the combined width of the two longitudinal battens), are laid across between the longitudinal battens and bolted to them. A ceiling plate, one half of which is attached to an end of each stretcher by means of ¾-inch No. 9 screws (reinforced with ¾₆-inch stove bolts if the ceiling is heavy), laps the edge of the longitudinal batten and is fastened to the latter by a ⅜-inch carriage bolt, which passes through a hole in the wood and is drawn up tight with a wing nut above the plate. Stretchers are not attached to the canvas. Therefore, they should be long enough to make a snug fit, and so prevent a sag in the cloth. The outer edge of this canvas at the sides can be fastened temporarily to the last two stretchers by a few tacks driven in part way.

If the ceiling is very wide, two stiffeners (1" x 3" battens on edge) may be pin-hinged across the stretchers to prevent sagging.

To fly the ceiling, two sets of lines with snap hooks are lowered and attached to rings in the plates. When the frame is in use, it is handled in a horizontal position. When it is not in use, one set of lines is detached and it is flied out of the way vertically like a drop. When the ceiling is taken on tour, it is lowered, the stretchers are removed, and the canvas is rolled up on the two long battens.

The *book ceiling,* a type frequently used where the flies are full of hanging scenery and space is consequently precious, is nothing more than a double frame hinged in the middle and suspended on three sets of lines instead of two. If the ceiling is rigged in the manner suggested in Figure 43, it may be kept in a closed, vertical position in the flies till it is needed, then dropped and opened out on top of a set, by manipulating it from the fly floor alone, without having to lower it to the floor to attach the other set of lines—a distinct advantage when the stage is cluttered with scenery and properties.

Ceilings, both single and double, are often made with sloping sides instead of square, in order to fit the shape of the top of the usual interior set. The shorter edge, of course, is upstage. If a ceiling piece is to be taken on the road, it must be so designed that it may be collapsed and packed into a small space, like the two above. If, however, it is to be used on one stage only, it is unnecessary to make its parts detachable. The stretchers can be fastened permanently to the longitudinal battens, the canvas tacked and

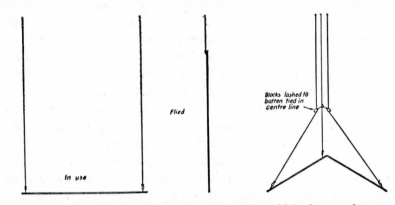

FIG. 43. Roll and book ceilings, the methods by which they are hung and flied. End view.

glued to the outer edges, and any type of simple hanging irons used in place of the more expensive ceiling plates.

Three virtues which should exist in every good ceiling are: lightness, tautness, and size sufficient to cover the whole set (except the backings) comfortably.

11. DROPS, BORDERS, AND TABS

If possible, drops (Figure 44) should be made of good duck or linen canvas, not muslin, because the material must be strong enough to support itself without the aid of a frame. To prevent wrinkling in hanging, seam the cloth horizontally. Use single straight seams and keep all the selvage edges on the back. Tack the cloth between double 1″ x 3″ or 4″ battens at the top and bottom, taking great care to avoid puckers. The battens are fas-

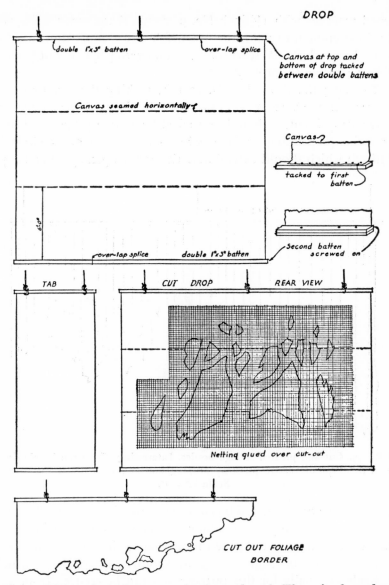

DROP

double 1"x3" batten

over-lap splice

Canvas at top and
bottom of drop tacked
between double battens

Canvas seamed horizontally

Canvas

tacked to first
batten

6'-0"

over-lap splice   double 1"x3" batten

Second batten
screwed on

TAB   CUT DROP   REAR VIEW

Netting glued over cut-out

CUT OUT FOLIAGE
BORDER

FIG. 44. Plain and cut drops, a cut border, and a tab. The units shown here
are considerably smaller in scale than those in general use on full-size stages.
Scale ⅛″ = 1′.

tened together with 1½-inch No. 9 screws. If the wood strips are not long enough to reach the full width of the drop, they may be spliced with the usual scarf splice, or an overlap splice, but preferably the former (Figure 29).

Tapering the drop slightly, that is, making the top two feet longer than the bottom, will cause the side edges to hang straighter.

If a drop is cut, it should be backed by a large piece of netting or scrim (depending upon whether a clear or a misty effect is desired) which should extend over the entire open space and sup-

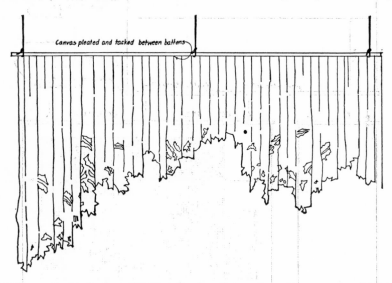

FIG. 45. Cut and pleated foliage border. Interesting effects can be obtained with this type of foliage piece by draping one or both ends of the canvas. Scale ⅛″ = 1′.

port the free branches and bits of foliage (or whatever the elements represent) that compose the silhouette. To attach the netting, turn the drop on its face and glue the netting to the back of the drop with some flexible adhesive agent. Rosine, a preparation which is made especially for this purpose and can be secured from any stage hardware company, is generally employed. It is melted for use in the double boiler arrangement described in the section on "Covering" (Chapter 4, Section 9), and applied with a brush. Some of the cold water pastes are fair substitutes. Whatever the agent is, it should be flexible enough not to crack when the drop is rolled. If the netting used is of the large mesh variety, it will be necessary to attach it to the drop by gluing little strips of cloth over the areas to be fastened.

Stretchers (Section 10) are sometimes used on the back of large drops to make them more rigid.

The border is made in the form of a shallow drop, commonly of only one width of 72-inch canvas, with no battens at the bottom. However, except as an occasional foliage or masking piece, the border is not used very much now.

The tab is made in the form of a narrow drop or border. Drops, borders, and tabs are flied by attaching sets of lines to their upper battens (Chapter 7, Sections 6 and 7).

12. CYCLORAMAS

Cycloramas, or *cycs,* are made of a variety of cloth materials hung from U-shaped wood or metal frames. They are commonly wide enough to reach well beyond the tormentors into each wing, and generally high enough to require no masking above, other than that offered by the teaser and perhaps a border (Chapter 2, Section 7). Made in several different forms, they serve a number of purposes.

The most common form is the drapery or curtain cyclorama (Figure 46). The cloth material, usually a dyed fabric with a surface texture that takes stage lighting well—such as velvet, flannel, poplin, monk's cloth, silk, satin, or duvetyn—is put together in vertical seams, reinforced with a strip of webbing at the top, and tied to the cyc frame by short cords which pass through grommeted holes along the webbed edge of the cloth. The grommets are placed 6 to 12 inches apart.

The frame itself is commonly made of three 1″ x 4″ battens, single or double depending on the reach and the weight of the draperies. A long batten supports the material at the rear, and two shorter ones, the *arms,* pivoted to its ends with 5″ to 8″ strap hinges, carry the material downstage and off.

As draperies are nearly always hung in folds, sufficient material must be ordered to allow for the gathering ("fullness")—generally twice the total width of the cyclorama. The bottom should be weighted with about a 1-inch chain run through a strong hem.

Gauze cycloramas, used in poetic and romantic plays, often

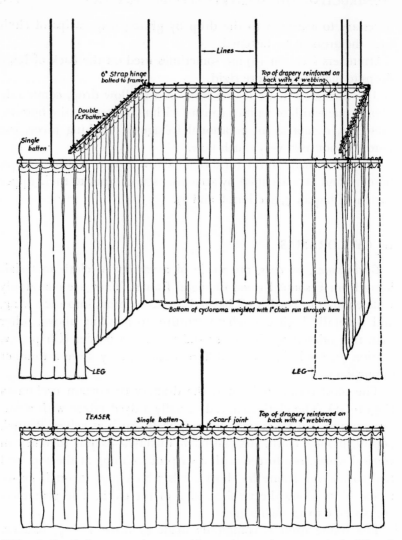

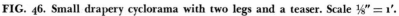

FIG. 46. Small drapery cyclorama with two legs and a teaser. Scale ⅛″ = 1′.

in the community theatre and occasionally in the professional, are made according to the same plan as the more substantial forms. The transparent material is scrim (Chapter 4, Section 5) dyed a dark blue. Under the usual schemes of lighting, scrim of this color succeeds better than that of any other color in blending into the atmosphere.

A *sky cyc,* used in place of the more common drop where it is advantageous to have an exterior backing extend around to the

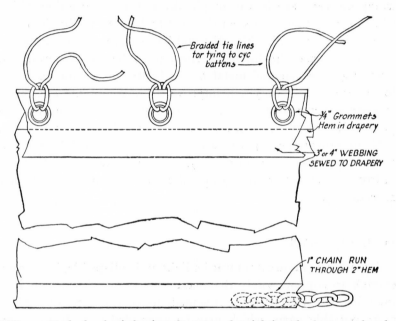

FIG. 47. Methods of reinforcing the top and weighting the bottom of cyclorama drapes.

sides as well as across the back (Chapter 2, Section 11), is made of wide strips of stout duck or linen canvas, sewed together in horizontal seams, and stretched tight between a wood or metal frame above, and either another weighted frame, or floor hooks, below. This form of cyc, which usually must be expansive enough completely to hide its edges behind the tormentors and teaser without the help of any other scenery, is always a pretty heavy unit. Consequently, the frame to which it is fastened must be strong. The larger units are frequently hung from 1½-inch, or even heavier piping in place of the pine battens employed for the smaller units.

The canvas, which is webbed and grommeted along the edge, is laced with a long continuous cord, not tied, to the pipe. The bottom edge is similarly laced to a free, curved pipe, or, to floor hooks—which are frequently merely stage screws in the stage floor. When a strain is put on the lines attached to the upper frame, the loose lashings above and below will adjust themselves, equalize the pull, and thus draw out the wrinkles which often appear in even the best behaved cycs. A latitudinal strain is often added by lacing the vertical edges to snaphooks snapped over guide cables, which are stretched between the grid and hooks in the floor and drawn tight by turnbuckles. If wood battens are used to support a large cyclorama, the hinged corners must be strengthened and made rigid by diagonal metal braces bolted to the frame. If the braces are curved, they will improve the shape of the cyc. Small cycs are sometimes hung from curved travellers (Figure 4) which permit the cycs to be pulled around out of sight when not in use.

If the downstage edges of a cyc cannot be masked by the tormentors or other pieces of scenery, two "legs" (tabs) may be hung in front of the edges of the cyc, parallel to the tormentors (Chapter 2, Section 7).

13. PLATFORMS

A platform (Figure 48) must be light and collapsible, but strong enough to support safely the maximum weight for which it is intended. If it is to be large, it is made up of a number of smaller, more portable parts, which may be assembled quickly in a performance to form the larger structure.

In unit form, a platform consists of two parts: a *platform top*, the floor piece on which actors stand and walk; and a *parallel*, the light folding trestle which supports this. The construction of the parallel is illustrated in the drawing. Each of the five sections is made out of 1″ x 3″ wood strips, cut and put together in the pattern shown. The parts are butt jointed, fastened with ¾-inch No. 5 corrugated fasteners, and reinforced with the usual corner blocks. Each frame is made rigid by a diagonal 1″ x 2″ brace in its upper-right-hand corner.

The five sections are fastened together with 2-inch back-flaps, and secured with ¾-inch No. 9 screws, two hinges being placed at each corner. The two end sections overlap the edges of the side sections, in order to make square outside corners. With this arrangement it is important that the hinges be placed as shown, otherwise the parallel will not fold. It should close one way only.

The platform top is made of 1″ x 6″ tongue-and-groove stock, held together by 1″ x 3″ cross battens fastened with 1½-inch No. 9

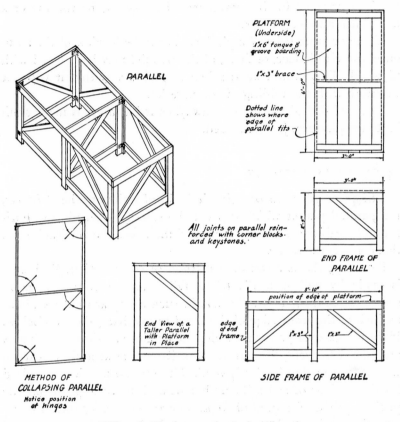

FIG. 48. Platform unit. Scale ¼″ = 1′.

screws. As the cross braces must fit inside the edge of the parallel, they should be cut so that they will be an inch shorter at each end than the width of the platform. Care must also be taken to see that the center brace clears the edge of the middle section of the parallel. (Plywood of ¾-inch thickness may be used for platform tops not larger than 4′ x 8′, and slotted angle iron has been substituted for wood in the making of platform frames.)

When two or more parallels are to be fastened together for mutual support, loose-pin hinges are used if the strain is not very heavy, and ⅜-inch carriage bolts, if greater strength is required (Chapter 4, Section 10). To prevent a tall, top-heavy single platform from rocking over, one or more legs of the parallel are secured to the floor by means of foot irons and stage screws, and the platform may be further stabilized, if necessary, by the use of a brace cleat and stage brace.

If one or more sides of a platform are to be in view of the audience, the visible face, or faces, of the parallel may be covered with plywood. This should be attached in such a way that it will not interfere with the folding of the parallel.

The inclined platform, or runway, called a *ramp*, is made similar to the platform just described.

14. STEPS AND STAIRS

The principal parts of a simple flight of stairs are the *stringers*, the parallel planks which support the steps; the *treads*, the horizontal boards that form the steps; and the *risers*, the vertical boards that connect the treads.

Figure 49 shows a common method of construction. Each step is made by nailing a 1″ x 8″ to 12″ tread across two or more stringers cut from 1″ x 10″ stock, in such a way as to allow about an inch of the front edge of the tread to overhang the step below. If the step is over 30 inches wide, one or more additional stringers are placed between the outside two. Risers, because they bear no weight, are made of ¼″ plywood. There is no absolute standard for dimensions of steps. Their height and depth depends on the pitch required of a flight of steps. The amount of 17 inches is frequently employed, however, as a standard over-all measurement of a tread and its adjacent riser; that is, if the tread is to be 12 inches deep, the riser will be 5 inches high, if the tread is to be 9 inches deep, the riser will be 8 inches high, and so on.

A flight of stairs, unless it is supported independently, is made to fasten to the platform to which it leads. A 1″ x 4″ batten is fastened with 1½-inch No. 9 screws across the stringers at the top, under the edge of the last tread, and a similar batten is placed just below its level on the parallel. A couple of brace cleats are

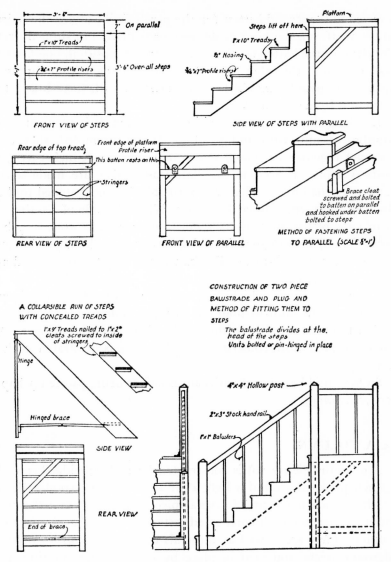

FRONT VIEW OF STEPS

3'- 8"

7" On parallel

1"x10" Treads

3/4"x7" Profile risers

3'- 6" Over-all steps

SIDE VIEW OF STEPS WITH PARALLEL

Platform

Steps lift off here

1"x10" Treads

1/2" Nosing

3/4"x7" Profile risers

REAR VIEW OF STEPS

Rear edge of top tread

Front edge of platform
Profile riser
This batten rests on this

Stringers

FRONT VIEW OF PARALLEL

Brace cleat
screwed and bolted
to batten on parallel
and hooked under batten
bolted to steps

METHOD OF FASTENING STEPS
TO PARALLEL (SCALE 3/8"=1')

A COLLAPSIBLE RUN OF STEPS
WITH CONCEALED TREADS

1"x9" Treads nailed to 1"x2"
cleats screwed to inside
of stringers

Hinge

Hinged brace

SIDE VIEW

REAR VIEW

End of brace

CONSTRUCTION OF TWO PIECE
BALUSTRADE AND PLUG AND
METHOD OF FITTING THEM TO
STEPS
The balustrade divides at the
head of the steps
Units bolted or pin-hinged in place

4"x4" Hollow post

2"x3" Stock hand rail

1"x1" Balusters

FIG. 49. Stationary and collapsible runs of steps, a balustrade, and a plug.
Scale 1/4" = 1'.

screwed to the second batten (on the parallel). To attach the stairs to the platform, the head of the former is lifted and slipped over the cleats of the batten on the parallel. In this position, one batten rests on top of the other. The cleats prevent them from slipping apart. The parallel should be well anchored with stage braces to prevent it from tipping over.

If a long flight of steps is to be constructed, it is planned as a number of unit runs and parallels. When assembled, they are fastened together by 2-inch loose-pin hinges or ⅜-inch carriage bolts (Chapter 4, Section 10). Balustrades, also, are made separately, attached to the edge of 1″ x 10″ planks, and fastened to the flight of steps with similar hardware. When the side of a staircase is in view of the audience, the entire construction work may be concealed by a triangular flat (*plug*) fastened by loose-pin hinges to the face of the stair case. The balustrade may be constructed as a part of this unit.

A narrow stairway which does not have to reveal its steps from the side may be built without cut stringers. The treads are merely nailed to cleats screwed to the inside of the straight stringers. A small, portable unit, constructed on this plan, is illustrated in the drawing.

Steps should be covered with canvas before being painted (Chapter 4, Section 9).

15. A COLUMN

A column (Figure 50) is constructed by nailing wide sheets of ¼-inch plywood around a light cylindrical frame. Wooden discs or rings, each made up of several pieces of 1″ x 6″ to 10″ stock fastened together with corrugated fasteners, form the core of the column. They are spaced at intervals equal to the width of the plywood sheets, and held in place by 1″ x 2″ strips running the length of the unit. The plywood strips are wrapped around this core and nailed to the edge of the discs, or rings, as well as seamed along the strips. The column viewed from one side only needs but one good face. In fact, small columns are often made in halves, that is, formed around half discs, called "half-rounds." This type of column, if it is not held erect by some other structure above, is secured by a brace cleat and stage brace fastened on the blind

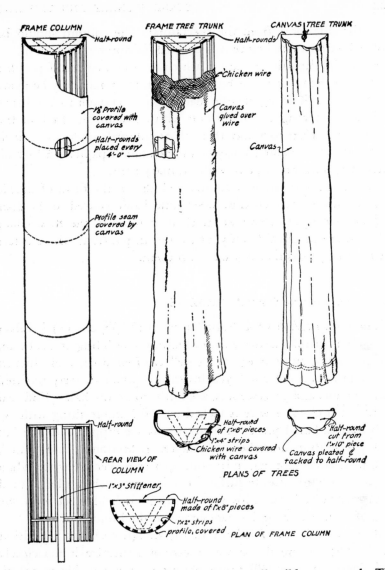

FRAME COLUMN

Half-round

⅛" Profile
covered with
canvas

Half-rounds
placed every
4'-0"

Profile seam
covered by
canvas

FRAME TREE TRUNK

Half-rounds

Chicken wire

Canvas
glued over
wire

CANVAS TREE TRUNK

Half-rounds

Canvas

Half-round

REAR VIEW OF
COLUMN

1"x3" stiffener,

Half-round
of 1"x8" pieces

1"x4" strips

Chicken wire covered
with canvas

Half-round
cut from
1"x10" piece

Canvas pleated &
tacked to half-round

PLANS OF TREES

Half-round
made of 1"x8" pieces

1"x2" strips

profile, covered

PLAN OF FRAME COLUMN

FIG. 50. Frame column, and a frame and a collapsible tree trunk. The "profile" indicated in the drawings of the column is plywood. Scale ¼" = 1'.

side (the side away from the spectators). The column should be covered with canvas before it is painted (Chapter 4, Section 9).

Bases and capitals, the use of which is to be avoided if possible because of the nuisance of building them, must generally be made more solidly. Molding may be made flexible enough to bend into a circle by making a series of cuts with a saw on the back or the front of the strip part way through at intervals of ¼ to ½ inch (Sections 23). Ornaments may be molded out of papier-mâché and, when dry, fastened in place with ordinary nails.

Columns are frequently constructed also in the form of simple canvas cylinders stretched between solid bases secured to the floor and wooden discs or frames attached to ropes in the flies. Cloth columns are practicable only, of course, in positions where actors are not likely to lean or brush against them.

16. TREE TRUNKS AND FOLIAGE

The construction of a "solid" tree trunk (Figure 50) involves the same principles as those employed in the building of a column, except that a more irregular "core" is often used, and chicken wire and canvas are employed instead of plywood. Irregularities, such as knots and excrescences, are built up on the half-cylindrical frame, then chicken wire is tacked over the whole thing with ½-inch staples. Small pieces of scrap canvas are dipped into the hot glue preparation described in Chapter 4, Section 9, and pasted, with their edges lapping, in irregular patterns over the wire. When this dries, a hard, uneven surface remains on which can be painted a suggestion of bark. This type of trunk is held erect with the help of a brace cleat and a stage brace on the blind side.

If the tree trunk called for in the design occupies a position on the stage where the audience cannot scrutinize it too closely and where no actor will brush against it, it is possible to substitute a much more easily built collapsible form for the rather elaborate framed kind described above. A wide strip of canvas is tacked in irregular pleats around notched discs at the top and bottom and hung by means of a screw eye to a line in the flies.

Realistic foliage is difficult to create on the stage, except in very expensive ways, and modern scenic artists consequently avoid its use as much as possible. Showing the lower portions of several realistic tree trunks in the foreground, the designer attempts merely to suggest masses of leaves and shrubbery in the background by using well-shadowed cut-out drops kept discretely behind much scrim. Where foliage must be shown downstage, cut-out cloth borders can be hung in silhouette. The canvas is frequently gathered or draped, after it is cut, to add to the depth of the foliage (Figure 45). The effect secured, especially in fairly dim scenes, is sometimes quite convincing.

Bushes and smaller shrubbery units may be constructed out of actual branches or sticks wired together and shaped up with papier-mâché, in accordance with the artist's design. To this skeleton are attached—by means of short lengths of fine wire—pieces of greenery secured from any concern that makes artificial flowers, or leaf and blossom forms cut from glue-stiffened cloth, crepe paper or felt. The bush is then painted.

Short lengths of vine and little plants can be made best out of artificial foliage materials bought in the five and ten cent store. At twenty cents a sprig, however, their cost precludes their use for quantitative effects.

17. ROCKS AND BUILT-UP GROUND

Rocks and built-up ground (Figure 51) are made by covering light, irregular frames of 1″ x 3″ stock with chicken wire tacked down with ½-inch staples, and covering the wire, in turn, with small pieces of canvas dipped in a mixture of hot glue and whiting, in much the same way as tree trunks are built. If the rock or ground is to be walked on, care must be taken to make the framework strong and rigid. The standard method for building a practical rock is to start with a number of vertical three- or four-sided frames, similar (except that these are irregular) to the sections of a parallel (Section 13). They are of different heights, some straight, some inclined, and some pointed. Placed edge to edge and edge to side, lengthwise and across, they are fastened together with nails, or better, with 1½-inch No. 9 screws. In the parts of the rock that must be practical, additional battens are nailed at short intervals between sections, and these are covered with pieces of planking arranged in different planes. If the rock is large, it should be made in a number of smaller units, pin-hinged or bolted together.

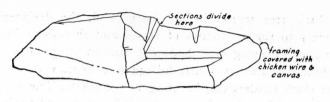

ROCK

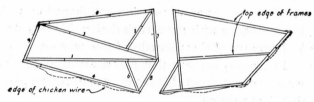
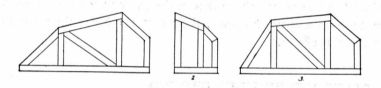

PLAN OF FRAMES - 2 SECTIONS

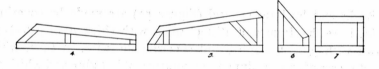

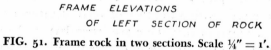

FRAME ELEVATIONS
OF LEFT SECTION OF ROCK

FIG. 51. Frame rock in two sections. Scale ¼″ = 1′.

Tufts and folds of brown burlap or felt attached to the surface here and there may be made to suggest patches of earth and knots of grass.

18. GROUND ROWS AND SILHOUETTES

Ground rows and other silhouette pieces (Figure 52) are made by nailing ³⁄₁₆- or ¼-inch plywood over flat frames of 1″ x 3″ stock,[4] which are put together with corrugated fasteners and reinforced with corner blocks in the usual way (Chapter 4, Section 8). The silhouettes are then painted and the outlines are finally

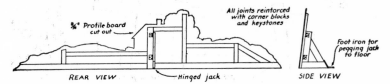

FIG. 52. Ground row, rear and side elevations. (What is designated here as cut-out "profile board" is ¼″ plywood.) Scale ¼″ = 1′.

cut out with a compass saw. The unit is made to stand up by hinging a triangular brace, called a *jack,* to its back. Small units may use an angle iron in place of the jack.

In an emergency a rather convincing distant mountain can be suggested by pinning a piece of light blue or violet tarlatan to the bottom of the sky drop.

19. WALLS AND FENCES

Walls and fences, made as independent units, whatever their design, must be fairly strong as well as lightweight (Figure 53). Heavy appearing parts should be made in skeleton form; that is, brick or stone parts, rails and posts should be shells only, put together with light lumber and covered (in the case of walls) with plywood, canvas, or chicken wire and canvas. Fence sections are made to stand up by means of jacks (Section 18).

[4] In the making of large ground rows it is not necessary to cover the whole frame with plywood. Strips of plywood can be cut for the shaped edge of the row, then the rest of the frame will be covered simply with canvas.

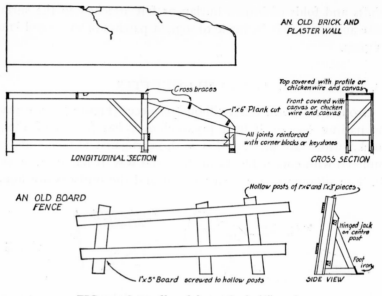

FIG. 53. Set wall and fence. Scale ¼" = 1'.

20. LOG CABIN WALLS

A simple method of suggesting the solid log walls of a cabin is outlined in Section 19 of the following chapter.

21. A BEAM

A large beam, or log, seen in three dimensions in a stage setting, is constructed as a light shell of wood, or wood and canvas. If it is small, it is built out of ½-inch planks put together in the form of a long, three-sided trough. If it is large, each of its faces may be made as a narrow batten frame covered with canvas. If it is irregular in shape, it may be modeled by the use of chicken wire and rags dipped in glue (Section 16). The beam is fastened in its position in the set by means of ⅜-inch carriage bolts and wing nuts or picture frame hangers and sockets (Chapter 4, Section 10).

Square posts and pilasters are made in the same hollow form.

22. IRREGULAR THREE-DIMENSIONAL COMBINATIONS

The construction of irregular three-dimensional units, such as dormer windows, alcoves, and perspective set houses—which have to be planned for two-dimensional striking and storage—is always something of a problem. A unit of this type, considered as a combination (often quite complicated) of a number of flat, or semi-flat parts, must be analyzed by the designer and carpenter and condensed into its simpler elements. Each part is laid out and built as an independent unit. The various members are then assembled by means of tight-pin hinges, loose-pin hinges, and ⅜-inch carriage bolts and wing nuts (Chapter 4, Section 10) in the least involved method possible under the circumstances.

Figure 54, by way of illustration, suggests how a small, irregular set house might be laid out. The front and end walls are constructed separately, covered with canvas, and then fastened together with tight-pin hinges in such a way that the three frames may be folded up backward like a double return (Section 4). The rear wall is constructed and covered, and fitted with loose-pin hinges to enable it to be fastened to the end walls (on the inside) when the little house is set up in the wings before the performance. A ridge pole cut to brace the top of the house is fastened to the two end frames by means of picture frame hangers and sockets (Chapter 4, Section 10) or shutter bolts. The roof (only the front half in this case is necessary because the back cannot be seen) is made in the form of a separate lid with a stop batten all the way around on the inside to prevent its slipping up, down, or to the side.

If the roof is carefully made and fastened in place with loose-pin hinges when the house is set up, no additional bracing is necessary.

The chimney, a light box frame covered with light profile board or canvas, may be pin-hinged or bolted to the ridge pole. The door and window in a house of this small size can, if they are not to be "practical," be simply built up on the surface of the walls in which they are supposed to hang. If the roof is supposed to be shingled it is quite sufficient to use two rows of real wood and to suggest the other rows with paint.

The house just described would be a small one. If a larger "practical" house were required, the walls could be constructed in the same way, but they would have to be either lashed or bolted together, and additional bracing would be required to keep them in position. The roof still could be fastened with loose-pin hinges. Door and window frames would be made separately and fixed in

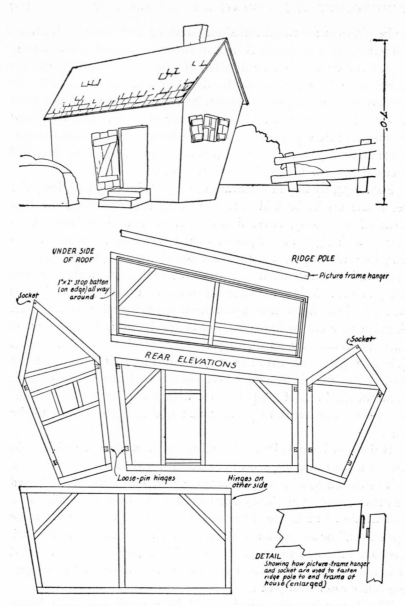

UNDER SIDE
OF ROOF

RIDGE POLE

Picture frame hanger

1"x 2" stop batten
(on edge) all way
around

Socket

Socket

REAR ELEVATIONS

Loose-pin hinges

Hinges on
other side

DETAIL
Showing how picture-frame hanger
and socket are used to fasten
ridge pole to end frame of
house (enlarged)

7'-0"

FIG. 54. Small set house. A set piece of this type may be combined effectively with set walls, fences, and ground rows in the background of various kinds of exterior scenes.

position in the usual way (Sections 6 and 7). If it were desirable
to bring the house onto the stage in one piece for rapid shifting
it could be flied by means of two piano wires (painted black to
make them invisible), each attached to an end frame; the opposite
ends of the wires are attached to fly ropes. Or the house might be
mounted on a wagon—that is, be bolted or pin-hinged around
the outside edge of a wagon built to its shape—with about ½-inch
clearance from the floor (Chapter 7, Section 11) and rolled in
from the side.

The above description of a knock-down house will suggest some
methods of approaching the problems of other irregular three-
dimensional pieces of scenery.

23. THE USE OF MOLDING

Decorative woodwork in a setting, such as that around doors,
windows, fireplaces, and pilasters, as well as bookcases, cupboards
and other standing properties constructed as scenery, should be
dressed with molding. The woodwork never looks quite convincing without it. Molding may be ordered in a wide variety of designs. The most generally useful for elementary construction on
the stage is 1″ panel molding. This is adaptable to many purposes.
It can be built up, when desired, by having a lattice strip placed
beneath it.

A length of molding can be curved to follow an arched line by
making a series of cuts with a saw part way through, about an inch
apart, on the edge to be made concave. To fasten the bent molding
in place, use 1-inch lath or finishing nails. Place them about 3
inches apart and drive them, not into the strip itself, but into the
saw cuts. This will prevent splitting the little segments of wood.

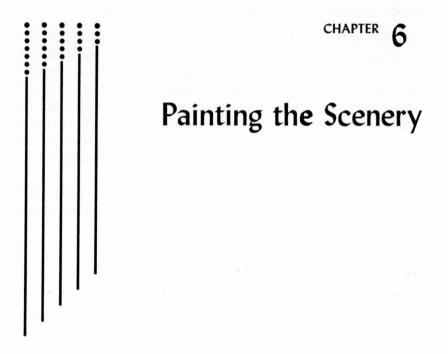

CHAPTER 6

Painting the Scenery

1. INTRODUCTION

THERE IS LITTLE work associated with the technical department of play production more fascinating than that of scene painting. To the uninitiated it often appears to be a rather mysterious and wonderful art; the ability to daub or splash a colored wash on flat canvas with an 8-inch brush and make the result look from a distance like a rough plaster wall, or sky, or mist-covered mountain, seems little short of magic. It is assumed by many people that the processes of securing such extraordinary effects must be difficult and complicated. As a matter of fact, they are usually quite the contrary. To become a real master of the art demands, of course, many years of study; but to learn to conceive and paint simple, attractive settings for the common type of modern play is no very difficult achievement. For this work, some understanding of drawing and composition, and a good eye for color, are essential. Anyone, however, who has done a little freehand sketching and painting in water colors should pick up the tricks of handling the larger medium of scene paints fairly readily. He must be prepared to use his materials freely and to do a considerable amount of experimenting.

2. THE TRICKS OF SCENE PAINTING

The first trick the artist learns is, obviously, to exaggerate. All painting for the stage must be done in a bold, straightforward way. Effects must be seen from a distance. Fussy details of design and color are consequently lost upon an audience. The smallest brush in common use in scenic work is two inches wide, and the ones more often employed measure from six to ten. It requires some courage to use these at the start, and a considerable amount of experimenting must usually follow before one acquires a sense of control over them. But in time they become as easy to manage as smaller brushes.

Another trick that must be learned is to paint for stage lighting. The latter can change not only the quality of color, but its intensity as well. Consider its effect upon make-up. "To appear natural to the audience one must be unnatural on the stage," was forcefully demonstrated by Cleon Throckmorton, at that time Art Director for the Provincetown Playhouse in New York, when he applied brilliant touches of green, red, and blue to the leaves of a real rose vine in a garden set to make the plant look from the audience like something more healthy and colorful than the pale weed it appeared to be before the artist gave it this assistance.

Scene painting can really be learned only through experience. The artist who is working in the medium of scene paints for the first time should not be discouraged if at the start he finds he has to do considerable repainting before he arrives at the effects he wishes to secure. Fortunately, scene paints are opaque and cheap and one coat may be applied on top of another as long as the glue will hold to the canvas.

3. PAINT MATERIALS

The following materials are required for painting:

Scene paints. Distemper, or water color, is employed almost exclusively on the stage, its advantages over oil being that it can be applied more easily and quickly, it dries more rapidly, it does not shine, it is cleaner to handle, it is far cheaper, and it is not inflammable. What is known as *scene paint* is the pure pigment in powdered form. Before it is used it must be mixed with glue and

A design by Mordecai Gorelik for Eugene O'Neill's *Desire Under the Elms*.

water. It is sold in sixty or more colors. Some of the most serviceable ones are the following:

Light chrome yellow	Magenta
Medium chrome yellow	Venetian red
Hanover green	Raw sienna
Medium chrome green	Yellow ochre
Dark chrome green	Orange mineral
Italian blue	Burnt umber
Ultramarine blue	Drop black

Other useful colors, some of which cost a little more, are: lemon
yellow, burnt sienna, vermilion, permanent red, purple lake,
light Milori yellow, malachite green, and emerald green.

Because of their cost, ready-made calcimine and other premixed
commercial preparations are not recommended except when it is
impossible to secure the pure pigments.

Whiting. By far the most useful pigment for the artist is ordinary
bolted whiting. He should estimate that he will use as much of
this pigment as all of the rest of the pigments put together. Only
good grade whiting should be used. Belgian and Danish whitings
are standard.

Common flake glue. Flake gelatin glue is preferable to ground
glue, though either may be used. These must be cooked. LePage's,
which needs no preparation except thinning with cold water, may
be employed in an emergency—only in an emergency, however,
because not only is it too expensive for general use, but also it
has a strong tendency to gray out any pigment mixed with it. Most
other cold water glues must be used judiciously.

Casein glue. This kind of glue, which may be mixed with cold
water, is coming into increasing favor where wearing and water-
resisting qualities are desirable, such as on woodwork. It is excellent for outdoor painting. Casein glue, however, is hard on brushes
and hands.

Non-rosin white casein. Some artists now use this in place of
separate whiting and glue for the primary coat. It can be mixed
with pigments for secondary coats. A product like Texolite has
the advantages of being ready for immediate use without the
necessity of adding other glue to it.

4. PAINTING IMPLEMENTS

For painting scenery, three different types of brushes will be found especially serviceable: one 8-inch and one 6-inch *priming* brush, for priming and covering large surfaces rapidly; one 4-inch *laying-in* brush, for smaller areas; and one 2-inch and one 1-inch *lining* brush for detail. There are a number of other types, such as round *foliage* brushes and special *liners,* which might be mentioned; but the three above will be found to be adequate for most purposes. They should all be of the good quality, long-bristle variety used in distempering walls. Brushes deteriorate very rapidly unless they are taken care of. After every painting they should be rinsed, shaken out, and dried in a flat position. Better still, drill a hole in each brush handle and hang the brush up on a nail. Never place a brush in boiling water. Other necessary implements for the artist are:

A yardstick
Charcoal sticks and chalk
A snap line (about 40 feet of heavy braided cotton cord)
A bow snap line (for shorter lines)
A pounce wheel (for making holes in a paper over which a pounce bag will be patted or rubbed)
A pounce bag (for chalk or charcoal marks)
A straight-edge beveled liner (for ruling short lines)
A 12-foot batten with a perfectly straight edge for ruling long lines
A large wooden compass (for describing circles and arcs)
A feather duster (for removing charcoal and chalk marks)
Stencil paper and frame
Several 2–3 gallon pails and smaller pans
Muffin tins (for holding small amounts of different kinds of color)
A gas, electric, or kerosene stove with at least two burners

5. THE PAINT FRAME

Another aid to the artist, found in the best equipped studios, is the *paint frame.* It is a large, rectangular, wooden skeleton, suspended from a set of ropes or cables, and big enough to accommodate a whole drop or set of flats spread out and fastened to it.[1]

[1] Paint frames are sometimes rigged on stages. See Figure 69.

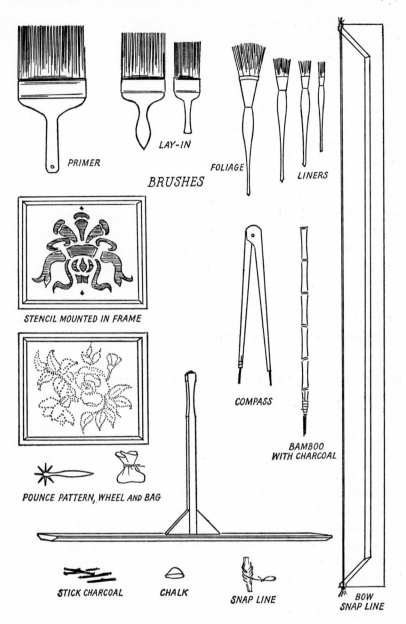

PRIMER

LAY-IN

BRUSHES

FOLIAGE

LINERS

STENCIL MOUNTED IN FRAME

COMPASS

BAMBOO
WITH CHARCOAL

POUNCE PATTERN, WHEEL AND BAG

STICK CHARCOAL

CHALK

SNAP LINE

BOW
SNAP LINE

FIG. 55. Painting implements.

Slots are cut in one or more floors to permit raising and lowering the frame through them, and to allow two groups of artists, if necessary, to work on a large piece of scenery at the same time. The frame is sometimes counterweighted and operated by means of a winch or some other manual device, but it is more often motorized for convenience in handling. Any type of flat scenery can be painted on this contrivance. This method of painting offers several advantages over the flat-on-the-floor method; it saves the artist's back by allowing him to do his work in an upright position; it spares his having to tramp over the surface of the canvas; and it gives him the opportunity to step back occasionally and view the progress of his labor. This is all important, however, only if scenery must be done in quantity. A university or community theatre should not worry itself over the problem of investing money in an expensive paint frame until it already has plenty of room in its workshop or on the stage, and until more important equipment has been paid for. Flats and drops can be painted very well on a large floor. Many of the busiest professional studios throughout the country use this method exclusively.

6. ELEMENTS OF COLOR AND COLOR MIXTURE

Before the scenic artist attempts to go very far into the methods of painting he should read and familiarize himself with the principles of color discussed in Chapter 12. The application of these principles to the pigments with which the scenic artist deals is, of course, quite different from that required for lighting, but the fundamentals are the same wherever color exists.

Generally speaking, the scenic artist is not concerned with *additive* mixtures (used in the composition of light) in which red, green, and blue are regarded as the primary colors, but with *subtractive* (Chapter 12, Sections 2 to 5) mixtures in which blue-red (magenta), yellow, and blue-green (cyan) are the primaries. Simply, this means that blue-red, yellow, and blue-green are the basic colors for pigmentary schemes and that under ideal conditions they may be mixed to make three other colors. Magenta combined with yellow makes red, yellow with blue-green makes green, blue-green with magenta makes blue. These second three are the second-ary colors.[2]

It is easy to see the relationship of these colors if one studies Figure 113. The three primaries occupy the circles. Where any two of them overlap (are mixed in accordance with the subtractive scheme) they produce a secondary color. This is assuming, of course, that the proportions are about equal. If much yellow is mixed with a very little magenta, the product will be orange rather than red. If much yellow is combined with a small amount of blue-green, the result will be yellow-green instead of green.

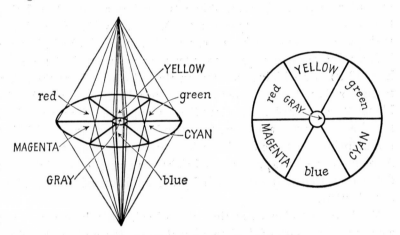

FIG. 56. Color wheel and color solid.

If all of these colors are arranged on the circumference of a wheel, such as that indicated in Figure 56, one can see other re-lationships. Colors adjacent to each other, such as yellow, yellow-green, and green, are *analogous*. Colors directly opposite each other are *complementaries*. Green is the complement of magenta (blue-red), blue is the complement of yellow, and red is the complement of cyan (blue-green). In the center of the wheel is gray, the abso-lutely neutral point. Colors are brightest when they are related to (nearer to) the outside edge of the wheel and dullest when they are related to the center.

[2] It will be noted that the secondary colors that result from mixing sub-tractive primaries are the additive primaries, and vice versa.

When two colors, represented by two points anywhere on the circumference of the wheel, are mixed, they produce a third color. If this were represented in a diagram, the third color, or blend, would be placed somewhere on a straight line drawn between the two original colors. The position of the blend on this line would depend on whether there was more of one of the original colors than the other in its composition. It will be seen that a point on this line (anywhere short of the extremities) is nearer to the hub of the wheel (grayness) than is a point on the circumference. This explains the fact that a mixture is never as intense in tone as a pure pigment. When two colors are combined they lose part of their intensity (saturation). If pure yellow is combined with pure magenta, for instance, a red is produced which, because it is a mixture, is not quite so intense as a pure red of the same hue. The more widely separated on the color wheel are the colors to be combined, the grayer or more nearly neutral will be the blend. When complementaries (directly opposite colors) are mixed together in correct amounts, they produce a pure gray. This is a useful principle to remember when preparing paint for scenery. A pigment which appears too bright may very easily be toned down or softened (neutralized) by the addition of a little of its complement.

We have just glanced at the color wheel. This, however, is not a complete diagram of the behavior of color. If we place the wheel on edge, we find that it is a cross section of a three-dimensional figure made of two cones with their bases placed together (Figure 56). The end points of the two cones represent white and black respectively and mark the extremities of the gray line passing through the center of the figure. What happens to a color when it is mixed with white or black can now be seen very clearly. Not only is it grayed but lightened or darkened as well. A cross section of the color solid may be taken at any point, between the extremities, to produce a perfectly proportioned color wheel. The only dissimilarity between a cross section taken near an end and one taken near the center would lie in the fact that the colors on the circumference of the wheel sliced near the end would be less widely differentiated than those on the wheel sliced near the center.

A color, then, has three characteristics, which are determined by its position in this figure. Its *hue* is determined by its position in relation to other colors on the circumference of the wheel—that is, by its redness, yellowness, orangeness, blue-greenness, and so on. Its *saturation* is determined by its nearness to the center of the wheel—that is, the amount of gray, or of its complementary, it has in its composition. Its *lightness* is determined by the amount of white or black it has mixed with it. A color of high lightness is called a *tint*, of low lightness, a *shade*.

If we were to list some of the more obvious characteristics of color the following would be included:

Magenta, red, and yellow are warm colors.
Green, cyan, and blue are cool colors.
Analogous colors are harmonious.
Complementary colors offer the greatest contrast.
Colors of high lightness are more "exciting" than those of low lightness.
A low degree of lightness gives a greater impression of dignity than a high degree of lightness.
A little bright color outweighs much grayed color.
Mixing colors always lowers saturation. The more widely separated are the hues, the grayer is the result.
The appearance of a color is always influenced by the colors surrounding it.

7. COLOR HARMONY

Harmony is, to at large extent, the result of good proportion.

Almost any color may be placed next to any other color, providing it is used in a correct amount. Two colors, which clash when combined equally, will usually appear well together in unequal quantities. Proportion involves balance. A little intense (saturated) color, for instance, as we have already noted in the preceding section, will hold its own against a considerable amount of neutral (grayed) color. The following rules for combining colors are founded on principles that operate under most conditions on the stage:

1. Various shades and tints of the same hue may be used together in any proportion.

2. Analogous hues (that is, those adjacent to each other on the color wheel) may be used together in any proportion, if they are used without a third color.

3. Complementaries may be used together in unequal proportion only.

4. Strict neutrals (grays), very light tints, or very dark shades may be used together in their own classes in almost any proportion.

5. Intense (highly saturated) colors may be used with neutral ones in almost any proportion, though balance, especially in the consideration of large designs, generally demands that the neutral colors predominate.

6. A neutral background may be used to tie together smaller masses of bright colors that would otherwise clash.

The greatest encouragement that can be given harmony is to keep the larger areas of the scene fairly neutral, and to sharpen visual interest by building up intensities in certain smaller points only.

8. PRACTICAL MODIFICATIONS

Whatever is said here about color mixtures and color relationships should be regarded as having to do with *principle*. The painter finds in practice that pigments seldom behave just as they should according to the color schemes. The reason for this is that complicating factors which prevent the conditions from being ideal are always present. Theoretically, a mixture of magenta and yellow will make red; practically it may make a dull, unpleasant brown. What the principle of color mixture (in its simplest form) cannot take into account is the effects of chemical reactions between ingredients, the difference of purity in the pigments, and variations in texture.

The fact that magenta, yellow, and blue-green (cyan) are called the three pigment primaries is based on the premise that the pigments being dealt with are transparent. Opaque pigments (such as many of those used in scene painting) tend to behave differently from the others. Since light does not penetrate them, and the effect created by a mixture of two of them depends on the visual blending of tiny spots—color particles of one pigment and color particles of the other—on the outer surface of the painting, the results often fit the *additive* mixture scheme more than they do the *subtractive*.

Backgrounds also influence effects. Painting done on a dark ground tends to be different from one on a light ground. There is a difference also when the pigments are transparent, or when they are applied loosely in spattering or dry-brushing and the ground shows through.

Another complication exists in the nature of surfaces. A shiny surface on one piece of painting may produce an entirely different color effect from a rough one on another, even when the hue, saturation, and lightness in both cases are identical.

Knowledge of how to deal with all these variants comes from practice. Skilled painters use the basic color principles as general guides, but general guides only; they are prepared to adjust proportions and relationships freely in the light of experience. Apprentice painters would do well to use a somewhat limited palette to begin with, and to learn thoroughly all of its idiosyncrasies before experimenting with new pigments.

9. PREPARING THE PAINT

Paint is prepared by mixing pigment with a solution of glue called *size water,* according to the following procedure: 4 pounds of flake (or ground) glue are placed in a 3-gallon pail of water, allowed to soak for at least an hour (or better, overnight) and then cooked on a stove. This pail is placed inside a larger one, with a little water and a block of wood or a brick in the bottom of the latter to prevent burning. When completely dissolved, the glue is further diluted to make size water. Four pounds of dry flakes will make from 6 to 8 pails of size water. (This is about the proportion of one cup of glue to a pail.) The more concentrated preparation may be kept as stock to be diluted as it is needed. Because time must be taken to remelt it every time it is used, however, it is wise to make up several buckets of size water at a time to prevent delay in painting. If glue is to be kept on hand for any length of time, a couple of teaspoonfuls of carbolic acid may be put in it to keep it from decomposing.

The glue solution should be warm when the pigment is added. Pour the powder into it slowly, stirring it thoroughly to prevent lumping, until the mixture has the consistency of coffee cream.

It is difficult to give any more nearly exact proportions for mixing scene paints as both glue and pigments vary. Veteran artists judge largely by the "feel" acquired through experience. If too much glue is used the paint, when dry, will draw and crack on the surface of the canvas; also the paint will have a tendency to look shiny, and dark stains may appear. If too little glue is used, the paint will powder on a hand rubbed across it. If too much pigment is used, the paint will seem stiff and heavy in brushing, and one stroke will pile up on top of the preceding one. If the mixture is too thin it will look transparent on the canvas.

The paint, when applied, should be at least slightly warm. The mixture in the bucket should be stirred from time to time to prevent the powder from precipitating. If the pail is set aside for a while and grows cold, it should be thoroughly stirred and returned to the stove briefly before being used again, care being taken that the glue does not burn.

Available on the market now are some new flexible glues, such as glycerin glue, which, though they are a little more expensive than the old flake glue, make smoother mixtures that attain more desirable results. These glues are generally also more convenient to use.

Certain of the pigments (Prussian blue, ultramarine blue, Van Dyke brown, most of the reds, lampblack, and the anilines) need to be "cut," moistened with a little alcohol, before they are mixed with size water.

10. SOME SUGGESTIONS FOR MIXING PAINTS

It is seldom necessary to use pure colors, except for accents. For most purposes they should be mixed with at least an equal portion of whiting for painting brighter blocks of color, and several times this amount for laying in lighter tones. On the other hand, the use of whiting should be avoided when it is not needed. Whiting exerts a strong influence over other pigments in a mixture; even a small amount dropped by mistake into a pailful of some dark paint (such as burnt umber or black) is apt to destroy its brilliance and make it appear chalky.

The various pigments may be mixed together in any proportion. Only in very unusual circumstances will an artist find just the tone of a color he wants without first blending two or more together.

A word of caution should be given to those experimenting with scene paints for the first time. Water colors invariably look darker when wet than dry, mixtures containing white being especially tricky deceivers in this respect. Those who have trouble in estimating in advance the result of a certain mixture would do well to mix their pigments in a dry state before adding any liquid.

It is difficult to match blends. Before painting a sky drop or the walls of a set, therefore, it is wise to mix enough paint to prevent running short at some critical point. Two 2- or 3-gallon pailfuls will take care of a drop 25' x 30', or a set of seven flats of standard width and 12 feet high, very nicely.

One of the less attractive qualities of the usual glue-mixed paint is that it may acquire an unpleasant odor after it has been allowed to stand in a warm shop for a day or two. Formaldehyde is a good preservative. Mix 2 quarts of this chemical with 3 gallons of paint. When spraying be careful not to breathe any of the mist. The use of carbolic acid has already been mentioned.

11. THE PRIME COAT

The first coat of paint is called the *prime coat*. Its purpose is to close the pores of the canvas and prepare a working surface for the following coats. Because whiting is the cheapest powder, it is commonly the chief ingredient used, but any other pigment may be employed equally well. Left-over scraps from the previous day's painting may be *boxed* together (poured back and forth into each other) and warmed up to prime the new flats. The tendency in professional studios is to prime a set of scenery with the tint of a color approximating the final tone of the scenery if the effect is to be smooth, and with a complementary to this tone if the effect is to be rough. To prepare a foundation for an open texture the priming is often done with several different colors. The only fixed directions for applying this first coat are to use a large brush and to spread the paint evenly, smoothly, and not too thickly over the canvas.

12. THE FOLLOWING COATS

One coat of paint should be allowed to dry thoroughly before another is applied; otherwise the damp pigments will mix and produce muddy spots. If the paints are properly applied, one coat will completely hide the preceding one (unless it is in extreme contrast or is mixed with an aniline dye—see Section 29). If it does not, it is probably too thin. If one coat picks up another, the fault lies in one of three possibilities: the fresh paint is too warm, that beneath it is still damp, or the under paint lacks glue. A little experience will quickly teach one how to avoid such conditions.

13. PAINTING OVER OLD SURFACES

Painting over an old surface often presents some difficulty. Scenic glue deteriorates in time and loses much of its binding quality. The paint on old scenery is often so powdery that it is caught up in the brush strokes and mixed with the new coat—disastrously so if the colors are dissimilar. The surface may be hardened somewhat by first sprinkling it freely with a strong solution of alum.

14. SURFACE TEXTURES

Irregular surfaces on the stage are, when viewed from a distance, more interesting to look at than perfectly smooth ones. For some reason, flatly painted scenery is never quite convincing; its chalky flatness reveals it to be what it really is, color-washed canvas. Even a slightly varied texture, scarcely recognizable as such from the audience, seems to "carry" where the flat one will not. The theory of *broken color,* which maintains that scintillation is secured by breaking up a desired tone into its simpler elements and placing these side by side in little blocks which the eye, at a distance, will blend into one, finds one of its surest proofs on the stage. A plainly tinted wall painted by spattering, one over the other, three coats—one magenta-gray, one yellow-gray, and one cyan-gray—has a suggestion of life which one painted with the same colors mixed together in a pail and applied flatly most clearly has not.

15. METHODS OF APPLYING PAINT

The following are the most common methods of applying paint to scenery:

Flat painting. The paint is brushed on smoothly and evenly. This is obviously the most simple method, and is useful for priming and laying on ground (base) colors. For a flat finish the paint must be applied in all directions, not in just parallel strokes.

Scumbling. Use is made of two or more brushes charged with different pigments which are brushed in irregular patterns around and through each other in such a way as to make the colors partially mix with each other. This method of painting is effective in producing mottled or rough surfaces, such as those that simulate old plaster.

Stippling. A large sponge, trimmed to present a flat surface, is dipped into a pail of paint, squeezed out, and patted gently over the canvas. In the use of this method, care must be exercised to cover evenly and to avoid undue spottiness. The textural pattern should be continuous. It will be found helpful to pat in spirals or semicircles and to turn the sponge constantly in the hand. Sponging is useful also for producing rough or patterned surfaces. Often a wad of newspaper, a squeezed-out cloth, or a rather dry brush is employed in place of the sponge.

Rolling. An effect somewhat similar to that obtained by stippling can be secured by dipping and wringing out a ragged piece of coarse linen or burlap and rolling it over the surface to be covered. This is an excellent method to use for imitating old plaster or rock surfaces. Most painters prefer rolling to stippling.

Spattering. A brush full of paint is shaken over the canvas or snapped by the wrist so that the paint falls in little drops. To insure evenness, it is well to start with one end or corner of a piece or group of pieces of scenery and proceed systematically to the opposite one. Be generous with the paint. A few tiny speckles will not be effective. At the same time avoid dribbling from an over-wet brush and dropping large spots which the audience will recognize as paint, thus destroying the illusion of texture. If it is difficult for the artist at the start to spatter evenly, he will find it helpful to snap the brush by striking the wrist of the brush hand against the wrist of the other hand at each shake of the brush. One secret of good spattering lies in loading the brush each time with the same amount of color, that is, always dipping the bristles the same distance into the liquid (never more than about three quarters of the way). Spattering is the method most often used for producing broken color impressions. It is often combined with one or more of the other methods (see Figure 57).

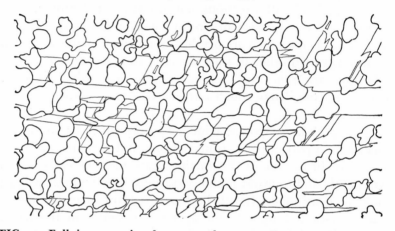

FIG. 57. Full-size spattering for a smooth texture. For a rough texture the spots should be three or four times the size of those shown here. This spattering has been applied over dry brushing.

Dry-brushing or dragging. In this method the painter employs a rather dry brush, working in one or several different directions. It offers a good system for simulating wood grains.

If a series of flats in a wall, or any other group of pieces which must be set together in a scene, is to be painted continuously by one of these methods, it is imperative that they be laid side by side in the proper order on the floor as a unit, to prevent dissimilarities.

There are few really standard ways of painting scenery. The successful artist is an inventor and experimenter. The suggested solutions of the various problems that follow should be appreciated as hints chiefly for beginners. These hints will be modified or disregarded as one discovers better methods.

16. INTERIOR AND EXTERIOR WALLS

The principles of broken color (Section 14) may be used in developing wall surfaces which are intended to appear either smooth or rough. For the smooth surface, which suits interiors better than it does exteriors, choose two or three colors which are nearly alike, such as blue-gray and yellow-gray, or light-cream, darker cream, and pink. Lay one of the colors on solidly as a ground coat; when it is dry, spatter the second evenly over the first until it nearly conceals it; then spatter over these two the third in the same manner. If the spattering has been properly done, it should present a surface which, from a distance, at first sight will appear perfectly smooth, but upon closer examination will be seen to have just enough texture to prevent it from looking monotonous and uninteresting. If a hard texture is desired, the spattering should be done on a perfectly dry surface; if a soft texture is desired, a wet surface should be used.[3] Avoid working over a partly wet and a partly dry surface, however, or the result will be uneven.

The use of more widely separated colors in spattering will suggest stucco. If two or more colors are cleverly enough applied by the cloth-rolling method, a very convincing effect of old mottled wall paper may be produced. If a more pronounced design is desired, simple figures may be cut in oil paper and stenciled onto the wall. In applying the paint through the stencil use an almost dry brush to keep the paint from running. Avoid any very conspicuous patterns or they will probably refuse to lie at rest on the surface. If the figures appear too vigorous when viewed from a distance, spatter them over lightly with a little of the ground color, to tone them back into the rest of the wall. Remember at all times that good scenery acts as an environment and must not detract from the action of the play.

If a warm gray is needed at any point, a serviceable one may be had by mixing together Venetian red and chrome green, plus enough whiting to bring the tint up to the lightness desired. One should never try to get a gray by using just black and white. What results from this mixture is a dull muddy color.

Old stained plaster, particularly effective for exterior walls, may

[3] If the different pigments tend to dry out too quickly for the right kind of blend, they can be kept moist by the addition of a little glycerin.

be suggested by scumbling and blocking in large irregular patches of various light and dark browns, or yellows, reds, and blues, and spattering this all over, while it is still wet, with the same colors. Keep the darker tones near the surface. As dark blue under the prevailing straw and amber lights of the stage looks nearly black, a little of this color may be mixed with a small amount of real black and sprinkled *very lightly* here and there over the plaster, to suggest holes and crevices. Guard against the appearance of large drops or you will give away your secret.

To give interest to highlights and shadows, and to produce other interesting qualities, through light reflection, in various kinds of textured wall surfaces, use is frequently made of aluminum (silver) powder (see Section 26), which is either mixed directly into the body paints before they are applied, or is made up with size water into a thin wash and spattered over the body coats (Section 17).

Brick walls should be handled thoughtfully. Rows of regular red rectangles with hard white lines between, seen so often on amateur stages, never look very convincing. Even the most evenly laid walls in actual life show many irregularities and signs of weathering. One good plan to follow in painting is to scumble in first the plaster effect (later to be seen between the bricks) in a full ground coat—not in one tone, but in two or three slightly different ones—then lay the bricks in lightly on top of this with a comparatively dry 2- or 3-inch brush. Vary red with a little neutralized orange, brown, and blue. It is well to keep the bricks in fairly straight lines, of course, but do not attempt to paint them too regularly. Knock off a corner here and there and touch occasional edges with darker blue to suggest stains. After the bricks have been laid in, spatter them all over very lightly with the same colors. Keep in mind that an *impression* is what one is trying to create, and that fussy details are lost on the audience.

The usual caution may be repeated: avoid extremes. In developing interiors or exteriors, guard against painting walls either too bright or too dull. They would be conspicuous in both cases.

17. SHADING AND TONING WALLS

In creating wall surfaces an artist must work constantly for variety. He should give special attention to large plain areas. Unless these are well painted, they are apt to appear bare even under the best lighting. It is not enough simply to suggest texture (see Sections 14 through 16). The artist should work for some difference between illuminated and shadowed areas. The light concentration on a high wall in a night scene, for instance, would naturally be near the bottom where the actors stand and walk in lamplight. In treating such a wall the artist might wisely lay his lightest tints here, and then shade them off gradually into deeper and deeper ones as he proceeds toward the top, until the wall appears to melt into darkness. The outer edges of the wall, away from the light source, might likewise be made to fade into the shadows.

Wall surfaces often seem more interesting when they are *toned* (tinted or grayed) with a light scumble or spatter of aniline dye dissolved in size water (Section 29). One or more tints or shades may be used. A thin wash of silver (Sections 16 and 26) may be used in the same way. By this kind of silver treatment, dull-looking walls may be given a remarkable sparkle without appreciably changing their color. The dye and silver powders may be mixed in the same bucket, if so desired, and thrown together.

Both shading and toning, if they are to be at all effective, must be done subtly.

18. IMITATING WOODWORK

Woodwork is very difficult to imitate satisfactorily with canvas and paint. When he is preparing a realistic setting, a professional scenic artist likes to use at least some real lumber on the stage. This he can do without great difficulty where door frames and moldings are involved; but it is obviously impossible to build a complete wooden interior to represent a shack or a log cabin. Where rough boards must be suggested with paint, lay a ground coat of gray-brown, rule the flats with charcoal to indicate positions of the planks, and scumble in each with shades and tints of brown, blue, and gray, using long strokes and avoiding making one plank exactly like the next. Alternate a couple of darker boards with a lighter one, and vice versa. Vary the ends, or the middles, of boards. Stain the edges of occasional boards. Now take a little yellow ochre, mixed with white, on an almost dry brush with the bristles spread, and with long sweeps suggest very lightly some pronounced graining here and there. If the pattern of the graining must be made more obvious, mix up a little black aniline dye (see Section 29) and sweep it on in the same way with an almost dry brush. If the brown and yellow show up too brightly, reduce their intensity with a little gray or blue. Finally, outline the boards lightly with blue accented with black, draw in a few knots, and drag and spatter a little light gray-blue over the entire surface to suggest the rough texture of the wood. A little real lumber seen in beams and supports will carry out the illusion.

In the more pretentious, formal type of interior which must be dressed up with baseboards, dadoes, cornices, wall paneling and shaped door and window trims, strips of molding may be indicated (when the use of real wood is considered impractical) by laying bands of suitable color and drawing on these, with a 1-inch lining brush, thin lines of highlight and shadow. Wherever the light may be presumed to strike an edge of the molding a line of high-light is ruled. In the hollows below this line (or above—depending on the direction of the light) the lines of shadow are placed. The color for the highlighted strip is commonly prepared by mixing the "local tone" (body color of the molding) with a little white, the color for the shadows, by mixing the local tone with a little dark blue or blue-black. If the lightness of the ground on which the lines of highlight and shadow are to be drawn is extreme, pure white and pure pale blue may be substituted for the mixed colors. The pigment should be applied with a full brush in long, clean strokes, the brush being carried the length of the straight-edge once only in each position. If the pigment is scrubbed on, the lines of light and shadow will look fuzzy, heavy, and uncon-vincing. To rule a crisp, thin line, the broader side of a small brush should be placed against the straightedge; to mark a softer line, the flat side should be turned to the canvas.

19. LOG CABIN WALLS

To suggest the walls of a log cabin, model the surface of the flats before painting by means of long strips of waste cloth—such as scrap canvas, flour sacks, and any other rags—dipped into a mixture of hot glue and whiting (Chapter 4, Section 9) and pasted on to suggest the roughly chopped edges of logs, with clay showing between. The raised portions should be 5 to 7 inches wide, and the spaces between 2 to 3 inches wide. Apply the rags hot, glue them firmly to the canvas, and wrinkle them to suggest the crude longitudinal grain of the wood. As the strips contract considerably in drying, avoid pulling them tightly when putting them on the flats.

Each log should run the full width of a wall. The flats composing a wall must therefore be laid together on the floor and done as a unit, that is, with the strips of cloth carried over the cracks. The flats may be cut apart afterwards. Corners, where two walls meet, must be carefully matched. As the log ends must seem to dovetail, the strips where the two walls join must be arranged in a stagger pattern. If the set is an exterior, the round ends of the wood at each corner should be shown.

When the log strips are dry, drag them in long, irregular streaks and blocks of dark and light grays, browns, and blues; then darken the edges, and put in bits of shadow with dark blue and purple under and above each strip to accentuate the thickness. Suggest clay in the cracks between by blotches of light yellow, blue, and gray. Paint boldly and freely and work for variety and contrast between the wood and the mud.

20. THE SKY

A large drop, high enough and wide enough completely to back up all exterior views, and painted pale blue, is generally used to represent the sky (Chapter 2, Section 11). As it depends chiefly upon lighting for its effect, its own tinting should be very soft. Mix not more than 3 or four ounces of Italian blue in a full pail of white, and apply the paint with a large, absolutely clean brush, taking great care not to streak. If it is a big drop, prepare two or three buckets of paint and box them thoroughly (pour them back and forth into each other) before starting. To run short and attempt to match tints in the center of the sky is disastrous. The sky may be given a little texture and a surface which will better reflect different qualities of light which may be thrown on it if it is spattered very carefully and evenly with pale, closely related tints of pink, purple, and blue (a fraction of a degree darker or lighter than the main blue). It may be given added scintillation by mixing into the paint a little aluminum (silver) powder (Section 26).

The old-fashioned practice of painting a landscape on the sky drop is now frowned upon by the best artists. Besides being difficult to do, it never produces very convincing results, and it limits the use of the drop. A simple sky may be used in every set of a play calling for a glimpse of outdoors, whereas a painted landscape fits the locality of just one scene.

If the drop must be rolled up frequently, the paint on its surface should be flexible. If to each 3-gallon pail of paint one adds ½ cup of glycerin, the paint can be prevented from cracking. Or one can use ready-prepared glycerin glue in place of the hard glue.

Sky drops which must be hung close up behind a window or door, or used to back up an exterior setting on a shallow stage, are difficult to light effectively and often have a hard, not very convincing appearance no matter how well they are painted. In such cases it is sometimes advantageous to hang a sheet of gauze just in front of the drop. This may be attached above to the same batten as that which holds the drop.

If a cyclorama is used to represent the sky (Chapter 2, Section 11), it is painted in solid or broken tints of very pale blue, and sometimes other colors, like the drop.

A dome (see same section) may be painted in the same way.

21. LANDSCAPE PIECES

The character of an outdoor setting is suggested better by a few plastic *set* and *built* pieces, such as ground rows, silhouette hills, rocks, trees, and fences placed in front of the sky, than by anything painted on the drop. The construction of these is described in the previous chapter (Chapter 5, Sections 16 through 19). When painting them one would do well to keep in mind that, except possibly for the sky on a cloudless day, there are no large masses of flat color in nature. Even a simple tree trunk will show a surprising number of colors—perhaps a dozen or more browns, grays, blues, and greens. Of course it would be impractical to indicate very many of these, but at least two or three tones should be used to indicate that a piece of scenery represents a tree trunk, not a painted post.

Rocks are never a dead gray. For painting the lighted side of a block of granite use warmer colors, perhaps a dull cream varied with a little rose pink, light brown, and pale blue; while in the shadows use cooler colors, blue, bluish-green, and purple. Greenish patches of moss may be added. A sandstone wall would be painted in the same way with the addition of a little yellow. Work freely in large blocks of color. Sprinkle the whole piece lightly, when finished, with a small amount of dark and light blue to break up the smooth surfaces and add texture.

Paint mountain rows in light greens, blues, and purples, and spatter them well with pale violet (ultramarine blue with a little Venetian red and white) to blend their outlines into the sky. Distant banks of earth may be suggested in much the same way by using burnt umber, ultramarine, and Italian blue. Wherever possible run a little of the sky color into the far-away objects.

In planning landscapes, keep colors as light as possible, vary the values of tints, and avoid black shadows. Paint objects in the foreground in purer, brighter colors than those in the background. The shadow colors should go on first, and the painting proceed step by step from dark to light.

22. FOLIAGE

To repeat the statement made in Chapter 5, Section 16, thoroughly convincing foliage is very difficult to paint. The tendency now is to avoid the use of definite shrubbery and other leafy pieces as much as possible. In out-of-door scenes calling for the presence of trees, an artist generally tries to design his setting in such a way as to draw the main attention to three or four bare, but convincing, solid-looking trunks rising out of sight behind the teaser in the more brightly lighted foreground, while merely *suggesting* masses of leaves, intertwining branches, and silhouettes of other trees (created by means of dark cut-out drops kept discreetly behind much scrim) in the shadows of the background. If a foliage piece, such as a masking border, must be used in the foreground, paint it in blocks to hint at clumps of leaves, rather than individual ones; then cut the edges and punch holes in the border (according to the characteristics of the foliage represented), and hang it in silhouette as much as possible. Dark chrome green, leaf green lake, and Hanover green are good foliage colors. They may be modified by mixing white into them. A few touches of neutralized red here and there will add roundness to the blocks of green. Some artists prime their foliage pieces with pure ultramarine and paint over it.

Vines and small bushes are made best out of materials secured at artificial flower shops, or five and ten cent stores. Their cost, however, precludes their use in quantity.

For other foliage suggestions see Chapter 5, Section 16.

23. MIST AND DISTANCE EFFECTS

Mist effects are created principally by the use of scrim, a dark blue theatrical gauze (Chapter 4, Section 5, and Chapter 5, Section 16). One or more thicknesses of it, in the form of a drop, are hung in front of the whole, or part, of a scene. If lights are carefully kept off of it, the gauze itself remains invisible but the objects behind it are blurred as though seen through a haze. If two or three small streaks of light are thrown across it a suggestion of fog is produced. The whole scene back of the scrim may be blocked out by removing the light from behind and bringing it up in front. This is the way the famous "transformations" of the old theatre were effected. The atmospheric vapors natural to a landscape contribute much to the impression of distance. Scrim, therefore, is useful for this effect also. With the aid of the right kind of lighting, a deep woods scene can be suggested very simply within a few feet of stage space by hanging, one behind the other, several foliage cut-out drops with pieces of scrim glued over the open spaces of each (Chapter 5, Section 11). From the front each receding silhouette appears dimmer than the one in front of it and consequently the feeling is conveyed that the last group of trees is quite far away.

Certain colors, also, give the impression of distance. Pale blues and violets are especially helpful in this respect. A little very light ultramarine or Italian blue spattered over a row of hills will make them appear ten miles closer to the horizon.

24. PAINTED SHADOWS

A word should be said about shadows. They are never black. They may be brown, green, purple, or almost any color except pure black, which is dead. The ideal plan, of course, is to arrange a set in such a way as to make the shadows fall naturally without painting; but where they must be made artificially one can use pigments that are neutralized complements to the prevailing colors in the lighting. Where an illuminated area is seen as amber or straw (yellow), the shadows are of blackish, or grayish, blue; where blue-green, of red; and so on. "Painted darkness," however, is at best a makeshift device. To be effective at all it must be subtle. It should not appear to have been laid in with a brush. Heavy streaks and blotches are worthless.

25. REPRODUCING FROM SKETCHES

A design for a picture drop or other large piece of scenery must occasionally be copied and enlarged from a small working sketch. As it is difficult, at close range to his canvas, for an artist to keep the various elements of an extensive composition accurately in proportion, he is compelled to make use of an analytical scheme of reproducing—in other words, to copy the design in small units. The following method is the one generally employed.

The sketch (Figure 58), made to a definite scale, generally ½ inch = 1 foot, is ruled off with a pencil in 1-inch squares. The drop, primed with a working surface (Section 11), is likewise ruled off with charcoal in 2-foot squares. These vertical and horizontal lines are drawn with either a long batten or a *snap line*. The latter is a heavy braided cotton cord, rubbed with a stick of charcoal, a lump of chalk, or a folded cloth containing a dry pigment, which is held against the canvas and pulled tightly at both ends. When it is lifted in the middle and allowed to snap back onto the cloth, some of the charcoal, chalk, or pigment rubbed along the cord is transferred to the canvas, making a distinct streak.

The design is now transferred from paper to canvas, square by square, chalk or charcoal being used for the outline sketching. The drop is then painted. If any of the black or white lines still show when the painting is completed, they can be dusted out easily with a feather duster or a dry rag.

It is sometimes advisable to work out a difficult detail or a repeat pattern at full size on a piece of wrapping paper first and then transfer this drawing to the canvas. After the drawing has been made on the paper, the paper is perforated along the principal

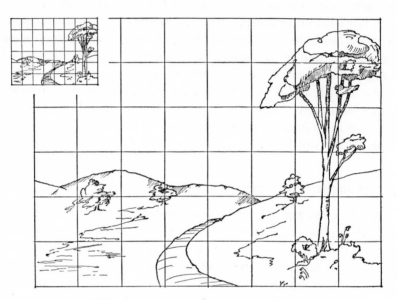

FIG. 58. Method of enlarging a sketch.

lines of the design with a pounce wheel, a small nail, or other pointed object, then the paper is turned over, the burrs are sand-papered off the little holes, the pattern is placed in position on the drop, and a small pounce bag is rubbed or patted over the perforations.

26. GOLD AND SILVER METALLIC PAINTS

Bronze and aluminum powders, which are sold in a number of different tints and shades, are used to represent gold and silver in scene painting. They are mixed with a bronzing liquid for applying to metal, and with a heavy glue size for painting on cloth and wood. Size water in its ordinary strength (½ pound of glue to 3 gallons of water—Section 9) does not bind strongly enough for metallic paints; the proportion of glue for these should be doubled. To prepare the water-color mixture, first make a thick paste of the metallic powder with a little alcohol and heavy size water used hot, stirring it until it is smooth; then mix in slowly more and more of the size water until the desired consistency is obtained. Place the mixture on the stove and bring it to a boil, stirring it constantly to make certain that it does not burn. If properly prepared, bronze and aluminum paints are thoroughly liquid when warm, and quite stiff when cold. When they are being used they must be kept warm by frequent reheating.

To make these naturally brittle paints a little more flexible for use on drops or other pieces that must be folded or rolled, add about a teaspoonful of glycerin to a pint of liquid, or use a glycerin glue.

If a metallic powder is to be mixed with scene paint it must be prepared separately, according to the directions given above, before it is added to the other pigment, otherwise it will separate out and flake off as soon as the paint is dry.

27. OIL PAINTS

Surfaces on small units, such as door frames and, particularly, furniture pieces, which have to stand constant rubbing from the hands or clothes of actors or must be cleansed now and then with a wet rag, are frequently painted in oil.

Oil paint consists of two parts: the *pigment,* a powder similar to that used in water-color scene paints, but ground more finely; and the *vehicle,* a liquid, the common ingredients of which are linseed oil and turpentine. The best work requires three to five coats. The first, called the prime coat, is composed of much oil and little pigment and turpentine; the intermediate, the body coats, contain more of the second and third elements; whereas the last, the finishing coat, is made up principally of turpentine for a flat surface, or oil for a glossy surface. For the temporary purposes of the stage, one or two coats of the same mixture is usually sufficient. A method very commonly employed in scene painting is to lay in the prime coat with an ordinary water-color paint made up with a strong size (Section 9), followed by a coat of shellac (Section 28), and to use oil paint in a single, final coat only. Shiny surfaces which reflect light are seldom desired. The most serviceable oil medium, therefore, is ready-mixed flat interior paint. It may be thinned, if necessary, with a little turpentine, and made to dry more rapidly by adding a small amount of dryer.

To avoid streaking, oil paint must be applied with considerably more care than scene paint (water color). Stir the paint well before using. Break up any lumps in the bottom of the can and see that all the ingredients are thoroughly mixed. Clean the surface to which the paint is to be applied. Brush the paint on with long, straight strokes, evenly, smoothly, and not too thickly. Two thin coats are better than one thick one. Be certain that one coat is thoroughly dry before applying the second.

Oil paint can be laid over a smooth surface of scene paint, but the reverse process is a little more difficult. Scene paint does not stick well to a very smooth surface. Shellacking the surface first, however, will help to make the water-color coat hold.

Oil brushes must be thoroughly cleaned with linseed oil or turpentine after every use and carefully kept separate from the water-color brushes.

28. SHELLAC

Shellac, a spirit varnish composed of gum dissolved in alcohol, lends itself to quick and easy methods of imitating surfaced woodwork. A convincing mahogany panel may be created by painting a piece of plywood or framed canvas with white scene paint, graining it with black, and applying over this a couple of coats of orange shellac stained with a little powdered dye of a dark reddish brown color, such as Bismarck brown. If a really nice piece of work is desired, one coat should be allowed to dry thoroughly, and should be sandpapered before the next is applied. In the absence of dye a few teaspoonfuls of burnt umber and Venetian red scene powder may be put into the shellac. Whole interiors are often done in this manner.

Shellac fulfills a number of other paint demands in an excellent manner. One of its best qualities is that of a water-proofing agent.

It is sold in two colors, clear and orange, is thinned with alcohol, and dries almost instantly.

Brushes used in shellac should be cleaned with alcohol immediately after service and kept separate from water-color and oil brushes.

29. DYES

Pure aniline dye, or its substitute, the commercial Diamond Dye, employed frequently for toning walls and draperies and occasionally for painting drops that have to be made very light and flexible, is prepared in the following way. Mix one ounce of dye with water into a paste, add a teaspoonful of salt and a quart of water, and bring to a boil. This is the standard method. A short cut is often taken in scene painting, however, by simply stirring the dye powder into very hot size water. If much painting is to be done with this medium, strong stock solutions of each color may be made up, kept on hand, and diluted with warm size water as needed.

The following colors will be found useful. They may be combined to form a wide variety of intermediate tones. To lighten a dye, dilute it; to darken it, add more stock.

> Brilliant red
> Wine red
> Purple
> Blue
> Green
> Yellow
> Seal brown
> Black

Dye may be applied with an ordinary scene brush. A little dye goes a long way; do not use it heavily. Dye, unlike distemper, is not opaque. One color on the canvas may be modified by brushing another over it; but it cannot be fully blocked out once it is placed. Light areas can be darkened, but dark areas cannot be lightened. It is recommended, therefore, that when the artist is doing any piece of work at all elaborate, he lay in his pale tones first, and proceed from them to his deeper ones.

Anilines are used quite extensively for "toning down" scenery

painted in the ordinary way. If the walls of an interior are too
lively, for instance, they may be grayed down effectively by
spattering them lightly all over with black or blue aniline (Section
17).

In an emergency in regular scene painting, whiting may be
tinted with a little dye to take the place of a color that has run
short. Seldom very satisfactory, however, the use of this method of
mixing pigments is not to be recommended as a regular practice.

Brushes used in dye cannot be thoroughly cleaned by simply
being rinsed in water. The bristles, which take up a considerable
amount of color, must be "bled" by being soaked for several hours
in a pan of whiting and water.

30. PIGMENTS UNDER STAGE LIGHTS

It is necessary to keep the lighting scheme of a production in
mind while painting scenery. Not only the intensities of pigments
are changed under stage illumination but often their hues as well.
Blue is one of the most conspicuous variants. Under straw and
amber (yellowish lights, complementary to blue), which are apt
to predominate in most interior scenes, an object painted dark
blue tends to become black, while one of light blue turns toward
gray. To appear normal, therefore, this color must be exaggerated
somewhat. Yellow, on the other hand, must often be softened.
Because so much depends on texture, the purity of gelatin mediums and the brilliance of illumination, it is difficult to give any
final rules for the selection of pigments.

The theory of the effect of colored lights on various pigments is
discussed in Part II of this book.

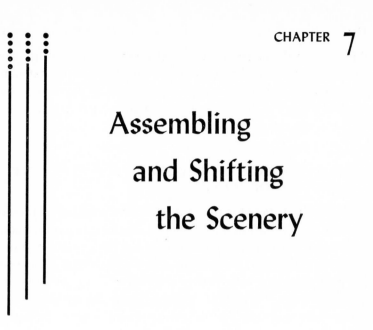

CHAPTER 7

Assembling
and Shifting
the Scenery

1. INTRODUCTION

As HAS ALREADY been remarked, one of the first requisites of good scenery is that it be designed for ready shifting. An audience pays money at the box office to see a performance, not intermissions. The latter should, therefore, demand as little attention as possible. In presenting one scene of a play an effort should be made to arouse the interest of the audience and lift its emotions to such a height that the audience will be able to sustain them during the dead interval needed for rest and change of scenery. A long or noisy shift makes this effort utterly futile. No change, however difficult, should occupy more than twelve minutes at most. Ten minutes is the average intermission between acts, and one or two, the maximum between scenes within acts. If there are many scenes, the time required for intra-act changes should be cut to the absolute minimum.

It will readily be seen how necessary is the planning of methods for assembling and taking apart scenery (*setting* and *striking*). So far as possible, these methods should be devised before the units of each set are built. Most of the time and temper so frequently wasted in refitting awkward pieces to the mechanical demands of

163

the stage could be spared by a little more thoughtfulness on the part of the person who lays out the working drawings (Chapter 3, Section 5). Efficient assembling and shifting does not, however, depend solely on the construction of the scenery: it depends also on the arrangement of the stage.

2. REQUIREMENTS OF THE STAGE FOR EFFICIENT HANDLING OF SCENERY

To design a stage for the most effective handling of present-day scenery requires a fine knowledge of engineering principles. The stage must be nicely proportioned and carefully organized in order to give a maximum of mechanical service in a minimum of space. No more complex in structure than some of its predecessors, frequently much less so, the modern stage is considerably better planned for economy and flexibility than the older ones. The degree to which it may be called "modern" clearly does not depend upon its size and complexity, nor the number of scene-shifting tricks it can boast. It depends on something more significant, its adaptability to the specific technical needs of each new play. Stages in this country are comparatively small. Most of the trick devices about which so much has been written require room which can be ill afforded. For that reason, over-elaborate machinery is apt to defeat its own purpose and become a hindrance rather than a help. Flexibility and expansiveness are the first two essentials of good equipment. In the following sections are described some of the more common methods of assembling and shifting scenery on the adaptable type of stage.

3. METHODS OF LASHING AND BRACING SCENERY

Two flats placed edge to edge are bound together by means of a system of "lashing" (Figures 32 and 59) described in Chapter 4, Section 10. The lash line, attached to the upper-right-hand corner of the flat on the left as one faces the back of the scenery, is grasped with the right hand, tossed up and over the left upper lash cleat on the flat on the right, back over a cleat on the first flat, then carried down over a lower one on the second, back to the first, and so on down to the last cleat on the right flat. It is carried over this cleat,

Above: *The House of Bernarda Alba,* designed by George Hamlin, University of Illinois.
Below: *Right You Are,* designed by George W. McKinney.

around the cleat opposite it on the left, and back to the right. The free end of the line is now passed under the flat section of line and pulled down snugly to tighten the lashing. While the left hand holds the rope taut, the right hand lifts the free end and passes a loop of it under the flat section once more to tie a slip knot. To loosen the lashing it is necessary only to pull the free end of the line.

Stop cleats, or small mending plates, are frequently placed on the edge of a flat which must be lashed to another to form a corner.

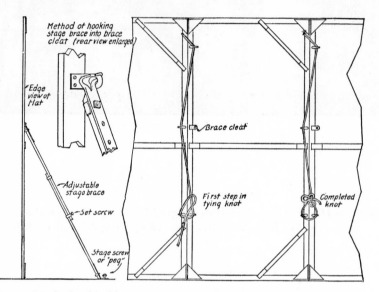

FIG. 59. Methods of lashing and bracing scenery. (See Fig. 32.) Scale ¼″ = 1′.

A substitute for the metal cleat is a small wooden block nailed or screwed ¾″ from the edge on the flat against which the edge of another flat is to be butted.

Flats needing special support, such as those on the edge of a set, in the center of a long straight wall, or holding doors or windows, are made secure by propping them from behind with stage braces. In each position where this is necessary the brace (made of two lengths of 1″ x 1″ wood held between clamps, and fitted at one end with a forked iron hook and at the other with an iron heel) is hooked into a brace cleat placed on any convenient part of the flat 8 feet or more from the floor; it is twisted so that its prongs clinch the plate as shown in the enlarged detail Figure 59; and

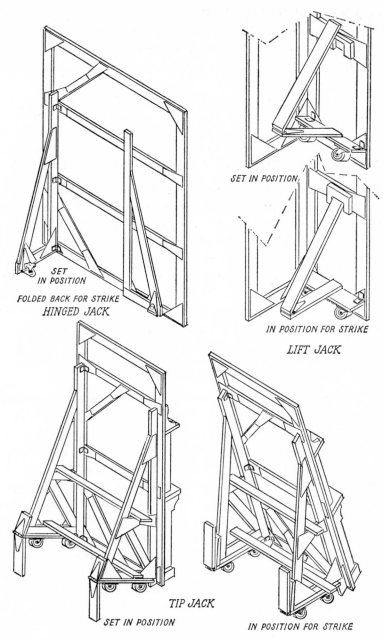

SET
IN POSITION

FOLDED BACK FOR STRIKE

HINGED JACK

SET IN POSITION

IN POSITION FOR STRIKE

LIFT JACK

TIP JACK

SET IN POSITION

IN POSITION FOR STRIKE

FIG. 60. Jacks.

then it is pegged firmly to the floor with a stage screw. The brace, which may be extended open to about twice its closed length, is held at the proper adjustment by means of a set screw placed in one of the clamps. Stage braces can be ordered from any firm dealing in theatrical hardware.

Another device for bracing certain kinds of scenery is the jack, illustrated in Figure 60.

4. METHODS OF BOLTING AND HINGING SCENERY

Heavier units, demanding strength, such as stairs, platforms and other built pieces, and certain lighter units which cannot conveniently be lashed, are fastened together by means of carriage bolts and wing nuts, or loose-pin back flaps and wire pins. The methods of using this attachment hardware are described in Chapter 4, Section 10, and under the construction of the various units which usually require them. On pieces of scenery which have to be put together or taken apart quickly, the bolts or hinges must not only be securely attached but must be in readily accessible places.

5. THE GRIDIRON AND THE FLY FLOOR

In order to fly scenery it is necessary to have some arrangement for hanging ropes from above. Every well-equipped stage has a gridiron (Chapter 2, Section 2) that extends over the entire working space and is built high enough to permit drops to be lifted completely out of view of the audience (Figures 61 and 62). The fly space on some professional stages reaches over 100 feet above the floor. The grid itself is constructed as a skeleton framework of steel I-beams, or wood beams, which is supported by the side walls and often vertical hangers from the roof. It is covered with an open lattice-work of steel strips, and it is slotted from front to back at regular intervals to accommodate the fly ropes. The slots are commonly placed about 15 feet apart. A narrow stage will have four slots, a wider one six or more. Above each of these slots, except one, are bolted large steel protected sheaves called *loft-blocks,* while above the last slot, situated directly over the fly gallery, are set up multiple sheave frames called head blocks.

Each set of blocks on an average sized stage (with a proscenium

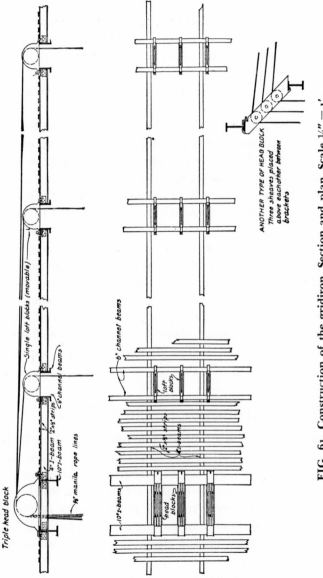

Triple head block

Single loft blocks (movable)

4-1-beam (2"x9' strip)
-10'-beam
6"-channel beams

3/4" manila rope lines

6" channel beams

loft blocks

(2"x9' strips)
6'-beams

head blocks

-10'-beams

ANOTHER TYPE OF HEAD BLOCK
Three sheaves placed
above eachother between
brackets

FIG. 61. Construction of the gridiron. Section and plan. Scale ¼″ = 1′.

opening 20 to 30 feet wide) generally consists of three loft blocks and one head block arranged in a row at right angles to the slots and parallel to the proscenium wall. A *set of lines,* made up of three or four ½-inch to ⅝-inch manila ropes (depending on the load), is attached to the center and the two ends of a hanging piece of scenery, passed over the three loft blocks directly above and the common head block at the side, then brought down and tied off on the row of belaying pins (the *pin rail*) on the fly floor (Chapter 2, Section 2, and Figure 62).

The fly floor, from which all the fly ropes are controlled, is a narrow floor, sturdily constructed, placed along one of the side walls of the stage, between the proscenium wall and the rear wall, some distance from the floor. It is situated high enough to clear all standing scenery—frequently 20 to 30 feet in the air. The pin rail, to which the fly lines are attached, is a double row of 17- to 21-inch hickory or iron belaying pins—commonly just short pieces of 1″ pipe—stuck through about 8-inch wooden beams or 5-inch iron pipes running the length of the gallery and supported by heavy wood or channel iron posts. The two rows of pins, set on the on-stage side of the gallery, are arranged one above the other.

A well-equipped stage has 15 to 30 or more sets of lines, with corresponding pins, placed about 9 inches apart and numbered from the proscenium back. The complete system of ropes, blocks, and belaying pins is termed the *rigging.*

6. GENERAL METHODS OF FLYING SCENERY

A line is attached to a drop, or other hanging piece, by tying it around the upper batten or into specially attached hanging irons. The three ropes in a set are called respectively the *short, center,* and *long line* as they are fastened to the near end, middle, and far end of the unit of scenery from the point of view of the flyman. The knots (Figure 63) used in making the ropes fast to the scenery must be those which combine absolute security with ease in untying. The bowline is commonly used for straight lifts, and the clove hitch for horizontal and bias pulls. If a quick attachment (*temporary* only) is to be made on a light piece of scenery, the slip knot may be employed. This knot, which will not hold well on a

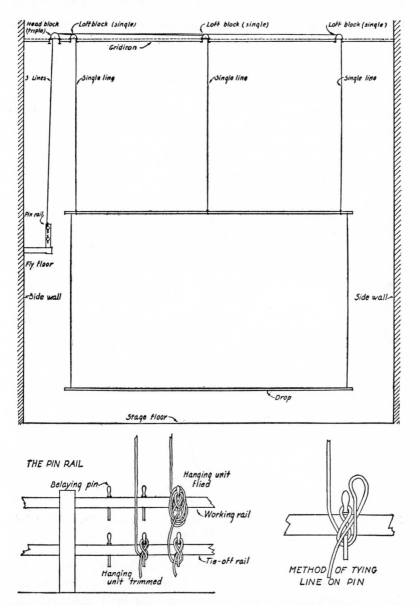

FIG. 62. Machinery for flying scenery. A general view of the gridiron and the fly floor, and a detailed study of the pin rail showing the method of tying off a line. (Usually there would be three lines together.)

batten, is useful only for tying a line into a ring or onto another line.

On units which have no free battens to which the lines can conveniently be attached, hanging irons are used (Figure 64). These are fastened vertically, ring end upwards, to the back of the unit, near the top, by means of ⅞-inch (or longer) No. 9 screws. If the weight on each iron exceeds 50 pounds, one or more ³⁄₁₆-inch stove bolts should be used with the screws.

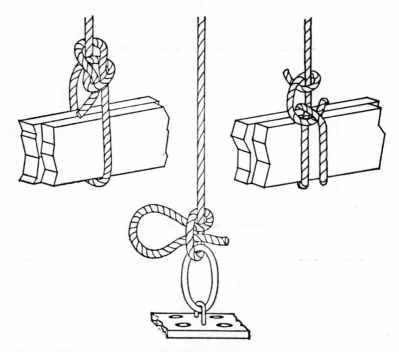

FIG. 63. Three knots commonly used on hanging scenery. The bowline, left; the clove hitch (plus a half hitch), right; and the slip knot, center.

The unit to which a set of lines has been attached is flied simply by pulling on the ropes. When it has reached the desired height, the ropes are made fast to a belaying pin. The method for *tying-off* is illustrated in Figure 62. The ropes are first carried around the lower end of the pin (from left to right), then up, across and around the upper end (from left to right), down around the lower end and up again, about two and a half times. The set of lines is finally made fast by making a loop, turning it over, bringing it down over the top end of the pin, and pulling it tight, as illustrated. The free ends of the ropes are coiled and hung over the same pin to prevent their getting tangled with other ropes. For the sake of clearness in the drawing only one line in each set is shown.

There are two rows of belaying pins on the pin rail: the lower one for tying the drop, or other unit, at *trim,* that is, when it is in position for the set, and the other pin for tying it when it is raised into the flies. This method of using the rail is found serviceable when a piece of scenery must be lifted and lowered during a per-

FIG. 64. Drop hanger and two types of hanging irons.

formance. Trimming takes time which can be ill afforded during a quick shift. However, by using the two pins, this can be done beforehand. The lower tie remains permanent. When the appropriate scene arrives the flyman loosens the ropes from the upper pin, lets them slide through his fingers, and when the slack is out he knows the drop or other hanging unit has come automatically to position.

Heavy pieces may be counterweighted by sandbags tied to the lines just below the head blocks (Figure 65). A whole rear wall consisting of three or more flats battened together may be balanced this way. A clamp is often used in place of rope for attaching the heavy sandbag to the lines.

A wide piece of scenery, such as a drop, may, in an emergency, be flied on two lines instead of three by using bridles as illustrated in Figure 65.

On a stage equipped with a low grid a tall drop may be *tripped* out of sight by attaching, from behind, a second, adjacent set of lines to the bottom batten. When both sets of lines are drawn, the drop is folded back and up into a space only half its height (Figure 65).

Hanging units may be breasted—that is, pulled slightly forward or backward, or around on a bias—by having upstage or downstage lines attached to them (Figure 65).

A unit is trimmed—that is, straightened so that it will hang squarely and without wrinkles—by having the short, center, or long line drawn up or let out slightly. It is said to be *on trim* when it is in exactly the right position for use on the stage.

A small sandbag should be tied into every set of lines not fastened to scenery to prevent the ropes from being pulled through the blocks when they are drawn up out of the way, and to force them to come down again with their own weight when released.

A word of caution. *Be sure that all hardware and knots used in flying are secure.* Some serious accidents have resulted from pulleys or hanging irons or sandbags breaking loose during a performance. Examine ropes from time to time for signs of wear. Safety is the first law of the stage as it is everywhere else.

7. SPECIFIC METHODS OF FLYING SCENERY

A drop or a border is flied by tying a set of three or more lines to its upper batten in the manner described in the preceding section.

A ceiling piece is suspended on two or three sets of lines, and lifted away or lowered to the standing set in the manner explained in Chapter 5, Section 10.

The larger types of cycloramas, unless specially rigged, as the one in the University Theatre at Yale, are generally too awkward to shift during a performance. All flying of other scenery has to be done inside of them. The smaller forms of cyclorama, however, are moved very simply. The rear batten is tied to a full set of lines and the downstage ends of the arms to another set of two lines. If there is no scenery above to foul, the whole thing can be lifted

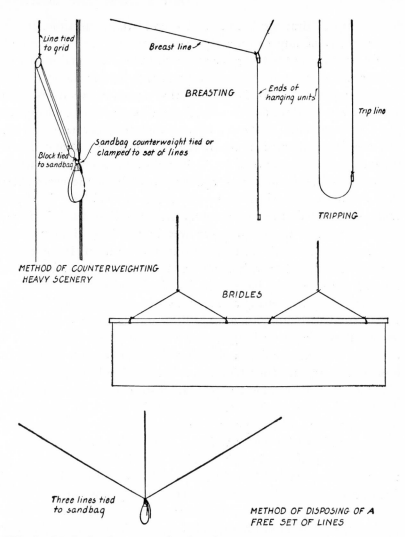

Line tied to grid

Breast line

BREASTING

Ends of hanging units

Trip line

Sandbag counterweight tied or clamped to set of lines

Block tied to sandbag

TRIPPING

METHOD OF COUNTERWEIGHTING HEAVY SCENERY

BRIDLES

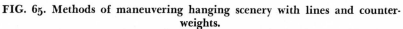

Three lines tied to sandbag

METHOD OF DISPOSING OF A FREE SET OF LINES

FIG. 65. Methods of maneuvering hanging scenery with lines and counter-weights.

straight up by drawing both sets of lines at the same time. If the cyclorama is of any considerable size, however, this method of handling requires the full stage room, or at least the major part of it. There is another method which permits flying the frame, canvas and all, into a space little larger than that occupied by a drop. Two adjacent sets of lines are employed. The two-line set attached to the downstage ends of the cyc arms is tied on a permanent trim, and the actual flying is done by the rear set alone. When this is drawn, the back, or curve of the U-shaped frame ascends first, while the arms fall down and back against the body of the cyclorama; then the whole thing is taken up as one flat piece. When the cyclorama is dropped, the permanently tied two-line set, which remained in slack while the piece was in the flies, tightens, and automatically pulls the arms back out into position. If the cyclorama unit is quite heavy, it is important to see that it is adequately hung. Extra lines may have to be installed for safety.

To speed up the setting and striking of a scene a complete back wall is frequently hung on a set of lines and flied like a drop. The several flats (single or hinged—see Chapter 5, Section 4) which compose the wall are first laid flat on the stage, edge to edge, face downwards, and fastened together to make a single rigid panel by placing two or more long battens, called stiffeners, across the back. They are fastened to the stiles of the flats by means of long screws or bolts, never nails. Ropes are tied into hanging irons attached at strong points (the center and two ends) to the back of the combination, and the wall is then raised and lowered as a unit. A side wall, also, may be flied in this way by tying to it single lines from an upstage and a downstage set. A whole box interior, with three walls, can, on occasion, be lifted from the stage as one piece by using one full set of lines which supports the back, and another set of two which supports the two front corners.

Heavy units should be counterweighted by large sandbags tied to each set of lines just below the head block, as described in the preceding section and illustrated in Figure 65. If the wall of an interior which must be placed under the edge of a ceiling is to be balanced in this way, a small auxiliary block and tackle will have to be attached to the sandbag to lift the latter slightly, and so give some slack to the fly ropes when the wall is in position on the floor, in order not to foul the overlapping ceiling.

Canvas tree trunks and light columns may be suspended on single, independent lines which, in this employment, are termed *spotted* lines.

If the emergency demands it, furniture and other properties may also be flied. As a rule, however, it is not wise to play too many tricks with the fly system. An overloaded grid is not the safest thing under which to perform.

8. THE COUNTERWEIGHT SYSTEM

In many of the newer theatres the fly gallery has been omitted and all flying is handled with a *counterweight system* [1] operated from the stage floor (Figures 66 and 69). In the unit form a pipe batten parallel to the proscenium wall and to the floor is attached to small steel cables, which pass over loft blocks in the grid—in the same arrangement as the Manila rope flying system (Section 5) —over a common headblock at the side, and down to a metal carriage with adjustable weights, which slides up and down the wall in a vertical track. The three or more sheaves (pulley wheels) for the cables and the one for a Manila rope, which compose the headblock, revolve side by side on a common shaft. The Manila operating rope is fastened to the top of the sliding carriage, passed up and over its sheave in the headblock in the grid, down and under a single block near the stage floor and up again to the bottom of the carriage. The latter, pulled up or down by this "endless" rope, in turn lifts or lowers the pipe batten it counterbalances. Scenery is attached to the pipe by means of trim chains. When a piece is flied to the proper height, the operating rope is fastened with a patent clamp lock. The balance weights are usually placed on the carriage from a narrow loading platform under the grid (see Figure 69).

Some stages today are equipped with both a counterweight system and the older rope system (Figure 67). The combination permits a flexibility of control impossible with one system alone.

---

[1] The "counterweight system" must not be confused with the use of counterweighting sandbags in the older method of flying scenery (see the two preceding sections and Figure 65).

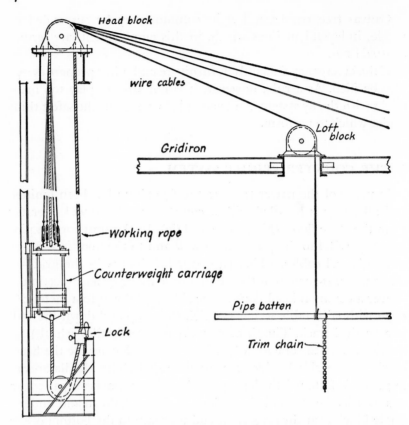

FIG. 66. Counterweight system. By means of this system scenery is handled from the floor of the stage instead of from the fly floor.

9. FLYING ON SMALL STAGES

On small platform stages where there is no possibility of constructing a regular gridiron, a makeshift device can be arranged in the form of a few stout pulleys fastened securely to beams in the ceiling. At a minimum, there should be two sets of pulleys to take care of the front and back edges of the ceiling, one to swing the pipe batten holding the front lighting units, and another to support the sky drop upstage. If the scenery is light, the lines may be tied off on a row of common lash hooks fastened to a board bolted to the wall on the side.

A little more costly, but a stronger and more generally satisfactory substitute for a grid on a small stage may be had by in-

FIG. 67. Combination fly system. This arrangement for flying scenery, which combines both the older Manila rope system, handled from a fly floor, and the newer counterweight system, operated from the stage floor, gives a degree of flexible control over hanging scenery impossible where either system is used alone. (Rigging installed on the stage of the Erlanger Theatre, Philadelphia, by Peter Clark, Inc., New York.)

stalling a system of light steel I-beams and underhang blocks (Figure 68). Four beams (about 4-inch), cut long enough to reach the full depth of the stage, are placed against the ceiling and secured to the front and rear walls. One beam extends back from a point above the center of the proscenium opening; two others from points about halfway between that and the side walls; and the fourth from a point near the right or left side wall of the stage. Standard steel underhang blocks with 4-inch sheaves are clamped

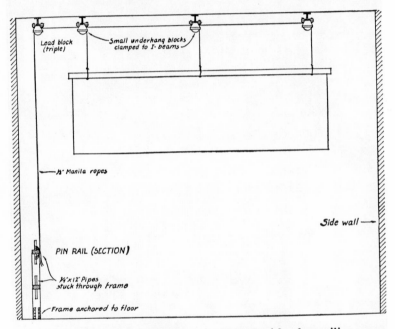

Lead block
(triple)

Small underhang blocks
clamped to I-beams

½" Manila ropes

Side wall —

PIN RAIL (SECTION)

¾"x 12" Pipes
stuck through frame

Frame anchored to floor

FIG. 68. Method of rigging a small stage with a low ceiling.

and bolted to the lower flanges of the I-beams in the same general arrangement of parallel "sets" as that employed in the layout of a regular grid (Section 5). Single blocks are attached to the three beams in the center, and triple blocks to the beam at the side.

A modified pin rail may be constructed by sticking 12-inch lengths of ¾-inch pipe through a 2″ x 4″ wooden framing anchored securely to the floor. This framing should, of course, be placed directly under the beam carrying the triple blocks.

The lines should be ½-inch Manila ropes. Cotton rope can be trusted only for the lightest of loads.

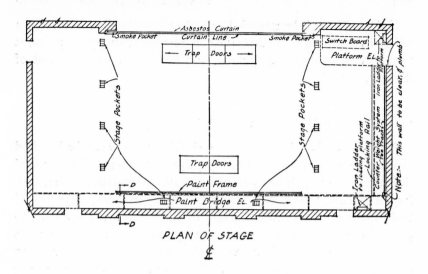

PLAN OF STAGE

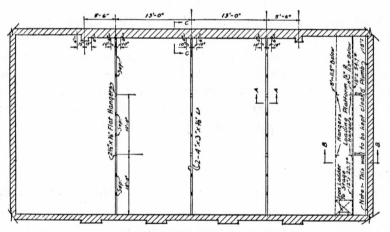

PLAN OF UNDERHUNG GRIDIRON

FIG. 69. Counterweight system and other features of the thoroughly modern equipment installed by Peter Clark, Inc., New York, on the stage of the Newark High School, Newark, N.J. (The set of plans on these pages was redrawn from records in Mr. Clark's office.)

If the ceiling of the stage is low, a drop may be flied out of sight either by tripping it, as described in Section 6, or by dropping it to the floor, rolling and tying it, and lifting it once more out of the way.

10. SPECIAL SHIFTING DEVICES

Practically all of the problems of shifting scenery can be handled satisfactorily with very simple equipment. Most of the novel shifting devices, such as hydraulic elevators, revolving tables, sliding platforms, tracks, and automatic flying systems, have found little favor on the crowded stages of this country. They tend to prescribe the type and form of scenery handled by them. This is especially true on small stages. Unless space permits their being completely ignored when types and forms of scenery which are not readily handled by them command the scene, such devices are better done without. As has already been said (Section 2), over-elaborate machinery tends to defeat its own purpose and become a hindrance rather than a help. A few of the simpler short-cut devices which do not destroy the flexibility of the stage, however, have occasionally proved very helpful. The *wagon* described in the following section, for instance, has been a valuable assistant to the shifting crew many times in recent years. Such devices should be considered, nevertheless, as special investments for particular plays rather than as permanent adjuncts of the stage.

11. THE WAGON

The *wagon* or *truck* is one of the few scene-shifting devices really favored by stage technicians in this country today. In principle, heavy groups of units are simply mounted on very low platforms fitted with casters and rolled into place for quick assembling and breaking—thus saving the considerable time and effort which would be required to put them together in smaller parts. Whole scenes are sometimes mounted on trucks. This last practice, however, is seldom employed on the stages of this country because of lack of room.

An ingenious use of the wagon system was employed in mounting a revival of Eugene O'Neill's *Beyond the Horizon* (Figure 70).

In the first production some years before, the last scene had to be omitted only because the scenery could not be changed in less than five minutes. This wait, almost at the end of the play, would have been disastrous. Cleon Throckmorton, who designed the settings, solved the problem for the second production by placing each of the two scenes—one, the interior of the farm home, and one, an exterior representing the brow of a hill—on a platform 6 inches high and just large enough to carry the body of the setting. This platform mounted on ball-bearing casters was rolled up to a per-

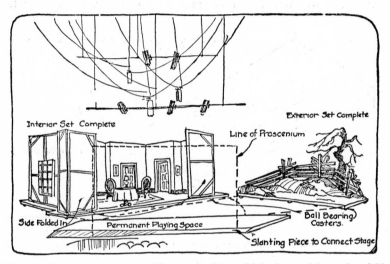

FIG. 70. Scenery on wagons. The method by which the problem of quickly shifting an interior to an exterior scene was solved in a revival of O'Neill's *Beyond the Horizon*. Sketch by Cleon Throckmorton.

manent platform, 6 inches high and 8 feet deep, built on the stage floor just behind the footlights. The permanent platform was used as playing space for both scenes, thus doing away with the continental practice of carrying the entire stage floor on each truck. In the interior scene, two end wings, which folded upon the truck when it was not in use, were swung out to join the edge of the proscenium, when the set was rolled into position, to complete the walls on the sides. In the exterior scene a sky drop and two returns were used to limit the view at the back and sides.

Because each wagon carried all properties necessary to the setting mounted on it, the time occupied by a shift was only that required to roll away one platform and bring up the other. The last change was cut from five minutes to less than one.

In the production of another play Throckmorton made use of much the same plan, except that—due to the fact that there were six complete scenes—he was unable to mount the body of each scene on a single truck. Side and back walls and porches of the interior scenes, and the various units of an elaborate Indo-Chinese street scene, were placed on a number of rectangular and triangular platforms and rolled together, according to the proper plan, as each scene was set. The most extended intra-act change by this

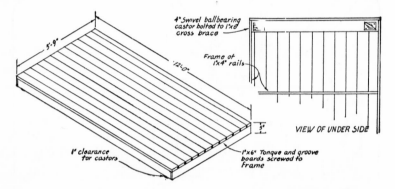

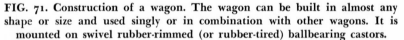

FIG. 71. Construction of a wagon. The wagon can be built in almost any shape or size and used singly or in combination with other wagons. It is mounted on swivel rubber-rimmed (or rubber-tired) ballbearing castors.

method occupied only two minutes. Without the help of wagons the same shift would have required eight or ten minutes. Recent uses of the wagon device have cut changes sometimes to a matter of seconds.

The general construction of a wagon is illustrated in Figure 71. In the unit form 1″ x 6″ tongue-and-groove white pine boards are screwed to a frame of 1″ x 4″ battens, or heavier lumber (depending on the intended load) mounted on 4-inch swivel ball-bearing casters, which are bolted to it on the inside. The truck should stand just high enough to permit the casters to roll easily. A truck unit, which measures, at most, not more than 5′ 9″ x 12′ 0″ over-all, can be used singly to carry individual units such as staircases; or it can be bolted to other trucks to form a larger platform on which a whole scene, such as one of the settings of *Beyond the Horizon* described above, may be mounted.

The use of an extensive wagon system for shifting scenery is a rather expensive one. It is not recommended for very small stages.

12. OTHER SPLIT-SECOND SHIFTING DEVICES

There are a number of other fairly simple split-second shifting devices which are used in this country from time to time. Mention might be made of the system in which the flats for a group of simple interior scenes are pivoted on two posts, one on each side of the stage, and opened in turn like leaves in a book. One leaf (made of two flats battened together) in each book forms a side wall of a set, while another folds out to meet a similar leaf from the other book to form the back wall. When the first combination is finished, it is hinged back to make room for the second, and so on.

Another method of reducing the time required for changing sets has been employed by the Theatre Guild in a number of its productions. A large, permanent frame is erected on the stage, and the back and side walls of the various scenes, put together in large panels, are each in turn set into and fastened to this frame. This saves the time which would be required for shifting if the units had to be lashed together and braced each time.

Two other methods make use of the *jack-knife* stage and the *revolving* stage. The first of these consists of two wagons pivoted downstage on each side just behind the tormentors. When one of the rolling platforms fills the proscenium opening, the other is back in its wing being set with a new scene. Then the first is swung back into the wing on the other side and the platform just set up takes its place. The revolving stage may be large enough to fill the whole of the proscenium opening. Sometimes it is placed down in the main stage floor, flush with the floor around it. This form of revolving stage is, of course, part of the permanent equipment. More often a low circular platform, made in sections bolted together, is put on top of the regular stage floor with a central pivot fastened in place temporarily. Settings are mounted on the platform in the shapes of irregular thin or thick slices of pie and revolved into place as needed. Often small circular platforms are employed to swing around only segments of scenery. Sometimes an installation includes two revolving stages, one beside the other. Sometimes one stage revolves inside of the other.

The methods for shifting scenery described in this section are suitable, of course, for certain types of plays only. Mention of them is included in this chapter to suggest to the stage technician how invention may be applied to the problem of very rapid changes. For most purposes the standard flying, lashing, and bracing methods are quite sufficient. The full service of the ordinary grid and gallery equipment is seldom realized on the nonprofessional stage. A few lines and sandbags in the hands of an experienced stagehand can be made to perform a remarkable number of feats. The young scenic designer is wise to make himself completely familiar with standard methods in the theatre before devoting much of his time to the invention of tricks.

13. SETTING THE SCENE

The exact plan adopted for the assembling of a group of scenic units varies, of course, with each scene. The following, however, is the general procedure for setting (putting together) a simple box interior (Chapter 2, Sections 4 and 5). After the ground cloth (Chapter 2, Section 2) has been laid, the ceiling is hung and lifted high enough to clear the flats; then the latter are lashed together in position, starting with one downstage end and continuing in order around to the other, stage braces (Section 3) being used where necessary. Door and window frames, if they have not already been bolted to their flats, are put into appropriate openings, and clamped in place with their strap hinges. The ceiling is let down again, trimmed and tied off on the lower pin rail. Lastly, backings are placed behind doorways, and the sky drop or sky cyclorama (Chapter 2, Section 11) is lowered. To strike (take apart) the scene, the ceiling is lifted two or three feet and a second tie in its lines made on the upper rail. The process of setting up is then reversed. An exterior scene is set and struck according to the same general plan.

When a group of scenic units is arranged on the stage for the first time, attention must be paid to proper placements and masking for good sight lines (Chapter 2, Section 10). The tormentors at the sides must be brought on far enough to hide the edges of the downstage flats; and the teaser at the top must be lowered to a position where it conceals the flies, the front edge of the ceiling (if there is one), and the overhead lighting units. When the exact arrangement of a scene has been decided upon it is a good plan to mark its position on the floor at the corners by means of a little dark paint (oil if permanent, water color if temporary). This will insure accuracy in reassembling the scene.

All flats and other units should be numbered prominently on the back for quick reference, and be stacked in a definite order before the beginning of the performance. When they are set up and struck during the performance they should be moved strictly according to this order. *Speed* and *efficiency* are two words which should never be forgotten when scenery is handled. Each shift should be plotted out carefully ahead of time and rehearsed until the station of every man and the sequence of his movements becomes absolutely clear. So far as possible, all methods and procedures should be strictly standardized. "A place for everything and everything in its place" is a motto that might well be tacked up prominently on every stage.

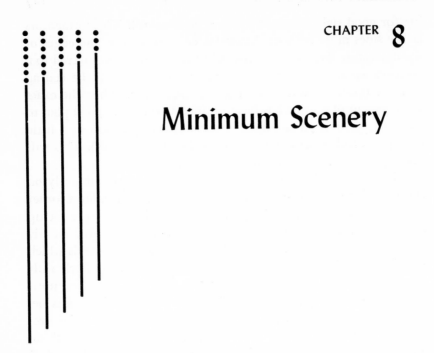

CHAPTER 8

Minimum Scenery

1. INTRODUCTION

THE SCENIC FORMS described in the preceding sections of this book are standard. In all essential features they are identical with the forms employed on the stages of New York. They have been planned to meet the requirements of general economy in construction and handling under normal conditions, but they do not take into consideration the abnormal or emergency conditions present in so many of our smaller school and community theatres.

"It is all very well," the instructor in stagecraft is reminded, "to talk of standard forms where one has the use of a properly equipped stage and has several hundred dollars to spend on a setting. But what does one do when his resources are limited to a simple platform stage and a budget of, say, twenty-five dollars for a setting? Must he forego all the pleasure of producing plays just because he cannot afford to mount them 'regularly'?" The answer is, obviously, "No." In the following sections are some general hints for designers and technicians forced to work under substandard conditions.

2. THE CYCLORAMA BACKGROUND

A program of special economy in stage settings necessarily involves some form of initial investment. The money-saver recommended for purchase or construction by the artist-technician who is required to provide a quantity of scenic environments on a frail allowance is a black cyclorama. Hung around and behind the acting area on the stage, the cyclorama is employed as a neutral background for small screens and other low-cut scenic forms placed in

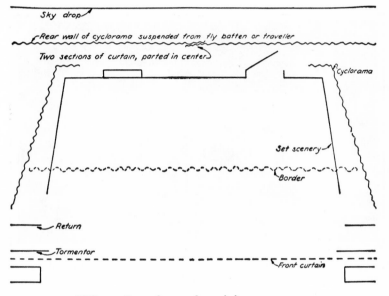

FIG. 72. Stage layout for minimum scenery.

front of it. It is surprising what attractive, dramatically effective, and at the same time inexpensive settings can be produced with this combination of black curtains and painted set pieces—if a person of ingenuity and taste handles the assemblage.

The material out of which the cyclorama indicated is made should be strong—it must stand up under much hard usage. The fabric should be closely woven, because the cyclorama must mask efficiently from the view of the audience all still and moving objects off stage. It should also have a rough or woolly surface. Fabrics with smooth surfaces tend to look shiny, and shine is one thing this cyclorama should not do. Cotton velour, with its heavy body and

deep nap, is ideal. Duvetyn is more commonly used. It lacks the
weight of velour; but it has a good surface, and it costs about half
as much as the other material. Rep is considerably stronger than
duvetyn, but it does not absorb light as well, and its price is higher.
Where both service and cost must be considered together, good-
grade duvetyn is probably the most generally satisfactory cyclorama material obtainable.

The method of constructing a cyclorama is described in Chapter 5, Section 12, and the way it is usually hung is shown in Figure

FIG. 73. Pen and wash drawing for *Ancient Heritage*, a play by Philip Parker.
Redrawn by Dan Rosen from the original sketch by Douglas Hume.

46. Where scenic set-pieces are to be placed within the enclosure
of the curtains, the rigging plan indicated in Figure 72 will be
found more satisfactory than that in Figure 46. In the arrangement
suggested here, the side walls only are tied to the U-shaped cyclorama frame. For sight-line purposes, the walls are raked outward
downstage while the upper corners are turned in and fastened to
the transverse batten of the U frame. The frame itself is suspended
on two sets of lines (run over stout pulleys securely fastened in
the stage ceiling if there is no gridiron).

The two sections comprising the back wall of the cyclorama are
hung independently from a fly batten or, better still, from a
traveller. Rigged this way, the sections may be lifted as a unit into

the flies, or parted right and left, to permit the ready passage of flats and furniture during scene changes. If a sky drop is included in the permanent stage equipment, the rear curtains are planned so that they may open up to a view of the drop.

The question will be asked, Why the choice of black for the cyclorama? The answer is that black is neutral. A black curtain with a soft woolly surface provides the least conspicuous, and therefore the most effective, background for other objects on the stage. Black absorbs light. A black cyclorama serves equally well for night and daylight scenes. Brown, blue, cream, and gray draperies reflect light. Their use as background is therefore limited.

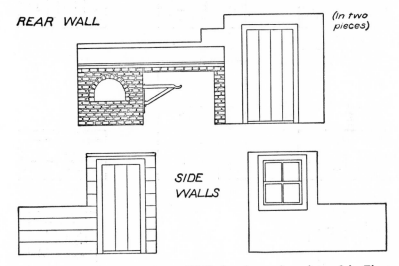

FIG. 74. Set of minimum scenery. Walls for the setting pictured in Fig. 73.

Because the cyclorama of black velour, duvetyn, or rep is such an efficient light-absorber, it possesses personally no radiant environmental quality. It should, therefore, never be used alone (except for occasional purely spatial scenes). Black, unrelieved by color, is depressing; an unvaried view of it soon grows tiresome to the spectator. The *feeling* of a cyclorama setting is imparted by the decorative and dramatic shapes placed in front of the cyclorama. Black curtains on the stage should be regarded purely as contrivances for masking from the audience the sides and top of the stage, and for providing a neutral or spatial background for the scenery proper.

3. THE SCENERY

The minimum type of setting used in front of the cyclorama should be at the same time decorative, dramatically effective, and very simple. The character of its design will be intense and com-

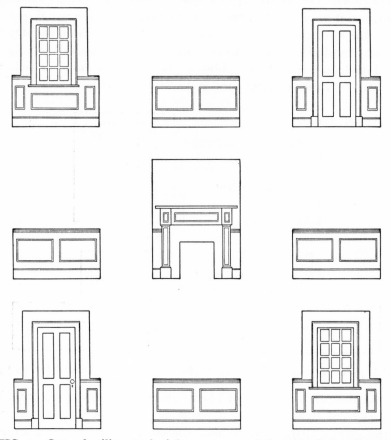

FIG. 75. General utility set of minimum scenery, designed by Robert Proctor.

pact; each detail in it—because there are so few details—has to carry a double load of responsibility for promoting the clarity, beauty, and expressiveness of the whole. Consequently, the composition of suggestive, minimum scenery has to be considered with extraordinary care.

Generally, the most practical approach to the design of this kind of setting is through selection. The artist, viewing on paper or in his mind's eye a full set of ideal scenery, determines what are the most interesting and eloquent features in it and centers his attention on these. Then he proceeds to cut down his original picture by reducing or eliminating the less valuable elements. The cutting begins with the upper, overhead parts of the set. Because the rear plane of the set, however, is naturally, by virtue of its position, more impressive than the sides, he will probably retain in his final design more of this rear part and less of the sides. The area of the back plane may be measurable not only by greater width but also by greater height. Because such architectural forms as doors, win-

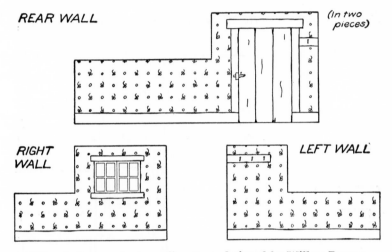

FIG. 76. Scenery for a small cottage, designed by Wilbur Dorsett.

dows and fireplaces tend to capture the audience's eye ahead of flat walls, the artist will let the former dominate the set and draw in just enough of the wall portions, perhaps, to unite the stronger elements and complete the character of the room.

Every detail in the suggestive, cut-down setting is prominent. For this reason the designer must give careful attention not only to scenic elements but also to furniture and other decorative and expressive forms used with them. Even the slightest lack of harmony between properties and scenery will destroy the sense of unity. The forms of the larger furniture pieces especially must be viewed from the standpoint of their effect upon the line and mass composition of the scenery, and the shapes of the two groups of elements —furniture and scenery—must be worked out so that they will complement each other. In the setting for *Stumbling in Dreams* (Figure 77), for instance, the piano on stage-right is naturally the most prominent object in the room. Because it is used repeatedly through the play, its presence is accentuated by spotlighting. The mass of the low desk on the opposite side of the room is insufficient to balance the form of the piano, so the wall behind the piano is reduced to a minimum and the main weight of the scenery is thrown to the other side.

Color may, and should, be used freely in the cut-down set. Because the over-all space occupied by this type of scenery is relatively

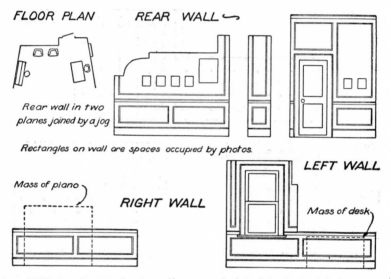

FIG. 77. Scenery for a studio room, designed by Samuel Selden.

small in comparison with the expanse of black behind it, all of the design elements may be exaggerated somewhat to good effect. This means that all the forms in a suggestive setting—walls, woodwork, furniture, and even costumes—may be a little more highly colored than equivalent forms in a regular realistic setting.

The construction of the scenery discussed in this section follows, more or less, the regular methods outlined in Chapter 4. Light wooden frames are put together with corner blocks and keystones, and then covered with cloth. Because strength in these smaller forms is not of prime importance a considerable saving in cost can be effected by the use of materials unsuitable for regular scenery.

Instead of white pine in 1″ x 3″ strips, the carpenter can use a cheaper wood (such as common yellow pine) in 1″ x 2″ strips; and instead of scene linen or duck, he can use a cheap grade of unbleached muslin.

4. LIGHTING MINIMUM SCENERY

If good lighting is necessary for complete scenic forms, it is doubly necessary for reduced forms. To obtain any degree of expressiveness at all out of his settings, the designer of minimum scenery must lean heavily upon an efficient electrical department. It is obvious that the essential qualities of a suggestive setting will reveal themselves rather timidly unless the atmosphere surrounding them is also suggestive. *Suggestive* lighting (as explained in later chapters) means *selective* lighting—adequately produced and flexibly controlled. Some stage electrical equipment is absolutely essential—however pinched the designer's budget may be. In fact, the smaller the general budget the more important it is for the designer to think of that equipment. If he has only $150 with which to rig his stage and prepare his first set of scenery, let him plan to spend at least half of those precious dollars on the lighting.

5. CONCLUSION

Minimum scenery is better than no scenery. Minimum scenery is not better, however, than complete scenery. The half forms described in this chapter represent (except in those plays where many shifts require a strict limitation in each scene) a rather severe compromise not only in size, but also in spirit, with the larger, more completely expressive forms. The artist who is forced to work for the time being under sub-standard conditions should guard against the temptation to avoid struggle by accepting those conditions as permanent. If he is worth anything as a theatre artist he will strive to improve his production machine until he is able to produce the type of settings he really wants to create. Let him remember constantly the eight requirements of effective scenery discussed in the first chapter of this book, and make it his purpose eventually to meet those requirements.

CHAPTER 9

New

and Experimental

Staging

1. INTRODUCTION

THE THEATRE is always growing, and growth means change. Playwrights experiment with new forms of drama, actors vary their approach, directors and designers try out new ways of staging, all working to make drama more evocative, more stimulating, more expressive. Even the architects who plan the auditoriums are busy. They ask each other questions about the best kind of shape, size, and equipment for the hall which the spectators occupy—questions concerning width and height, acoustics, sight lines, traffic lanes, seating, illumination, and many other factors—then try to do something about improving these.

The principal problem in which all people in the theatre are interested is the relationship of audience to performer. Driven by a desire to build a more and more exciting place for action and response, many minds have labored toward the evolution of a "perfect stage" and a "perfect auditorium," each considered as a separate area of planning.

For nearly three hundred years very little was done about the link between the two. Throughout this period it was generally assumed that the connecting link between acting area and spec-

196

tator's chair was the proscenium arch. Early in this century, however, especially in Europe, a few revolutionaries challenged this idea. In recent years the voice of protest has become stronger. Now the desire for trying new arrangements is clearly evident in this country. In time the question may be answered in favor of the traditional forms. Until then, however, the technical director and the designer would do well to keep their eyes and minds open and be prepared to shift their staging methods to get the best results from the elements, both human and technical, with which they deal.

It is true that this book is a manual of scenic and lighting methods, not a treatise on theatre architecture. Nevertheless, it is appropriate to devote a few pages here to experimental efforts to solve actor-audience relationships, for two reasons: first, the designer may find himself having to modify the visual forms of his scenic elements to fit the peculiar requirements and opportunities of new playhouses already erected; and second, having studied the many complex problems involved in making scenery an effective support to acting, he may wish to offer suggestions on a new building in which he will work in the future.

2. SETTINGS FOR THE ARENA THEATRE

One of the liveliest of theatre developments in recent years has taken place in the *arena*, sometimes called also the *theatre-in-the-round*. In arena theatre the acting area, usually square or rectangular, is placed in the center, and the spectators encircle it. Players' entrances and exits are made down aisles between sections of the audience. Sometimes the acting is done on a level with the lowest seats, sometimes it is raised a foot or two. Ideally, the surrounding audience chairs are banked (sloped up) to give the spectators better vision. There are no definite rules about the size and shape of the arena space, or about the relation between the acting and audience areas, except two: the front seats should be close enough to the playing space to keep the feeling intimate, but not so near as to inhibit the actors' freedom of movement; and the rear seats should be so arranged that people sitting in them can hear and see easily every part of the performance, including the entrances and exits.

Generally speaking, arena staging uses no scenery. Occasionally,

Arena theatre, or "theatre-in-the-round." The Penthouse Theatre, University
of Washington, planned by John Ashby Conway.

directors staging plays with multiple locales have found it advantageous to mark off one part of the playing space as a sitting
room, another as an office, another as a street corner, and to erect
one or two low scenic set pieces to help the spectators visualize the
different places. One device that has been used is to give floor areas
in the different spaces different colors by means of rugs or painted
pieces of canvas. Since, however, this kind of arrangement tends
inevitably to corner the action during each of the several scenes, it
is usually frowned upon. In arena theatre, the actors are supposed
to play equally to every part of the audience, and this cannot be
done if their actions are restricted to specific areas.

Sometimes, of course, the whole play may be set outdoors. In
this case, the use of a scenic rock, or one or two tree trunks (not
so large as to interfere with lighting or sight lines) may help to
create a sense of locale. Generally, however, the responsibility for
creating a feeling of surroundings rests with the actors, assisted
by the lighting director. This does not mean that there is consequently nothing for a designer to do. There is much for him to do

in the selection and construction of properties—pieces of furniture, utensils, bits of machinery, and various portable objects, which will *suggest* by their form and style the kind of surroundings which would naturally go with them. Thus the properties help the actors create an illusion of scenery.

And, of course, there are always present the problems of texture and color, and of the composition of the various blocks, lines, and contours of physical objects in relation to the costumes and the movements of the players. All of these details are especially important in arena staging, and the designer will find himself busy attending to them.

3. THE HORSESHOE THEATRE

A modification of the arena is the *horseshoe,* or *three-quarter-round,* theatre in which the audience sits not on four, but on three sides of the central acting area. The fourth side is reserved for a

A production of *On Borrowed Time,* designed by Richard Wilcox. Theatre 170, Department of Theater Arts, University of California at Los Angeles. (See Fig. 80.)

simple scenic façade whose form suggests an environment for the performers working in front of it. Perhaps what is selected for this pictorial plane is a prominent window, door, or fireplace, with some of the surrounding wall attached to it, or, if the place of action is outdoors, a tree or a rock. In the horeshoe theatre, like the arena, players make their entrances down aisles through the audience; commonly, however, they make their exits through the scenic façade or around its edges, in order to seem to carry with them some of the environmental image.

The designer's problems in the horseshoe are similar to the ones he has in the arena, except that to these he now must add special consideration for the design of the scenic background. Into this one screen or three-dimensional shape (or group of shapes) he must concentrate much of the planning that he would distribute throughout the three planes—plus through-door or through-window vistas—if he were working on a conventional proscenium stage. This does not mean, of course, that he will try to crowd into one wall all the forms which would ordinarily be found on the three walls, but he will have to capture and place in the one wall as much as he can of the sense of place and mood desired for the scene as a whole.

4. MODIFICATIONS OF THE PROSCENIUM STAGE

The majority of theatre workers still seem to prefer the proscenium type of stage, since for them it is, in the long run, the most flexible. On it they can construct settings covering the wide range from illusional realism to theatrical formalism in a variety of forms impossible to set up in the arena or horseshoe theatres.

Still, there clearly are disadvantages to be met on the proscenium stage. One exists in the hard line of the arch which limits the sides of the acting area. Another is in the elaborate, expensively equipped stage house which frequently requires for the operation of all its machinery a crew of technicians as large as the whole acting company put together.

One solution which has been offered for the first difficulty is a plan which extends the frontal acting area right and left out beyond the edges of the proscenium frame onto two small side stages. Sometimes these side spaces take the form of plain little nooks, with no access except through the main opening or by steps from the side aisles of the auditorium. More often they have special doors of their own opening through the proscenium wall to backstage. The University Theatre at the University of Oregon runs the front of its stage in a concave curve beyond the right and left edges of the proscenium arch to provide two side spaces for action. Entrances and exits to these small supplementary stages are made behind louvers, two on each side. The upstage louvers have door openings.

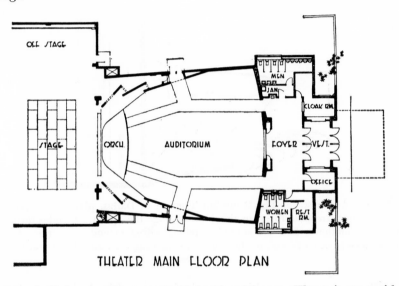

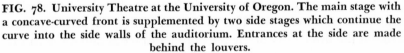

THEATER MAIN FLOOR PLAN

FIG. 78. University Theatre at the University of Oregon. The main stage with a concave-curved front is supplemented by two side stages which continue the curve into the side walls of the auditorium. Entrances at the side are made behind the louvers.

Arch Lauterer and some of his associates have tried to solve the mechanical problem of scene changing by eliminating the conventional flies and suspending all hanging pieces, such as drops, drapes, and the rear walls of sets, from trolleys running on tracks attached to a low ceiling. The scenic units can be shifted laterally, instead of vertically, by a minimum crew.

Generally speaking, there have been no recent changes in the proscenium stage that affect the technical director and designer except in so far as they may necessitate the replanning of scene shifts.

5. THE APRON, OR OPEN, STAGE

A form which has had considerable promotion in the United States in the last several years, though it is by no means new to Europe, is the *apron,* or *open,* stage. Its principal feature is a raised promontory which sticks out into the auditorium much like the forestage of the old Elizabethan playhouse; but it also has a transverse, conventional stage, at the back. Scenery hangs, or is set up, behind this.

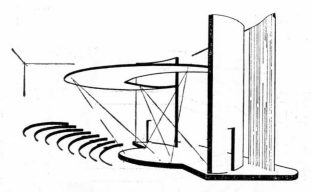

FIG. 79. Apron stage. The Roundup Theatre in Dallas, planned by James Hull Miller. In some forms of this kind of stage the apron protrudes farther into the audience and the slotted hanging ceiling extends over the whole interior—the seats as well as the platform—making the auditorium and stage one room.

The apron stage combines certain features of both the horseshoe and proscenium forms. The audience, sitting in a wide curve around the three sides of the big apron, can see action on both this front platform and the transverse part of the stage behind it (see Figure 79). Actors make their entrances and exits through portals right and left at the ends of the transverse portion of the stage, or behind tormentor screens framing the central façade, or through some part of the scenery in the middle. This scenic element may be quite flat, or it may have depth.

James Hull Miller, a principal proponent of the apron stage in this country, thus describes some of its characteristics: "Not as radical as central [arena] staging, nor as conservative and illusory as the picture frame [proscenium arch] setting, it depends more on a free-style theatricality and flair which has been the mainstay of production style over the ages . . . The apron stage supplies the intimacy of arena while retaining a portion of the visual spectacle." [1]

The scenery for this form (sometimes simply drapes) is shifted laterally by trolleys running on overhead tracks, or by hand, into the wings. Usually only properties and light set pieces are moved onto the apron. The lighting of all parts of the stage is affected by units mounted above slots in a hanging ceiling over the acting area.

The development of the modern apron stage has moved in two directions: one toward a kind of compromise with the old proscenium stage which exploits the thrust-out apron but retains something of the conventional arch and a modified stage house behind it; and one toward what its promoters call a purer, more historical form, with no arch and no fly space. In this development the slotted ceiling (for lighting) is continuous from front to back, over both the spectators' seats and the actors' platform, making the whole space in effect one room.

6. OTHER EXPERIMENTAL FORMS OF INDOOR STAGING

One of the most interesting of the explorations into new staging is the experimental Theatre 170 at the University of California at Los Angeles. A made-over classroom, it has no fixed stage or audience space. The acting area is placed sometimes at one end of the room, sometimes at one side, or in a corner, or in the middle, and movable seating is arranged to fit the acting. Figure 80 shows nine different plans for nine different productions.

John Ashby Conway's proposed theatre for the University of Washington goes back to the use of the proscenium frame. However, what he has put behind the frame is quite novel (Figure 81). The principal parts are an inner revolving disc, and an outer revolving ring on the inner edge of which is mounted a circular cyclorama wall. The wall has one break in it which may be oriented to the proscenium opening. When the ring is given a partial turn the wall seals the opening. Since there is a shallow space on the ring in front of the wall, actors can deliver before-the-curtain

[1] James Hull Miller, "Initial Factors in Theatre Planning," *Educational Theatre Journal*, Vol. VIII, No. 2 (May, 1956), p. 91.

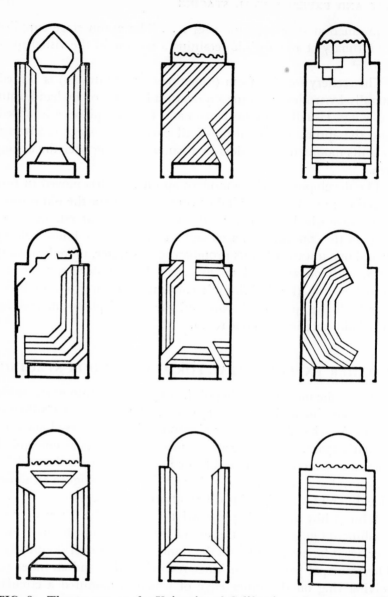

FIG. 80. Theatre 170, at the University of California at Los Angeles. The seats and acting space are here arranged in nine different ways for nine different plays (starting with the left row, bottom to top): *The Cherry Orchard, Blithe Spirit, Twelfth Night, Ah, Wilderness!, Suspect, Volpone, Mourning Becomes Electra, The Late Christopher Bean,* and *The Great God Brown.*

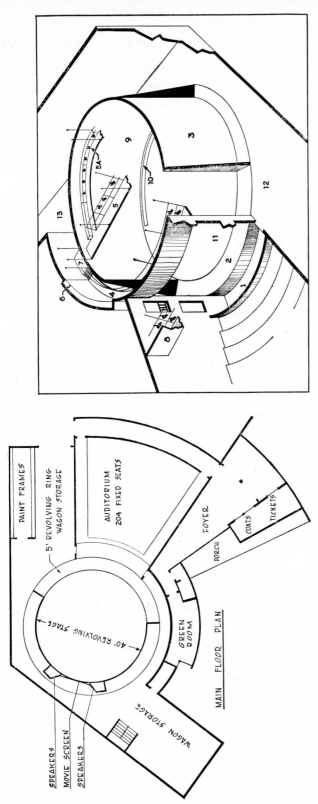

FIG. 81. Proposed theatre for the University of Washington in Seattle, designed by John Ashby Conway. The circular shell mounted on the revolving ring serves as a cyclorama when the front is open. When it revolves a quarter turn it closes the opening. (1) Hydraulic lift which can be used as elevator, orchestra pit, forestage, or will carry extra rows of seats. (2) Revolving ring which operates independently, carries the cyclorama, motion picture screen, and two side stages. (3) Side stage. When used in conjunction with the forestage, will allow a set eleven feet deep. Two proscenium doors and balconies are available if needed. (4) First lighting bridge. Conway suggests the switchboard and sound control be placed up on this bridge. (5) Second lighting bridge, connected with (4) via (7). (5a) Connecting lighting bridge for cyc lighting. (6) Top of switchboard. (7) Connecting platform, connects (4) to (5). (8) Beam, entered through door in wall from wagon storage (12). (9) Plaster cyc. Revolves on its ring, making a sight barrier between forestage and mainstage. (10) Light pit. (11) Revolving stage, 40-foot diameter. (12 and 13) Wagon storage.

speeches or play transitional scenes here. In fact, since the ring has considerable circumference, a whole series of short scenes can be given in front of the wall, one after another, with the ring taking a quarter turn—forward, or forward then backward—for each shift. (One segment of the wall is reserved for a motion picture screen.) A forestage in front of the ring gives additional depth, when needed, to the front scenes.

On the main part of the stage—that is, on the central disk—the scenic artist can create one permanent setting that will not move, or a number of temporary settings back to back that will be revolved into view as they are needed. The circular wall behind the scenery serves as a sky backing in every scene opening to the outdoors. Reserve elements may be mounted on wagons stored in the rooms set aside for their use on stage right and left. With the use of the two revolving sections and the wagons, the artist and his technical associates can handle easily and swiftly an almost unlimited number of scenes in one play, or present one show in the afternoon and change to a completely different one in the evening.

The forestage is movable by means of an hydraulic lift. If the frontspace is not needed it can be dropped all the way down to provide a pit for an orchestra, or halfway down for a level area for additional auditorium seats. Heavy properties, usually kept in the basement, can be brought up to the stage on the elevator and later returned to storage the same way.

One of the principal advantages of this theatre design is that it places practically no restriction on the width of the auditorium. The sight lines would be good even if the boundary of this segment were increased almost to a semicircle.

7. OUTDOOR THEATRES

The recent development of outdoor historical drama, more usually referred to as "symphonic drama" in several parts of the United States, has necessitated considerable revision in amphitheatre forms. Open-air plays are typically composed of varied elements: dramatic episodes, both mass and intimate; choral and dance groups; and general visual spectacle. There is much physical movement and the story moves swiftly; no waiting at any point can be tolerated once the action starts. Since the presentation takes place in the open where there can be no proscenium arch on which to hang a traveller track, the changes from scene to scene have to be effected without the help of any front curtain.

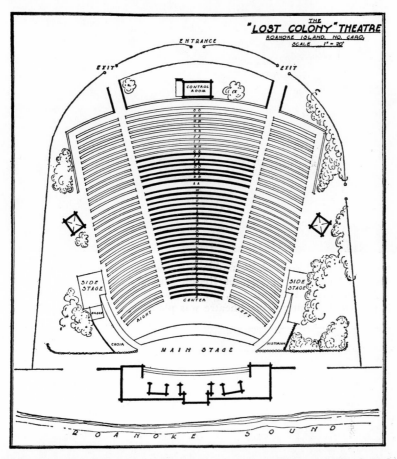

FIG. 82. Ground plan of the Waterside Theatre on Roanoke Island, N.C., home of the presentation of Paul Green's outdoor drama, "The Lost Colony." Designed and constructed by Albert Q. Bell.

The solution for this problem is the use of a main stage, on which the big scenes are played, and two flanking side stages, on which are put the smaller transitional scenes. Lighting (the instruments for which are mounted both behind the proscenium walls

Two outdoor theatres for historical ("symphonic") dramas. Above: Hunter Hills Theatre, Gatlinburg, Tennessee, setting for Kermit Hunter's *Chucky Jack*. Below: Lake Matoaka Amphitheatre, Williamsburg, Virginia, where Paul Green's *The Common Glory* is presented. Hunter Hills Theatre was planned by John B. Lippard.

of the main stage and, for the most part in two tall towers on each side of the auditorium) controls the visibility for the audience. It directs attention away from the action on one stage to the action on another, thus permitting scenery to be shifted on the darkened stage without any pause in the continuity of the performance.

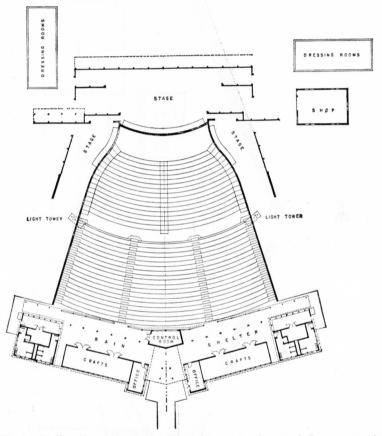

FIG. 83. Indian Fort Theater at Berea, Kentucky, home of the presentation of Paul Green's outdoor drama "Wilderness Road." Designed by John B. Lippard, landscape architect.

The treatment of the scenic factors varies from drama to drama. For Paul Green's *The Lost Colony*, on Roanoke Island, North Carolina, there is a three-dimensional setting, depicting the settlement in the New World, placed toward the rear on the big main stage. This is not revealed. however, until the beginning of the sec-

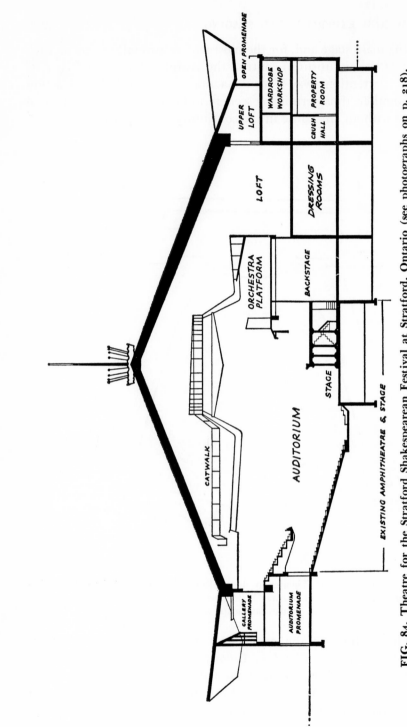

FIG. 84. Theatre for the Stratford Shakespearean Festival at Stratford, Ontario (see photographs on p. 218).

ond act. For the first-act settings tall screens are set up in three layers in front of the settlement to suggest, in turn, the reed fence of
an Indian village, the stone outer walls of an English garden, and
the brick and plaster walls of a tavern courtyard.

The right side stage, on which the natural island shrubbery has
been preserved, is retained chiefly for wilderness scenes; while the
left stage, a little more bare, can be set up easily with interior
scenes.

The main stage of Matoaka Lake Amphitheatre at Williamsburg, Virginia, where Green's *The Common Glory* is performed,
reveals the lake at the rear. Here there is no permanent setting of
any kind. All the scenic elements are mounted on wagons which
roll in from the wings to make a variety of interiors and exteriors.
The side stages in this theatre are quite small and are placed close
down against the proscenium walls. There is no effort to set
realistically the scenes presented in these little areas. The backgrounds are simply suggestive vignettes.

The modern outdoor theatre, when it is skillfully and sensitively
lighted, is a wonderfully flexible instrument for those who enjoy
epic imagery. A piece of action can be held for a moment in the
tight grip of one small spot of light, then with the lift of a dimmer
handle, suddenly be given freedom to sweep three hundred feet
from one bank of the theatre, down to the central stage, and up to
the other side, with no limits except the deep surrounding woods
and the lofty stars.

8. CONCLUSION

One brief chapter cannot do much in the way of describing all
of the staging experiments that are now in progress. What it can
do is to suggest a few of the directions which these experiments are
taking, and perhaps stimulate the reader to do some fresh thinking
of his own.

Which is the best direction to follow? No one can give a final
answer to that. Each designer and technical director must analyze
carefully all the factors in the particular situation in which he
works, then attempt to find the best solution to *all* his problems
considered as a whole.

And it is important for him to think of the solution in terms of its long range implications. If he is not planning to rebuild his stage plant every few years, what he designs must be flexible enough and sturdy enough to be used for many different kinds of plays over a long period of time.

STAGE LIGHTING

By HUNTON D. SELLMAN

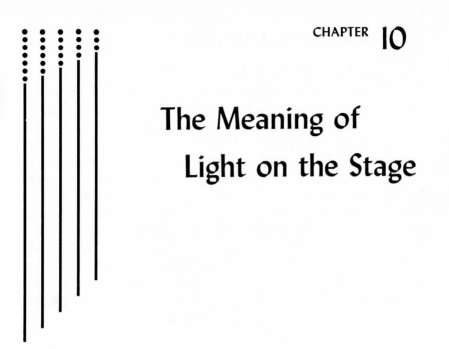

CHAPTER 10

The Meaning of
Light on the Stage

1. INTRODUCTION

WHEN THE HOUSE lights dim and the footlights add a warm glow to a rich velour curtain, the audience is in the mood for something special. These spectators will not be satisfied with a literal transcription of the mundane activities of the family next door in their conventional living room. Instead, the magic of the theatre must pull them forward in their seats and must command their full attention; it must say to them, "This is no ordinary place and this dialogue is not from the daily newspaper." Here will be a carefully organized dramatic story told with action and emotion. It may be a play by Sophocles or Shakespeare or O'Neill, brought to the stage by the finest professional actors or by a talented group of university players. In any event, the first visual impact of scenery and lighting must set the stage for something extraordinary. Beyond a doubt, this magic touch is created by means of light, living light revealing living actors. Light is magic in the sense that it can command attention, establish mood, enrich the setting, and create composition. Light might be said to paint with the painter, act with the actor, and create with the director and playwright.

215

Used with imagination, light is, indeed, the magician of the theatre.

For two thousand years light was merely illumination, usually from the sun. Of course there was an occasional exception in the pyrotechnics of the Middle Ages; and in the Renaissance candles and oil lamps may have helped in the masques of Inigo Jones. In the eighteenth century Garrick's De Loutherbourg is said to have used the "magic lantern" for the theatre's first lens-projected scenery. It remained for Adolph Appia late in the last century, however, to conceive of light as the partner of music and drama. He wrote about it, designed with it, and demonstrated the effective use of light according to his original ideas in a distinguished production of *Tristan and Isolde*. In more recent years Robert Edmond Jones, Donald Oenslager, Jo Mielziner, Stanley McCandless, and Thomas Wilfred, to mention only a few, have developed the use of light as an art of the theatre. Yet lighting as an art is just beginning. The possibilities are unlimited.

2. BACKGROUND

Adolph Appia, distinguished revolutionary in design and light at the turn of the last century, pointed the way in his writings and stimulating designs.[1] He called the familiar light of his time (from borderlights and footlights) *general illumination (Helligkeit)*. According to Appia this kind of light was inadequate, useful perhaps, but there must be a new kind of light, a form-revealing light (*gestaltendes licht*) to give objects on the stage their natural third-dimensional quality—there must be living light for living people. From Appia's *gestaltendes licht* the contemporary concept of *specific illumination* has developed.

Recent developments in incandescent lamps and the improvements in design and construction of instruments and their control have not made Appia's ideas obsolete. Even today artificial light can be divided into two kinds which correspond to the two kinds of light in nature. Direct sunlight is a shadow-producing, form-revealing light that may be called *specific illumination*. In the theatre, or on the stage, specific illumination is produced by spot-

[1] Adolph Appia, Die Musik und die Inscenierung (Munick, F. Bruckman, 1899).

lights. The other kind of light, *general illumination,* like sky light in nature, is a shadowless illumination produced on the stage satisfactorily by striplights and floodlights. When these two kinds of light are properly produced, controlled, and distributed according to good stage lighting standards, the basis for effective results has been established.

3. CONTROLLABLE PROPERTIES OF LIGHT

These two kinds of light have three properties, *quantity, color,* and *distribution,* over which varying degrees of control are possible. The *quantity* of light is controlled by the number of sources of light, their size, dimming control, and color filters. From the point of view of the audience, the quantity of light influences visual acuity, fatigue, and mood. The amount of light needed for the stage has always been determined by a mixture of guesswork and experience. More research is needed but good judgment has helped to establish a reasonable range of illumination for the stage. Acting area light usually ranges between two and forty lumens [2] per square foot. These figures mean very little, of course, unless such factors as color, reflectance, contrast, size of the object, distance from the observer, and the nature of the surface are known. Such obvious things as avoiding glare by preventing very high contrast and removing brilliant sources from the sight of the audience should always be remembered. By all means a sufficient amount of light to prevent eye fatigue should be provided on an acting area. When members of the audience are straining to see with insufficient light, they frequently miss important parts of the play. Since muscular control of the iris in the eye and changes in the retina, called adaptation, require time, we must control our changes in illumination accordingly, especially from light to dark. For example, an audience can see a dimly lighted scene more clearly (and with less strain) if the house lights are dimmed slowly and if the house is left dark for a few seconds before the curtain rises, than if the house lights are snapped off and the curtain is

[2] A lumen per square foot, or a foot-candle, is the illumination on a surface one foot from a source of one candle power. The usual illumination meter indicates illumination in foot candles, which is numerically equal to lumens per square foot.

Two views of the stage of the permanent Stratford Shakespearean Festival Theatre at Stratford, Ontario. Designed by Tanya Moiseiwitsch.

opened immediately. The reason for this is that adaptation takes place in a few seconds when light becomes brighter, but it takes as much as several minutes for adaptation from light to dark. Everyone has had the experience of stumbling about for a while upon entering a cinema theatre from bright daylight. A number of quick changes of scene with widely different levels of illumination will tire an audience much more rapidly than lighting slowly changed, or kept at a single level of illumination, because in the first case the eye has been overworked. There is evidence that higher levels of illumination make people more alert, and we know by experience in the theatre that audiences enjoy a sophisticated comedy in bright light more than they do one in which the lighting is at a lower level. Bright light for comedy and dim for tragedy is an old but useful rule.

The control of *color* is just as important as the control of quantity of light. In producing plays in the fifteenth century not only was quantity of light different in comedy and tragedy, but colors differed also. Warm colors were used for comedy and cool ones for tragedy. This conception of color is still in general use today, but there are many exceptions in which color is used intelligently in defiance of this rule.

In working with color on the stage, one is interested in it both objectively and subjectively. Objectively, a source of light is selected, modified, and reflected before it reaches the eyes of the audience. On the other hand, the director is more interested in how color affects the minds of individuals in the audience. This is the subjective, or psychological, aspect. The color of the source is modified by the reflector, lens, and color filter, and by some means of dimming. This controlled color is further modified by the reflecting surfaces of scenery, properties, make-up, and costumes before it reaches the eye of the observer who sees the final result as a pattern of color. Mixing colors additively by dimming and varying the proportion of colors from two or more sources is another phase of color control. The discussion of color continues in Chapter 12.

Distribution is the term used to indicate the way in which light of any quantity or color is spread (distributed) over the acting area and the background. Obviously, the three controllable properties are closely interrelated. Distribution depends upon the use of both kinds of light, specific and general, to produce different levels of illumination on the acting area and on the scenery, and upon variety in color over the same surfaces. The fact that scenery, costumes, properties, and even the actor's make-up vary considerably in their ability to reflect light, and in the way they reflect it, is a highly important consideration in the lighting distribution for a play. Even when an actor moves about the stage he changes the distribution of light, because his body and costumes are reflectors like any part of the setting. A successful distribution of light on the stage depends on the length and angle of the shadows, the depth of shaded areas and their contrast with highlights, and the difference in levels of illumination, without the extremes which are sometimes called "dead spots" and "hot spots." These last are merely evidences of too much contrast, or insufficient blending of general illumination with specific illumination.

Thus the controllable properties of light take their place in an analysis of stage lighting. In a single sentence the whole matter can be expressed like this: Both general and specific illumination can be controlled and changed in quantity, color, and distribution to accomplish the five functions of stage lighting discussed in the following section.

4. THE FUNCTIONS OF STAGE LIGHTING

The functions of stage lighting are generally agreed upon by those who work in the theatre, but the names of the functions and their divisions differ somewhat. For purposes of discussion the functions are divided here into five:

1. Selective visibility
2. Revelation of form
3. Illusion of nature
4. Composition
5. Mood

1. *Selective visibility*. The most important thing that light can do on the stage is to allow an audience to see comfortably and clearly. Visibility depends upon the amount of illumination, the size of the lighted objects, the amount of light an object reflects, contrast with its background, and the distance between the object

and the observer. This is a general statement, applicable to the
stage as well as elsewhere. Obviously, light at all times should
be sufficiently bright for comfortable vision without fatigue; but
large numbers of people every day are working and reading under
insufficient illumination. The theatre is only a minor offender in
this respect, but settings are frequently seen in which extreme
contrasts are annoying. For example, table and floor lamps are
frequently too bright and sky cycloramas are very often too light
in contrast to the level of acting area lighting. On the other hand,
many productions are lighted with insufficient contrast; in other
words, everything on the stage is evenly and monotonously illuminated. The mean between these extremes is preferred, and visibility is a matter of degree. That is, visibility must be selective if
the audience is to see only what is intended for it at any moment.
In Arthur Koestler's *Darkness at Noon,* the main curtain is not
closed except during the intermission, and scenes are played on
different levels and at different places on the stage. The scene in
progress, however, is the only one illuminated while the others are
obscured by darkness. Light, in a sense, opens the curtain for each
small scene and guides the eyes of the audience in the direction
the producer intends—to the place where sound and movement
occur.

By lowering the level of illumination, visibility can be reduced
until an object completely disappears or is left inconspicuously
in shade or shadow until one wishes to have it appear. This method
of lighting is always effective with a permanent set when changes
are made by moving from one part of the stage to another. Color,
too, is concerned with visibility. Under ordinary lighting conditions visibility reaches the maximum in yellow and drops off in
blue, green, orange, and red. Because of this fact, higher levels of
blue light are necessary for a night scene than would be if yellow
light were used. On the other hand, monotonous uniform distributions of blue light in large quantities quickly bring fatigue to the
eyes of the audience.

2. *Revelation of form.* This is a function that is easily ignored
and overlooked. When plays are lighted with general illumination alone, actors, properties, and pieces of scenery all look flat and
uninteresting. There are no highlights, no shadows, no variety in
the distribution of light. The walls of a set have as much light on

them as the actors' faces have, and in fact every object, every surface, is at the same level of illumination. This is anything but
form-revealing light. In order for objects to appear in their natural
form, the distribution of light must have a high degree of variety
produced by different levels of illumination. In the first place,
there must be that form-revealing, shadow-producing light which
we call specific illumination. Appia said that shade and shadow are
equal in importance to light itself. In one of the notebooks of
Leonardo da Vinci there appear some pertinent comments on the
subject. He says, "Shadow is the withholding of light. It seems
to me that shadows are of supreme importance in perspective,
seeing that without them opaque objects and solid bodies will be
indistinct both as to what lies within their boundaries and also as
to their boundaries themselves. Consequently I treat of shadow
and say in this connection that every opaque body is surrounded
and has its surface clothed with shadows and light." And again,
"Excess of light makes things seem hard; and too much darkness
does not admit of our seeing them. The mean is excellent." One
of the fundamental demands of depth perception is the harmonious
relationship between the scenery and the actor, and the way light
contributes to this relationship. For example, if the angle of illumination and the position of the actor are such that the shadow
of the actor falls halfway up Mount Whitney on the drop, any sense
of depth is immediately destroyed, and any sense of theatrical
illusion is reduced to a ludicrous absurdity. The scene designer
can paint a natural haziness in the outlines of the distant objects,
and light can participate by keeping distant objects dimmer than
those in the foreground. As discussed under the subject of projected
scenery, the slides for projection (both for lens and Linnebach
projectors) can be made to suggest objects at different distances by
the sharpness or softness of their outlines.

Separation of the actor from his background, even from the
wall of a set ten feet behind him, is a highly important part of
the function of form revelation. It can be done in three ways.
First, the background should have considerably less light, perhaps
one fourth to one twentieth of the light on the actor. Furthermore,
the light on the background should be general illumination. The
actor, as mentioned above, is lighted with specific illumination.

The second factor in depth perception is the use of some intense, specific illumination from the side, avoiding high levels of general illumination or monotonous levels of specific illumination from the front. The third method, so common and so effective in television, is back lighting, with specific illumination highlighting the hair of the actress as well as her shoulders and neck. If back lighting is impossible, some sources directly overhead will aid in separation and in the perception of depth.

Revelation of form, then, is accomplished essentially by specific illumination. But specific illumination monotonously applied can easily approach general illumination in making a scene flat, dull, and uninteresting. The angles and direction of specific illumination, together with carefully applied highlights balanced by shade and shadow, make the difference. Contrast and variety in color also is a part of this difference that compels the interest and attention of the spectator.

3. *Illusion of nature.* This function includes the use of artificial light to create the illusion of natural light that indicates time of day, locale, and season. It includes also the simulation of artificial illumination in interiors to indicate light from chandeliers, bracket lights, and other luminaires commonly found in interiors. These are merely *motivations* (apparent sources) for the actual acting area lighting, and are almost never used as real sources of light for the acting area. The sources of outdoor and interior illumination are a part of design too (see Section 8).

By the amount of light and the color, one can distinguish between the intense tropical sunlight of a South Sea island, and the weak cold sunlight of northern Norway. With the same variables the romantic moonlight in *Cyrano de Bergerac* can be differentiated from the cold moonlight in *Mourning Becomes Electra.* In plays of naturalism, and perhaps sometimes in plays of realism, the vertical angle of sunlight and moonlight may be important. In a play with a single set, suppose that the first act takes place in the morning with the sunlight coming in a window at stage left. In the second act the time is mid-afternoon, and the angle of the sun will be different and will enter through a different window. A sunset should not be seen through the same window where the morning sun appeared. The length of shadows may be important

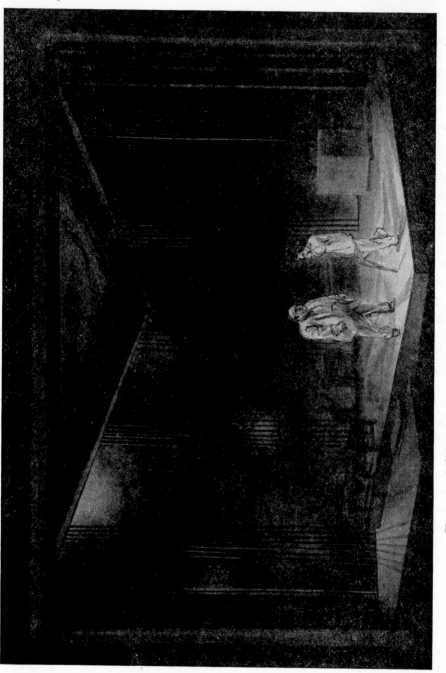

Tennessee Williams' *Cat on a Hot Tin Roof*, designed by Jo Mielziner.

in certain plays to indicate the time of day, and foliage patterns (see Figure 104) on the walls of buildings assist in this function as well as in that of composition.

The color of sunlight is actually almost white, or at least it is a very much lighter tint of yellow than unmodified incandescent light. While cool white sunlight might help create an appropriate mood for tragedy and melodrama, it would not have sufficient contrast for comedy. In keeping with the theory that theatrical exaggeration increases the effectiveness of all the elements of dramatic production, the amber color for sunlight has become an appropriate convention for comedy. Varying from a pale greenish yellow (usually unpleasant for comedy) to a pinkish or orange yellow, a shaft of sunlight is considered a pleasing motivation for the acting area light. It should be placed and directed not only for this function but also for design, in so far as its pattern falls on the walls of a set or other objects.

Moonlight, too, is concerned with color. Natural moonlight, as everyone knows, is sunlight reflected from the surface of the moon, and accordingly is yellow in hue. But if one used yellow moonlight on the stage, it would be confused with sunlight and would also be a distraction because of its "unconventional" color. It is reasonable to suppose that the cool color for moonlight developed as a convention because of its association with the blue night sky. Shafts or beams of moonlight produced with spotlights are conventionally some tint of blue, depending on the taste or discretion of the artists concerned. They might be anything from greenish blue to lavender blue, the latter being good for very romantic scenes. "Steel" blue or pale blue-green are the usual colors for moonlight.

4. *Composition.* Composition is the use of light as an element of design. If one turns a borderlight and footlights on three walls and a few pieces of furniture, he illuminates a box set and the first function, visibility, may be accomplished. But if one can succeed in creating, according to the principles of good design, a distribution of light, with variations in quantity and color, he is composing a picture with light. This requires general illumination of the right tonality and quantity; it requires specific illumination from an angle best suited to each object, so that the highlights are accurately placed and the shadows are massed and formed as a part of the design. Shadow patterns, too, are use-

ful for design as well as for representations of nature. Design in light is not static like a painting in oil or water color, but is a mobile painting in space, changing continually and following the drama as an accompaniment. Lighting should focus the attention of the audience and build a new design with every movement of the actor.

Light, as an element in stage design, may vary from a projected image on a cyclorama with only actors in front of it, to a design in space with no reflecting background at all. The director builds the composition with actors, and light reveals this composition as a mobile design. With a small amount of dust or reflecting vapor in the air, the design may be extended to include the shafts and cones of light from spotlights. In a simpler way projected images on a cyclorama or drop may become a part of a design with other elements of wood and canvas. Light, motivated by sunlight or moonlight, may be a pattern of foliage or grill work decorating a wall. Light may isolate a small group of actors into a unit, by ignoring the rest of the set and moving with them from place to place, thus forming a whole series of compositions as the scene develops. Without light, design cannot exist; and without design, lighting is only illumination.

5. MOOD

This function includes the emotional and psychological effects which light can have on an audience and, being intangible, is a difficult one to accomplish. The problem might be divided into the influences of (1) color and (2) light and shade; or, following the terminology used in Chapter 12, of (1) chromatic colors and (2) achromatic colors.

One way to create a mood by means of light is to use three-color striplights to tone the acting area and the walls of a set with a tint (a mixture of three primary colors) appropriate to the scene, such as a warm tone for comedy and a cool one for tragedy. A romantic comedy might add a pink tone to the basic color of the set through the general illumination. In a tragedy one might mix a blue-green tone for the walls.

If the costumes are not distorted, the acting area tints can provide a mood color. For comedy, one might project pink from one direction and lavender from another. Further comments on the mood and symbolism of color appear at the end of Chapter 12. Turning to achromatic color, brighter light suggests the mood for comedy, and dim light seems more appropriate for serious plays or tragedy. Bright highlights and deep shadows (strong contrasts) suggest a mood of mystery and melodrama. Fluorescent and phosphorescent effects suggest supernatural characters and objects. Light from directly overhead, or light limited to the face, suggests the supernatural. Motion picture melodramas have exploited the emotional effects of shadows, especially in the horror films. Everyone has seen the distorting effect of a face lighted from below, or the terrifying impression of an enormous shadow on a wall. The shadows of prison bars and of a noose have become clichés of early crime films. The shadow of a cross is still a symbol that may create a religious mood.

The creation of mood by means of light should be a subtle thing that affects the audience without calling attention to itself. The red of a sunset in Euripides' *Hippolytus* may coincide with the messenger's report of the death of Hippolytus, but if it becomes more interesting than the messenger's speech, the sunset is an exaggerated distraction rather than a reinforcement of mood.

CHAPTER 11

Lighting Instruments

1. INTRODUCTION

MOST OF US, when we need a new suit or a new electrical appliance, set out with a common goal. We want a good buy; we want our money's worth. The best defense against getting less than this is a thorough and sound knowledge of the article we wish to purchase, and perhaps an impervious armor against high pressure salesmanship. Fortunately for the directors of college, school, and community theatres, ethical standards in lighting equipment salesmanship have improved in the last twenty years. Most of the representatives of lighting equipment manufacturers are college graduates or men of considerable experience in the commercial theatre. They help architects and engineers with specifications for new or rebuilt theatres, and are genuinely helpful to workers in the educational and community theatre.

Catalogues, too, have greatly improved with better photographs, diagrams, and useful data to help us make better selections. Committees of the Illuminating Engineering Society have been influential in persuading manufacturers to publish more complete and unbiased information about their equipment. There is still more to be done, however. For example, it would be highly desirable from our point of view to have the efficiency, or the actual amount of light as measured by an independent testing laboratory, stated under each instrument in the lighting catalogue. No doubt, it will take some time to persuade all of the manufacturers to do this. Since the salesman and the catalogue will continue to present a somewhat prejudiced point of view, the people who actually use this equipment day in and day out should make the final selection. Training, actual experience with lighting equipment, and shrewd purchasing ability are still needed, and the only substitute for these three essentials is authoritative and unbiased technical advice. Because one manufacturer makes the best spotlights, it does not follow that his floodlights are equally good. And again, the idea of buying three borderlights instead of one in the hope of multiplying the amount of good lighting is about as intelligent as buying two station wagons for one family, when the second car is used entirely for transporting one person to work. Accordingly, the purpose of this chapter is to show how to prevent this sort of mistake and to discuss the best that is available, so that directors and technical workers will be able to select lighting instruments more intelligently and handle them more effectively.

This chapter presents the requirements and specifications for good lighting instruments, compares the instruments, and suggests a basis for judgment in their selection for various functions. For purposes of discussion we shall classify everything used in stage lighting as (a) instruments, (b) accessories, and (c) control equipment. In the present chapter, the first two will be discussed, and in Chapter 14 the third will be considered. Instruments will be analyzed and explained under these headings: spotlights, striplights, floodlights, special instruments, and accessories.

2. STANDARDS FOR JUDGMENT

While there is a convenient method of controlling the output of an incandescent lamp by dimming it from the control board, the lighting instrument itself (and its accessories) plays a more important part in the control of light. The quantity and distribution (see Chapter 10, Section 3) of light are affected by the size and shape of the whole instrument; the size, shape, material, and reflecting surface of the reflector; and the size, shape, and type

Above: *The Man Who Married a Dumb Wife*, designed by Russ Smith, Wayne University.
Below: *The Lady's Not for Burning*, designed by Edward Anderson, University of Michigan.

of lens, as well as other details mentioned below. The distribution of light from an instrument should be studied more carefully than is possible by taking a quick look at the wattage and price in a catalogue. For example one should know whether a striplight produces a narrow wedge of light or a wide spread; whether color mixing occurs three feet from the striplight or six feet away. Concerning a floodlight it is important to know that the distribution is even, not spotty, when cramped circumstances cause the floodlights to be placed six feet from the cyclorama instead of twelve. The angle of spread at a useful distance with different lenses, the evenness over the lighted area, and the spill light beyond the direct beam are important matters in the selection of spotlights. A rough estimate of the distribution can be determined by studying the instrument under actual conditions of use (advisable in any case), but accurate comparisons that tell the whole story for many uses should include an examination of the candle-power distribution curves made by an impartial testing laboratory.

Any careful study or comparison of lighting instruments for the stage should include the following considerations also:

Size. It should be obvious to anyone who has worked on a small stage that "the smaller the better" is true of almost anything backstage. That is, a lighting instrument should be as small as possible consistent with the efficient control of the three properties. When a small size reduces proper ventilation and consequently the life of the lamps, the efficiency of the reflector, and even causes breakage of lenses, anyone knows that reasonable limits have been exceeded.

Ventilation. Each incandescent lamp, according to its size and wattage, requires sufficient space and movement of air around it to maintain normal life and efficiency. Nearly all manufacturers now provide this satisfactory condition in their instruments. These better instruments have leak-proof holes and slots that distribute almost no unwanted light. Many are still a little too hot for comfortable handling when the instruments need adjusting and focusing.

Weight vs. durability. Lightness is certainly a desirable quality in a lighting instrument if no sacrifice is made in strength, rigidity, and long life. Most instruments, however, are subjected to rough treatment and careless handling, and so require rugged construction. From catalogue pictures it is sometimes difficult for one to see why similar spotlights should be as different in price as $60 compared with $90. On close comparison of the actual instruments it will be obvious that the construction of one is so far superior to the other that, in a television studio, the one costing 50 per cent more will last four times as long. The cheaper one may, on the other hand, be entirely satisfactory in a college theatre producing six plays a year.

Efficiency. The efficiency of a lighting instrument cannot be determined without an illumination meter. Efficiency, as the term is used here, means the amount of light emitted from the instrument, divided by the amount of light emitted from the lamp. Striplights and floodlights are nearly always more efficient than spotlights, and in any one type of instrument efficiencies will be found that vary from 5 to 30 per cent. When one is purchasing a considerable number of lighting instruments, it is well to have efficiency tests on instruments of different manufacturers made by an impartial testing laboratory. A general idea of efficiencies of each type of instrument will appear in the detailed discussion of that instrument.

Adaptability. For those community theatre workers who own a few instruments only, instruments with the highest degree of adaptability for several purposes are the best. For example, a certain spotlight might be useful as a beam spotlight, a bridge or teaser spotlight, or for lens projections (see Section 11), but in making it adaptable something might be sacrificed that would limit its usefulness for any one of these purposes. A very good striplight, however, can be made to serve equally well for a teaser or border striplight, footlights, or for cyclorama base lighting.

Standardization. It is well, in planning and accumulating equipment over a period of years, to select items that have interchangeable parts, easily replaced parts, and a minimum number of different sizes in accessories such as lenses, screws, bolts, color frames, and lamp sizes and bases. The use of one standard size of stage connectors will save endless hours of interchanging, and will reduce the number of connectors and cable necessary to be kept in stock. On the other hand, it is nearly impossible to standardize to any great extent when one buys a few instruments each year and wants to keep up with improvements as they are developed.

Price. Good lighting equipment certainly is not cheap, but as in many other markets, money cannot be saved by buying poor equipment that is inefficient, obsolete, or poorly constructed and frequently out of service when needed. The manufacturers and dealers have small discounts for educational institutions. When inquiring concerning prices one should mention discounts to schools.

This basis for judgment should orient the prospective purchaser and serve as a guide for comparing instruments of various types. A more detailed description and analysis of them follows.

3. CONVENTIONAL LENS SPOTLIGHTS

A good spotlight should consist of several thoughtfully designed and well-fabricated parts. First, it needs a strong, light sheet metal hood, or enclosure, that is well ventilated and properly reinforced with steel. The size of the hood is determined by a number of factors, but it should be as small as is practicable, making it possible to focus sharply a lens of the longest focal length needed for the application of the instrument.

Different manufacturers have placed the access door (for removing or replacing the lamp) on either side, top, bottom, front, or rear of the instrument. For spotlights to be used in the ceiling of the auditorium, the rear access door is preferable; for a teaser spotlight, that is, one hanging from a batten behind the teaser, a front door is much more convenient if the instrument is adjusted from a ladder on the floor. This is an illustration of the difficulties attendant upon building a completely adaptable instrument.

Since the cost of spotlights is already high, custom building would be out of the question. One needs to compromise and accept one or two undesirable features in order to get the best combination. Twenty-five per cent more light from a spotlight justifies having an access door in the wrong place.

The focusing slide, lamp socket, and reflector should be a unit assembly which will slide easily within the hood and which can be quickly and easily held in any position. Strips of metal that move with this assembly should be placed under the socket to prevent light from spilling through the slot in the bottom of the hood.

There are at least two improvements in this method of moving the lamp back and forth. One is a spiral screw controlled by a crank at the rear. The other is a simple lever mechanism with a calibrated scale on the front and the rear of the instrument, allowing the operator to record the position of the lamp for a more accurate change in focus from scene to scene. Each of these is good, but adds considerably to the cost of the spotlight. The old method is still satisfactory.

Reflectors. The light that falls on the lens is actually a very small part of the total output of a spotlight lamp; so a spherical reflector is mounted directly behind the lamp socket, mentioned above, to increase the efficiency about 40 per cent. This reflector must have a regular reflecting surface, such as polished aluminum,[1] so that light falling upon it will return directly to the center of curvature of the reflector, which should be at the center of the lamp filament. If the reflector mounting is designed and set by the manufacturer to prevent any misplacement when it is returned to the spotlight after necessary removal (for dusting or relamping), many irregularities in the distribution of light will be avoided (see diagram in Figure 85).

Lenses. A lens is a piece of glass or other transparent material shaped in such a way that it will bend or refract a ray of light passing through it. Unlike window glass, a lens must have non-parallel surfaces. While some lenses are thinner in the center than they are near the outer edge, most lenses used in stage lighting instruments are thicker in the center. These are called converging lenses, that is, lenses that bend the rays of light into a beam or cone of light. Most converging lenses are either double convex or plano-convex. The first has two curved sides, and the second has one plane side and one curved side (Figure 85). The curved surfaces are portions of a sphere; the plano-convex lens might have been sliced from a glass ball.

Each lens is said to have a focal point to which parallel rays of light converge after passing through the lens. Theoretically, if a source of light were placed at this focal point, the rays of light, after passing through the lens, would continue in parallel lines. The focal length of a lens is the distance from the focal point to a point within the lens. Notice the line drawn through the mid-

[1] Alzak, a patented process, is the best known method of treating aluminum for long wear and a high reflecting surface.

dle of a lens perpendicular to the plane face in Figure 85. This is called the optical axis, and will serve as a convenient base line on which to study optical images and along which to make measurements and calculations. If a bright object is placed beyond the focal point above the optical axis of a converging lens, an image of this object will appear on the opposite side of the lens, below the axis and upside down.

Such a condition would be undesirable in a spotlight, since this image might fall on the scenery or on an actor's face. If a spotlight were designed for a specific lens, the slot or other focusing device would not allow the filament of the lamp to reach the focal point,

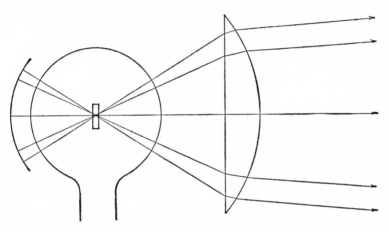

FIG. 85. Plano-convex lens and spherical reflector.

and at the other end would not allow the lamp to touch the lens. Three-eighths of an inch clearance is usually allowed to prevent cracking the lens or melting the bulb of the lamp if the two come too close to each other. Within this focal range, a good spotlight will produce a narrow beam by pulling the lamp assembly (reflector and lamp) to the rear of the hood, and when the lamp is near the lens a sufficiently wide spread of light should result. The most useful diameters in spotlight lenses (plano-convex) are 4½ inches, 6 inches, and 8 inches. Useful focal lengths vary with the diameter but it is desirable to have a short focal length to increase the efficiency of a spotlight (explained below), even though this requires thicker glass, is more expensive, and provides more uneven illumination.

To solve the problem of excessively thick glass, the Fresnel type lens was developed for spotlights (see Figure 86). The concentric ribs, or steps, are elements of lenses of nearly the same focal length but of different diameters, cast from heat-resistant glass in one flat disc. As mentioned above, the concentric ribs tend to make shadow rings in the light beam, and so require a diffusing (not completely, of course) pattern on the back of the lens. For any given diameter the focal lengths can be much shorter (8 x 5 [8-inch diameter, 5-inch focal length] Fresnel instead of 8 x 10 plano-convex), allowing the filament to be nearer the lens, and thus increasing the efficiency with a relatively narrow beam of light and no chromatic

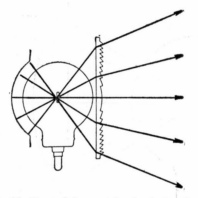

FIG. 86. Fresnel lens and spherical reflector.

aberration (color bands in the beam). These flat Fresnel lenses are very satisfactory for the stage under circumstances where the "soft edge" spill light outside the center of the beam is not objectionable. They are very satisfactory for "first pipe" batten [2] mounting for stage area lighting when the walls of the set tend to control the spill light. Sometimes funnels are used to cut part of the spill. In space-stage lighting (see page 226), where every possible trace of spill light must be eliminated, plano-convex lenses are always used and funnels (see page 276) are added to the spotlights. The flat Fresnel lens is never used for balcony front, beam, and ceiling port positions because the spill light would be excessive on walls and proscenium arch. In ellipsoidal spotlights a concavo-convex Fres-

[2] First pipe means a suspended pipe batten just upstage from the teaser. Outlets are distributed along its length where instruments may be connected.

nel lens with no diffusing pattern is used interchangeably with the plano-convex lens either to make possible a lens of slightly smaller focal length, or to save money. Spill light is a little more noticeable with this lens than with the plano-convex. See end of this section for ellipsoidal spotlights.

Lens and spotlight efficiency. One can see from Figures 85 and 86 that the basic problem of spotlight efficiency (output divided by input), or getting the most out of a conventional spotlight, is rather simple. The closer the lamp is to the lens opening, the larger the solid angle of light. This solid angle is a cone with the filament at the apex; the base of the cone is the opening for the lens. It is obvious that the angle in Figure 86 is greater than in Figure 85. Stated another way, that lens which allows the lamp to be nearest to it will produce the greatest amount of light on a specific area. Any lens will allow proximity of the lamp, but some lenses will spread the light so far that it is no longer useful in lighting a specific area. In a general way, then, the best lens is the one that produces a fairly narrow beam with the lamp as close to the lens as possible. Since moving the lamp away from the lens (to produce a narrow beam) loses light, the better approach is to move the focal point of the lens toward the filament. This, of course, is leading to the shortest workable focal length for any given diameter. Obviously, the largest practicable diameter will increase the amount of light, too. Actually, efficiency is concerned with the ratio of the diameter to the focal length. Theoretically, an 8 x 5 lens should produce twice as much light as an 8 x 10 lens. Furthermore, since the ratio of 8 to 12 is the same as that of 6 to 9, a lens with an 8-inch diameter and 12-inch focal length should have, theoretically, the same efficiency as a lens with a 6-inch diameter and 9-inch focal length. The following explanation of the graph in Figure 87 should help to understand spotlight lenses better, and perhaps help to select the best one to use under various circumstances, from both the theoretical and practical points of view.

The graph in Figure 87 was made to compare the efficiency of lenses of various diameters and focal lengths. Both plano-convex and Fresnel lenses were studied and many thousands of readings were taken with voltmeters and illumination meters to obtain the data from which these curves were drawn. Most of the curves for the plano-convex lenses are short and approach a straight line because the lamps used were of the G (spherical) type and would not allow the filament to go closer to the lens. The curve for the 8″ diameter and 10″ focal length was extended by adding readings taken with a T (tubular) lamp that could be placed somewhat closer to the lens. These additional data were added when this study was continued to include Fresnel lenses whose focal lengths

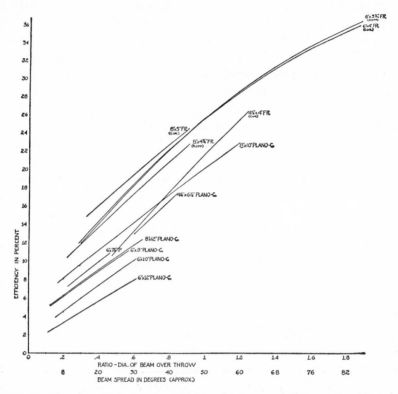

FIG. 87. Showing efficiency of spotlights with lenses of different focal lengths and different diameters.

are so short that one must use lamps that can be placed nearer to the lens. These points, at the extreme right in any of the curves corresponding to beam spreads of 60 degrees or more, are of academic interest only, because an extreme flood focus in a spotlight is rarely useful. In fact, one can be deceived very easily by the manufacturer of a spotlight with a 6-inch diameter Fresnel lens who says that his spotlight has an efficiency of over 35 per cent. As one can see from the two curves extending into the upper-right-hand corner, his claim is true; but look down below at the spread of the beam—over 80 degrees, more of a flood than a spot. The graph's usefulness lies in comparing lenses in this way. Take some reasonable spread of light for a spotlight, such as 20 degrees, follow up from the lens of lowest efficiency, the 6 x 12, to the highest, the 8 x 5 Fresnel. Logically, the 8 by 4¾ Fresnel curve should be almost superimposed on the 8 x 5, like the two 6-inch Fresnel curves that lie between the two 8″ lens curves. One possible explanation for the deviation from the expected results in the case of the 8 x 4¾ Fresnel is this: All Fresnel lenses have a diffusing pattern on the back that prevents circular shadows in the lighted area, at short throws particularly. Considerable amounts of stray light that are hard to measure are caused by this diffusing pattern, and some lenses have more of it than others.

Some practical considerations, too, come into the selection of lenses. An old rule of thumb that can be followed is to use a short focal length for a short throw and a long focal length for a long throw. This rule is satisfactory if one understands its meaning and uses, according to the curves in the graph (Figure 87), the shortest focal length for any given diameter of lens that will produce an even distribution of light without chromatic aberration (irregular color bands in the lighted area). For example, one might want to use an 8-inch diameter lens spotlight on the first pipe (or bridge) part of the time, and at other times move it out front to a ceiling port or beam position, where the distance to the stage is probably three times as great as that from light bridge [3] to stage. At the shorter throw one could use a 10-inch focal length and produce a 35-degree beam spread for ordinary area lighting. From the curve one can see that the efficiency is nearly 16 per cent. For another play this spotlight might be needed out front, perhaps fifty feet away from the stage. Now, in order to have about the same size lighted area on the stage, the beam spread has to be cut to 8 degrees. But to make the beam narrower, the lamp must be moved further back in the spotlight. Referring again to the curve opposite 8 degrees, one finds the efficiency reduced to 8 per cent,

[3] A steel frame with a narrow walk-way and battens with outlets, suspended by two sets of lines from the gridiron, is a better device for mounting area spotlights. Two pipe battens, one above the other, provided with electrical outlets, usually form the upstage side of a bridge (Fig. 91).

that is, cut in half. But now there is more trouble. In trying to get a narrow beam with this lens, the lamp was moved too near the focal point and there is a lot of chromatic aberration—another unsatisfactory, uneven beam of light. There is nothing else to do but to change the lens to one of longer focal length—the 8 x 12. We can see from the graph that our efficiency has dropped to nearly 6 per cent, a 25 per cent loss of light, but we have gained a more even beam of light that will enhance the appearance of the actor and his costume. To regain the lost light we change the size

FIG. 88. Major 1000 watt spotlight with yoke and pipe clamp.

of the lamp to 1500 watts instead of the usual 1000 watts, if our circuit will allow it. This is a good example of increasing the adaptability of a spotlight by changing the lens.

Mounting. All good spotlights are designed for mounting either on a floor stand or with a yoke or suspension arm for mounting on a pipe batten (see Figures 88 and 89). Since the suspension arm supports the instrument on one side only, the yoke, which supports the instrument from both sides, is the preferable method of mounting. To fasten the yoke or arm to a pipe batten, either a "C" type clamp (Figure 89) or a "two part" clamp (Figure 88) is used, but the "C" clamp is much more convenient to attach to a batten when only two hands are available. The usual method of attaching a spotlight to a floor stand is to screw the smaller adjustable piece of pipe, attached to the stand, into the threaded hole in the yoke. When other means of fastening the pipe clamp to the yoke are used, special methods may be needed in mounting the spotlight on a floor stand. Several manufacturers make adapters that mount spotlights on vertical battens, such as tormentor mountings.

Color frame guides. Adequate guides for color frames should be provided on the front of each instrument. By far the best type of

FIG. 89. Six-inch Fresnel lens 500 watt spotlight by Century.

color frame is open at the top and closed on the sides and bottom (see Figure 90). Side openings may cause frames to fall on actors, crew members, or spectators. The color frames (Section 11) and their guides on spotlights should be standardized. It is rather annoying to find that the 6-inch frame from one manufacturer is $\frac{1}{16}$ inch too large to go in the guides of a 6-inch spotlight from another manufacturer.

Small spotlights. The small spotlight (called baby spotlight), with $4\frac{1}{2}$-inch or 5-inch plano-convex lens for the 250 watt or 400 watt lamp, seems to be almost obsolete. Its principal replacement is a 6-inch Fresnel lens instrument, with a short hood for a lens of 3½ to 4 inches focal length. A 500 watt lamp with a T20 bulb (see Section 10), or even the 750 watt, is recommended for this spotlight. One can see clearly that the larger diameter, shorter focal length, and a larger lamp with very little increase in instrument dimensions give this spotlight many advantages over the old baby spotlight. The new instrument has become the common area spotlight for bridge or first pipe for many small and medium size stages. At a cost of about $25, this is a good buy and a useful instrument under all circumstances where the spill from a Fresnel lens

FIG. 90. Eight-inch Fresnel lens spotlight for 1000–2000 watts by Kliegl.

is not objectionable. Funnels (see Section 12) tend to cut some of the spill when it is too great.

For even more restricted spaces, where less light is needed, a spotlight of about one third the size of those mentioned above is available, with a 3-inch Fresnel lens and a lamp of either 100 watts or 150 watts. This instrument is light enough to be screwed to the back of scenery as well as clamped to a pipe; or, resting on a round, flat metal base, it can be hidden behind properties.

Larger spotlights. Several manufacturers make a complete line of Fresnel lens spotlights, from the 3-inch lens and lower wattage lamp, mentioned above, to a 14-inch lens with a 5000 watt lamp, made primarily for television. Larger theatres find the 8-inch lens instrument with 1000 or 1500 watt lamp preferable (see Figure 90) as an area spotlight from bridge or first pipe. Instruments designed for Fresnel lenses are shorter but are less adaptable than those made for plano-convex lenses (see Figures 85 and 86). Those made for plano-convex lenses are more adaptable in that the plano-convex lens can be replaced with a Fresnel lens when desired. The hood

FIG. 91. Lighting bridge in the theatre at the University of Iowa.

is too short in the Fresnel spotlights to allow a change to a plano-convex lens.

Spill light definitely is undesirable when a narrow beam is needed to light a small area while other parts of the stage are kept comparatively dark. Here, the plano-convex lens is needed badly. At least a few spotlights made for this type of lens should be in the equipment stock of every theatre, especially in the college and community theatre.

Ellipsoidal spotlights. The ellipsoidal spotlight represents one of the few radical changes in spotlight design since the nineteenth century. Its name is derived from the shape of its reflector, which is one half of an ellipsoid. Through a hole in the closed end, a lamp, burning base up, is placed so that its double plane filament is at one of the focal points of the ellipsoid. With the lamp in this position, direct emanation is reduced to a minimum and the reflected light converges (theoretically) to the second focal point. While the reflector has a highly polished surface, this surface is broken up slightly to make the light fill a hole in a metal plate, sometimes called the *gate*. The gate is near the second focal point of the ellipsoid, where the rays of light cross on their way to the lens (see Figure 92). The lens can be a single plano-convex, two plano-convex lenses (to shorten the focal length), or a concavo-convex Fresnel lens. The lens, or lens system, behaves like an objective or projection lens, and the whole instrument is a pro-

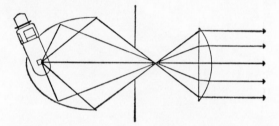

FIG. 92. Ray diagram of ellipsoidal spotlight.

jector with elements corresponding to those of a lantern slide projector (see Section 6 of this chapter). The gate is like a slide holder, and the lighted area on the stage is the image of the gate. These instruments are sometimes made with an iris at the gate, but more often, for ordinary stage purposes, four shutters are placed against the gate to make the beam of light larger or smaller, and to change it into irregular shapes. Because it operates as a projector, the focal length of the lens must be shorter than the distance from the gate to the lens. The efficiency of the ellipsoidal spotlight seems to be between 25 and 30 per cent, in spite of some manufacturers' claims that would give it from three to four times the efficiency of conventional spotlights. As they are now designed, those with a 6-inch diameter lens produce a wider beam than the ones with an 8-inch diameter lens. The instrument with a 4½-inch diameter lens produces an even wider beam. One should buy them according to the spread needed for a specific throw. It is a little short-sighted to buy a 6-inch lens ellipsoidal spotlight for a long throw, and then lose half the light by pushing the shutters halfway in to obtain a narrow beam. Larger instruments are made for 1000 watt and 1500 watt T-shaped, double plane filament lamps, and smaller ones for 750 watts, 500 watts, and smaller lamps of the same type. These lamps are made for base-up burning, while most spotlight lamps burn base down. Although these instruments are more expensive than common spotlights, they are rapidly replac-

FIG. 93. Ellipsoidal spotlight by Century 6-inch lens, 500–750 watts.

ing conventional spotlights for all out-front positions, balcony, front, ceiling beam or ceiling port—antiproscenium positions (see Glossary). The built-in framing shutters in the ellipsoidal spotlight are a great convenience in shaping the beam of light to fit between tormentors, to cut off the spill light from the teaser and to frame the lower part of the beam to the curtain line (see Figures 93 and 94). For larger outdoor theatres or civic auditoriums, where spotlights are mounted three hundred feet from the stage, there are special ellipsoidal instruments for 3000 watt and 5000 watt lamps, including blowers for cooling, and other accessories. Arc spotlights, too, are common under such conditions.

4. STRIPLIGHTS

Striplight is used here as a general term that includes border-lights, footlights, cyclorama border or footlights, and backing striplights. Older striplights (now obsolete) consisted of an open painted trough, with sockets and wiring compartment below. A few of them still can be found and, although they are inefficient and ineffective in the control of distribution and color, they are not

FIG. 94. Ellipsoidal spotlights by Kliegl, 1000–2000 watts.

totally useless. If one has unfortunately fallen heir to one or more of these, chances are he will need to consider other purchases before he decides to replace the striplights. If they are properly wired in three or four circuits and used for supplementary lighting of low intensity, they can serve a very useful purpose, even if they are inferior in design. The warning is essentially against purchasing new ones of this class when much better striplights are available. The old ones are still useful as worklights.

One of the two best types of striplight units (Figure 95) consists of a row of individual reflectors, each containing one lamp and a round glass color-medium that completely covers the mouth of the reflector. The reflector should be of Alzak aluminum, with either a specular (polished) or a diffuse reflecting surface. Alzak has a reflectance [4] of at least 80 per cent. The diffuse surface tends to spread the light a little more than the polished surface. The shape of the reflector is a combination of parabolic and spherical, which

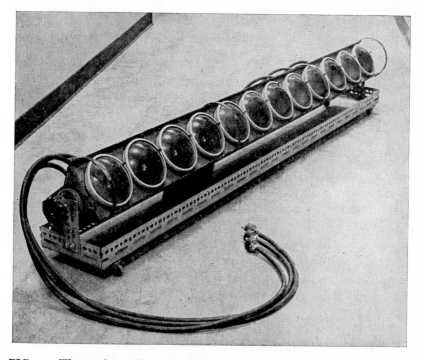

FIG. 95. Three-color reflector striplight section (major) in punched steel angle iron frame for use as cyclorama footlights.

seems to produce the best distribution in striplights. The reflector with a parabolic shape tends to send out light in straight lines if the source is placed at the focus. A spherical reflector was explained above (see Section 2 and the ray diagram in Figure 85). Striplights should be wired in three or four circuits for the three primary colors, blue, green, and red (see Chapter 12), and pos-

[4] The reflectance is the amount of light reflected from a surface, divided by the light falling on that surface. It is usually expressed in per cent.

sibly one for white light. The color roundel, which is placed in the mouth of the reflector, is of heavy heat-resistant glass that is not easily broken in normal use. These color media are readily interchangeable. Reputable dealers carry five or six colors in stock. Variations in distribution are possible by changing the reflector surface (an expensive process), lamp, and color roundel. For a sharp, narrow wedge of light, when the surface to be illuminated is at a considerable distance, the specular (polished) reflector, clear lamp, and clear roundel might be indicated. For the maximum spread at close range, one can use the diffuse reflector, inside frost lamp, and the diffusing color roundels. Various other combinations of the three may give better results under special circumstances.

The second satisfactory type of striplight came into common use with the development of the PAR 38 and R40 150 watt spot and floodlamps (see Section 10). Since these lamps have built-in reflectors, the reflectors mentioned above for the first type of striplight are omitted in this one. This second type (Figure 96) consists of the wiring channel, with screw sockets for the lamps, and a sheet-metal housing to protect the lamps and secure the color roundels. Associated with this striplight is a widespread color roundel that allows color mixing near the instrument when it is necessary to place the striplight unusually close to a surface such as the cyclorama. Changes in distribution are made possible with this striplight by changing from the spot type to the flood type of lamp, or vice versa.

The purpose of striplights, borderlights, and footlights is to produce general illumination; a more wedge-like distribution of light is possible with these two types instead of allowing it to spill over everywhere, as was the case in the earlier models.

Borderlights. A borderlight is just a striplight hanging from a pipe batten overhead to produce general illumination on the acting area from above. Since the new striplights will produce a wedge of light, the light can be restricted in part to certain areas. For example, by tipping the borderlight downward, most of the illumination can be kept off the scenery, or any part of the light can be directed to the set by rotating the instrument on its axis. The usual method of mounting is by means of chains. More accurate manipulation becomes possible, however, when the instrument is attached by short arms and pipe clamps, one at each end, in a similar manner to the arm-and-clamp method of mounting a spotlight. Borderlights with individual reflectors are made for lamps from 75 watts to 500 watts, but 75 watts to 150 watts is sufficiently large for the average theatre. This is true because the three small sizes, 75, 100, and 150 watts, can be placed on 6-inch centers, and it is preferable to have like colors near each other to make the distribution as nearly even as possible. An instrument

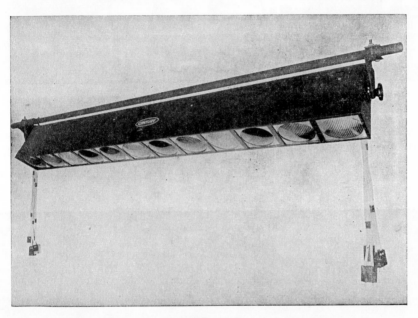

FIG. 96. Century striplight for use with R40 lamps.

with 150 watt lamps is composed of reflectors on 6-inch centers, while one with 200 watt lamps is on 8-inch centers. There is exactly the same wattage [5] and illumination per foot, but the units of the same color are 6 inches farther apart in the larger one, and the larger one is more expensive—two definite disadvantages.

In the past it has been the accepted practice to have several borderlights on a stage, extending from one side of the proscenium arch to the other. In other words, a 36-foot proscenium opening would require a 36-foot borderlight. While these are satisfactory

[5] Total number of watts. See Chapter 13 on electricity.

Above: *A Streetcar Named Desire,* designed by Sam M. Marks, presented by Purdue Playshop, Purdue University. Below: *Thieves' Carnival,* designed by Wendell Josal, University of Minnesota.

for lighting rehearsals, orchestra, and band practice, striplight sections from 6 to 7½ feet long, with line connectors at one end and load connectors [6] at the other, are three times as useful (see section on accessories). If a section is provided with a studbolt extending from each end it can be attached to a batten with hangers (Figure 96), or set on the floor with feet or carriages with casters (Figure 95) for ground row and cyclorama base lighting. These sections are also excellent for direct or indirect footlights.

Footlights. Usually footlights consist of a striplight concealed from the house by proper recession near the edge of the stage floor outside the curtain line. They should be of very low wattage and need not be longer than three-fourths the width of the proscenium arch. Footlights should be carefully placed to avoid spilling light on the proscenium arch or on the teaser when it is at its lowest useful position. They should not be placed higher than 3½ inches above the stage floor. Like other striplights, they might well be made in 6- or 7½-foot sections, so that less than the full width can be used when desired. Again, like striplights, they should be wired in three circuits for the primary colors. The same colors should not be farther apart than 18 inches in order that they will blend well and no spottiness will occur when only one color is in use.

Since the illumination from footlights is directed upwards, as well as backstage, large shadows are likely to appear on scenery, because each source of light produces a separate shadow of every object in front of it. This is one of the most objectionable characteristics of ordinary footlights, but the difficulty can be overcome by reversing the striplight to send its illumination in the direction of the audience. To receive this illumination a long trough-like, properly shaped (spherical is a desirable shape) reflector of polished aluminum (with a "broken" or partly diffusing surface) is provided to direct the illumination back to the stage. This reflector acts as a line source of light that does not produce shadows of objects that stand perpendicular to it as the actor does. In this manner, then, indirect footlights solve the problem of annoying footlight shadows.

Most of the epithets hurled at footlights come as a result of their being used as a primary source of light, but this criticism does not

[6] See Section 14.

apply to footlights of good design that are used for their intended purpose. Color in footlight illumination adds to the general tonality of the setting, but the primary purpose of footlights is to soften facial shadows and to diminish excessive contrasts in the actors' faces caused by illumination from beam spotlights placed in the auditorium ceiling. This function requires illumination of a very low level, and is akin to the function of borderlights and any other source of general illumination—that of blending and reducing contrasts in the distribution of specific illumination from spotlights. One can do very well without footlights if the angle of spotlights in the auditorium ceiling is fairly low, 35 to 40 degrees, except when actors wear broad-brimmed hats. If this angle is about 60 degrees, footlights are necessary in any case. They are, however, more often too bright than too dim.

Backing striplights. Another type of striplight is cheaper and simpler than the ones discussed above. It, too, is divided into compartments for small wattage lamps (100 watts or less), but is wired in only one circuit. This striplight is useful in two, three, or four compartments and serves well, as its name implies, for low level illumination in small "backing" areas off stage from doors in interior sets. It is useful, also, for corridors, behind archways, and, on occasion, it is placed on the floor between ground rows. There are other ways (R40 lamps or small floods) of lighting a backing, but the backing striplight is rugged and convenient to mount. The hook on one end can be hooked beh'nd a flat in a brace cleat or a screw eye, and it will drop into the end of the pipe on a floor stand.

5. FLOODLIGHTS

The old box type floodlight is now obsolete. While a few of these are still in use, floodlights that are more efficient, lighter, more easily mounted, and more suitable in light distribution to the needs of modern stage lighting, are now preferred by technical workers in most theatres. Figure 97 illustrates one of the best, which consists of a spun-aluminum reflector with a diffuse reflecting surface (guides for a color frame to drop in at the top should be added for the theatre), a mogul receptacle, and a small yoke with

pipe clamp. The shape of this reflector is ellipsoidal,[7] but a parabolic reflector is common also, and equally good. When floodlights
are mounted above on battens to light the cyclorama or perhaps
a drop, cramped stage conditions may demand that the floodlight
batten be four or five feet from the surface to be illuminated.
Under such conditions, the ellipsoidal shape will probably produce
a smoother distribution. Many of these floodlights are made for
750 or 1000 watt lamps, but the one illustrated in Figure 97 is

FIG. 97. 500 watt scoop or floodlight for television by Kliegl. For theatre,
color frame guides are added.

smaller, being intended for a 500 watt lamp. The 500 watt size has
the advantage of taking less space in mounting and is of ample
intensity for college and community theatres.

A floodlight produces general illumination similar to the distribution of only one unit in a striplight; by the same token, the illumination from a whole row of floodlights is similar to the distribution of one striplight, but probably greater in spread. Floodlights can be used interchangeably with striplights in some cases,
one taking the place of a short strip for illuminating backings,

[7] See discussion of ellipsoidal spotlights, page 244.

several replacing a borderlight to provide the general illumination for the acting area, or most important of all, a number of them, on a batten, lighting the cyclorama from above. In this case they are more satisfactory than any other instrument for this purpose. In some cases they are mounted close together in rows on a pipe batten and connected in two circuits, one light blue and one dark blue, for changes from day to night scenes. Perhaps better than a single batten mounting for cyclorama lighting, would be a rectangular pipe frame of several short battens, supporting a large number of floodlights. This frame is hung fifteen or twenty feet from the cyclorama to produce a more even distribution of light over the surface than that produced by a single, longer row, placed closer to the cyclorama. These floodlights are exceedingly useful instruments for many purposes.

6. LENS PROJECTORS

The projection of images by means of lenses has been a part of scenic and lighting effects in the theatre since the eighteenth century. While the continental theatre displays effects produced by lens projectors frequently, the directors and designers in the American professional theatre have never been much interested in this expensive piece of optical equipment.

A relative of the scenic projector, the *effect machine* (called a *sciopticon*), has "astounded" the American theatre going public since the early part of this century. This instrument produces a mediocre image of rain, snow, clouds, angels, bluebirds, and rippling water in the moonlight. These are only a few of the crude hand-painted effects from a long list offered for rental or purchase in older catalogues of lighting equipment (see Figure 98).

The basic item of a sciopticon was a spotlight with a 1000 watt lamp and 6-inch (sometimes 8-inch) condensing lens. To the spotlight was added a second condensing lens whose frame held the light steel drum with guides to hold an objective (image producing) lens shown in the diagram in Figure 99 and in the photograph, Figure 98. Within the drum was a revolving disc with a transparent painted effect, illuminated by the spotlight and projected to the screen by the objective lens. The disc was rotated by a clock mechanism, or by an electric motor and reduction gears

FIG. 98. Sciopticon or effect machine equipped with motor instead of clock
mechanism.

(Figure 98). These effects were ingenious but fairly crude. The
objective lenses were inexpensive and poorly corrected. For a
photographed or painted still slide, a $3\frac{1}{4}$" x 4" slide holder was
substituted for the disc of the sciopticon.

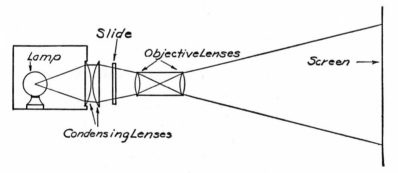

FIG. 99. Elements of a lens projector.

In the "still" version of the combination above there was nothing more than a crude lantern slide projector, somewhat like the
type used for illustrated lectures. In fact, this type may be substituted if it is possible to find one with an objective of short focal

length, or if space allows it to be placed far enough from the surface that receives the image.

To project a complete scenic background that will fill an ordinary drop at the rear of an average stage requires something better than the combination of parts mentioned above. It may be clearer after a brief look at the simple calculation below, but in general the whole picture can be summed up in this way. On a small or medium size stage the acting area is likely to be quite near the scenery or cyclorama, and area light reflections and spill

FIG. 100. Modern lens projector for stage and television.

will wash out a projected image. Since a lens projector is an inefficient instrument (probably a little more than 5 per cent of its illumination reaches the screen), the newer, better-built projectors are made for 3000 or 5000 watt lamps. The other problem, even more difficult, is the objective lens. This lens should be as large as possible, 2½ inches to 3 inches in diameter, and the focal length must be less than 5 inches in order to produce an image 25 feet wide at a distance of about 20 feet or less. Unfortunately, many of our stages have less depth than 25 feet and many productions might require a wider image than 20 feet. Lenses that produce rectilinear, sharp images from a 4 x 6 slide are very expensive.

The whole instrument costs from $1200 to $3000 depending on the wattage of the lamp (3000 or 5000), and the quality and focal length of the lenses (Figure 100). Thomas Wilfred, of Clavilux fame, has recognized the merits of complete scene projection for many years, and almost alone, with the exception of a few of us in the academic theatre. Wilfred is known internationally for his development of the art of light and his beautiful and exciting effects of color and form from his Clavilux. In 1927 he applied his imagination and equipment to the production of Ibsen's *Warriors*

FIG. 101. 5000 watt Multiplate scenic projector (lens) by Thomas Wilfred, Art Institute of Light.

of Helgoland, at the Goodman Memorial Theatre. Those who were fortunate enough to see this production were enthusiastic in their praise of Wilfred's projected effects, not as pure spectacle, but as an integral part of the production.

Since the war, he has devoted much time at the Art Institute of Light to making scene projectors for educational and civic institutions. He builds two projectors, a Uniplate model and a Multiplate model (Figure 101), in which the lamp is of 5000 watt size, the slide, 5 x 6 inches, and the objective lens is approximately 2½ inches in diameter and 5 inches in focal length. The slide and objective lens produce an image of one foot in width for each foot of distance to the screen. The Multiplate unit is only 12 inches thick (upstage to down) with a 45-degree mirror to turn the image, thus saving valuable mounting space. Ten 5 x 6 slides can be set up in advance and shifted by pushbutton remote control.

While this type of equipment is expensive, some schools find it a valuable money saver for scenery. Professor John Conway, supervising designer of the Theatre Department at the University of Washington, handles the scenery for several theatres and considers these scene projectors indispensable.

The television industry has stimulated a new interest in scene projection. Television studios use scene projectors frequently, having taken over and adapted many techniques from motion pictures. Both motion pictures and television have done more "rear screen" projection than projection from the front. In rear screen projection the screen is translucent and the projector is "behind" the screen, that is, on the opposite side from the actor. This makes it possible for the actor to play nearer the screen. Most stages would have insufficient depth to set up a projector 20 feet behind a screen and have any acting area remaining in front. On the other hand, if the projector is mounted above the stage on a batten or bridge, the scene can be projected over the actors' heads without much difficulty. Kliegel, Century, and Bode, among others, have made scene projectors for television that could be used in the theatre as well.

The same general rule concerning lenses for spotlights applies also to lenses for projection; use a short focal length for a short throw and a long focal length for a long throw. This rule is too general, however, for the determination of image sizes, and the simple formula of relationship, familiar to every student of elementary physics, is needed.

$$\frac{1}{p} + \frac{1}{q} = \frac{1}{f}$$

p is the distance from the object (the slide) to the lens; q is the distance from the lens to the image projected on a drop or other surface; f is the focal length of the lens.

This formula is for thin lenses, but it may be applied to thick lenses (lenses used in spotlights and projection instruments are thick) if p, q, and f are measured to the principal planes. In plano-convex lenses made of crown glass (nearly all lenses used in stage lighting are of this type), one principal plane is parallel to the plane face of the lens, within the lens, and two-thirds of the lens thickness from the plane face. The other is tangent to the convex face of the lens. Both are parallel to the plane face and perpendicular to the optical axis. p, q, and f are measured to the nearest principal plane. The sizes of the slide (S) and the image (I) are related to the p and q distances in this way.

$$\frac{S}{p} = \frac{I}{q}$$

When q is large compared with p as in the following problem, p can be considered as equal to f and the relationship becomes

$$\frac{S}{f} = \frac{I}{q}$$

S is either dimension of the slide, I is either dimension of the image, and f is the focal length.

Problem. A lens of what focal length should be used to project an image 28 feet wide with a 6-inch slide if the distance of projection is 24 feet?

$$\frac{6}{f} = \frac{28 \times 12}{24 \times 12}$$

$$F = 5.15 \text{ inches}$$

Problem. What size image can be projected from a 5″ x 6″ slide with a 6-inch focal length lens if the projection distance is 20 feet?

$$\frac{5}{6} = \frac{I \times 12}{20 \times 12} \qquad\qquad \frac{6}{6} = \frac{I \times 12}{20 \times 12}$$

$$I = \frac{100}{6} \qquad\qquad I = \frac{6 \times 20}{6} = 20 \text{ feet}$$

$$I = 16\tfrac{2}{3} \text{ feet}$$

The image is 20 feet by $16\tfrac{2}{3}$ feet.

The cost of a large stock of objective lenses is prohibitive for most nonprofessional organizations, but a few lenses of different focal lengths can be combined in various ways to produce a large number of focal lengths. The following relationship is used to find the focal length of the combination:

$$F = \frac{f_1 f_2}{f_1 + f_2 - s}$$

in which F is the equivalent focal length of the combination; f_1 and f_2, the focal lengths of the two lenses; and s the distance between them.

Problem. Given two lenses, one 8 inches and the other 12 inches in focal length, what would be the equivalent focal length if they were placed 4 inches apart?

$$F = \frac{8 \times 12}{8 + 12 - 4}$$

$F = 6$ inches—the focal length of the combination.

The problem of "distortion" has caused some difficulty in projection because it is frequently inconvenient or impossible to keep the slide parallel to the surface of the screen or cyclorama on which the image is to be projected. By distortion is meant deviation from the original design, as when parallel lines become diverging or converging, or portions of the image become large while other portions are reduced. In projecting over the heads of actors from a batten or bridge, it is necessary at times to tip the projector down in order to place the image in the proper vertical position. Figure 102 is a case in point. The designer's intention was to project an illusion of the ancient city of Nineveh onto the background behind the hut of old Tobit, which was on the outskirts of the city. When the projector was tipped down, a "normal slide" produced an image that was spread at the bottom and caused parallel walls of buildings to converge toward the top. To correct this distortion, the optical axis was tipped below normal and the angle was measured; the same angle was used in tipping the positive lantern slide away from parallel to the negative when the positive lantern slide was being printed in the photographic enlarger. This common practice in correcting distortion produces a slide like the one in Figure 103, the final result being an image as shown in the opening and closing of *Tobias and the Angel* in Figure 102. While Wilfred recommends painting the 5″ x 6″ slides, many craftsmen would consider this a tedious task on so small a surface, and the 3¼″ x 4″ slides (used here) would be even more difficult.

Although it is certainly simpler to use a single slide with an objective lens of shorter focal length, such an expensive lens was not available for this production. By tracking down some extra parts, two lens combinations of approximately 6-inch focal length were assembled. Fortunately, the hut itself covered that portion of the cyclorama where the two parts of the image would meet,

FIG. 102. *Tobias and the Angel* at San Diego State College, designed by Don W. Powell and directed by H. D. Sellman. The scene is the outside of Tobit's hut with skyline of the city projected by a lens projector on cyclorama behind.

so there was no objection to producing it with two projectors. It is very nearly impossible to join two images without an unsatisfactory matching of edges from each part.

When a slide is hand painted, the brush strokes appear messy and obvious when they are "blown up" into an image perhaps 16 feet by 24 feet. The brush strokes or minor imperfections can be concealed by adjusting the lenses until the image is very slightly out of focus; a slightly fuzzy outline tends to make an object seem farther away.

Although lens projectors are an expensive investment for the average college theatre, they certainly can save expense and labor. In the opinion of the writer, projected scenes or parts of scenes are not appropriate for every play. The lens projector, capable of producing fine detail, will serve a useful purpose in more realistic or naturalistic circumstances than the Linnebach (next sec-

FIG. 103. Slide with distortion made to produce normal image when projected at non-perpendicular angle from lighting bridge to cyclorama.

tion), but even it is not appropriate for every realistic play. Projecting images of wallpaper or other patterns on three walls of a box set with three projectors may be interesting experimentally, but it could hardly be recommended for every contemporary realistic play.

Another effective use of the lens projector is illustrated in Figure 104. The slide was made by photographing tree foliage against the

sky as a background. Five or six different shots will give one a good
stock with sufficient variety. Positive lantern slides of the nega-
tives, shot in the above manner, can be placed in the projector
with an amber color medium for sunlight, or light blue for
moonlight shining through the trees. Such leaf patterns add
variety, naturalistic detail, and an aesthetic touch to wall surfaces
in all sorts of exterior scenes. Distortion is not a problem in this
type of image.

Such patterns and images appear natural because we see similar

FIG. 104. State University of Iowa production of E. P. Conkle's *Prologue to
Glory*, directed by Sidney Spayde and designed by A. S. Gillette; lighting by
H. D. Sellman. The pattern on the walls is a lens-projected leaf pattern.

patterns of sunlight or moonlight, and shadows of various objects,
around us every day. Painted sunlight and leaf shadows look de-
cidedly unnatural unless they are part of a stylized or "period"
setting. Seeing a projected scene or pattern beside a painted one
is particularly distracting and inappropriate because it invites
comparison between what psychologists call different "modes of
appearance." A projected pattern will never look painted, and
vice versa. To the writer, at least, it seems satisfactory to have a
painted foreground or wall of a set, and a projected pattern of
distant objects on the cyclorama. This is not distracting, perhaps

because distant objects always have a hazier outline than do objects in the foreground. Projected effects actually give the appearance of being farther away.

In a recent professional opera production there were solid, conventionally painted scenic forms right and left in several scenes, with a fairly wide expanse of blue-gray cyclorama between. In one scene there was a projected pattern on this cyclorama that

Photography by Dorothy Conway

FIG. 105. Lens-projected background in *Old Maid and the Thief*, opera by Menotti, University Playhouse, University of Washington. Designed by John Ashby Conway, with respectful bows to Mary Petty's *New Yorker* cartoons.

seemed unattached to either side and was, to the writer, completely incomprehensible. In another scene this space was filled with a handpainted pattern of a serpent-like Nile, with suggestions of pyramids along its banks. This might have been acceptable but for two massive stone columns that must, because of their size, have belonged to the foreground. In places, however, the sketchy lines of the pyramid forms crossed over the huge columns. In a final scene this same space was filled with a photo-

graphed rectangular rope pattern that seemed to suggest prison
bars through which could be seen fragments of architectural ruins.
Not only did the designer attempt to project patterns of light onto
painted forms to suggest the walls of a room, but he tried to suggest distant landscape at the same time. Furthermore, he mixed
styles by painting some slides, and employing photographs for
others. Some interesting sets that make good use of lens-projected
effects appear in Figures 105 and 106.

Photography by Dorothy Conway

FIG. 106. Lens-projected background in *Barber of Seville,* University Playhouse, University of Washington. Designed by John Ashby Conway.

7. LINNEBACH PROJECTORS

While the more expensive lens projector is better for a sharp
image and the projection of fine detail, the Linnebach, or shadowgraph, projector is better for broad, wide-angle effects in which
detail is unimportant. The lens projector is limited in spread to
very little more width of image than the projection distance,

perhaps a 24-foot width for a projection distance of 20 feet. On
the other hand, the Linnebach will cover a whole cyclorama
through an angle of 180 degrees if desired. The lens projector
works well when projecting images on a plane or almost plane
surface, but the Linnebach can project a slightly fuzzy image on
a cyclorama of any shape, as well as on a plane surface (drop).
Lamps of lower wattage (500 watts to 2000 watts) are satisfactory
in Linnebach projectors, too.

On the realistic side, city skylines or distant hills and mountains are about all one can expect from Linnebach projectors be-

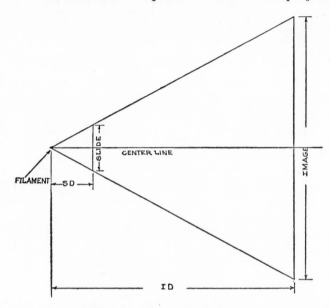

FIG. 107. Linnebach diagram.

cause they are really at their best in expressionism, stylized
images, and fantasy.

The Linnebach projector is so simple that any craftsman in
the nonprofessional theatre can construct one, at least with the
help of a sheet metal shop. Basically, it is a socket and lamp inside a black box with guides for the slide. Theoretically, one
needs a point source of light which will produce a sharp image
or shadow of the opaque and transparent elements in the slide.
Since the smallest filament in a lamp producing enough light is
probably ½ inch wide by ⅝ inch high, the image inevitably will

have a fuzzy outline. Anyone who has stood between a light source and a wall knows that the closer one is to the source, the larger the image or shadow, and the fuzzier the outline of the shadow. Each part of the filament tends to make a separate shadow of the slide. A general rule, accordingly, is to use the smallest filament possible and to have the slide as far as possible from the filament. A number of practical considerations, however, must enter here. Unless the stage is quite small, a 1000 watt lamp is needed. Projection lamps have the smallest filaments, but their life is short. Keeping the slide as far as possible from the lamp has its limits because the Linnebach hood will become unwieldy and the material for the slide is hard to find in pieces larger than 20″ × 50″.

The calculations of slide and image size are quite simple since they deal with the simple proportion in the corresponding parts of similar triangles. It is well to lay out the whole problem graphically to scale on the ground plan and longitudinal section through the stage. Referring now to the diagram in Figure 107, it should be clear that the apex of both triangles is at the filament of the lamp in the Linnebach hood. The base of the small triangle is the slide S and its altitude is the slide distance (filament to slide) SD. The base of the large triangle is the image on a cyclorama or drop (screen) and its altitude is the image distance (ID) measured from the filament to the image on the drop or cyclorama.

$$\frac{S}{I} = \frac{\text{slide distance (SD)}}{\text{image distance (ID)}}$$

Problem. In a Linnebach projector the lamp filament is 2 feet from the slide, and the projection distance (filament to drop) is 18 feet. If the slide is 20 inches high and 36 inches wide, what will the size of the image be?

$$\frac{20}{I} = \frac{2 \times 12}{18 \times 12} \qquad \frac{36}{I} = \frac{2 \times 12}{18 \times 12}$$
$$I = 15 \text{ feet} \qquad I = 27 \text{ feet}$$

The image will be 15 feet by 27 feet.

When a plane slide is used to project an image on a flat drop, there is no distortion of the image if the slide and drop are parallel. This is not difficult if the projector is mounted on a batten or bridge and the image is projected over the actors' heads. The projectors are sometimes placed behind scenery, such as a ground row, since a very wide angle is possible with this instrument. Again, the slide and image can be kept parallel. If it is impossible to keep the slide vertical like the drop, the resulting distortion can be corrected by laying the image out on paper in plotted squares and working back to the slide.

On stages large enough for a sky cyclorama, the Linnebach projector is ideal for covering this surface with any sort of appropriate image (keeping in mind the Linnebach's limitations mentioned above) all the way around to the downstage extremeties, up to 180 degrees. If the cyclorama is a semi-cylinder, the hood shape and slide must be the same to avoid distortion problems. In fact, if the cyclorama is a deviation from a true semi-cylinder, with a flatter area in center rear and a slightly shorter radius where it turns downstage, it makes no difference. One simply shapes the hood and slide of the projector to duplicate that of the surface on which the image is projected. No distortion results if the projector is centered with respect to the image, and the slide and image are parallel.

Sometimes it is desirable to have more than one Linnebach projector mounted along a batten or lighting bridge, so that the hood is not centered. For example, a different image may be needed for each of several scenes, with no time for changing the slides between scenes. Or perhaps the play calls for a transformation, such as that in *Blue Bird* when the graveyard turns into a fairy garden. If the two Linnebachs are side by side, one is dimmed down as the other is dimmed up. There are many such transformations in fantasy and expressionism. In Kaiser's *From Morn 'Til Midnight* the tree changes into a skeleton as the bank clerk watches it. Again, it is a matter of two projections, one dimming out as the other is dimmed up. To prevent distortion, when the projector is moved from the center, the lamp should be moved a proportional distance in the same direction in the Linnebach hood. It is simple enough if an adjustment for moving the socket is provided when the Linnebach is built.

Linnebach slides are easier to paint and construct than lens projector slides, since they are so much larger. A very simple slide can be cut from cardboard, with a distant mountain as a horizon outline, and open sky produced by a single light-blue sheet of color medium. Plastic sheets, heavy enough to prevent buckling, can be used as Linnebach slides without being framed. Colored plastic or gelatin shapes can be glued to the surface to form a design; special transparent lacquers, such as Craftint, made to adhere to plastic sheets, are available to those who wish to paint the design. One must be careful about solvent for thinning or correcting mistakes; some solvents tend to dissolve the plastic sheets and make the slide transluscent. This will diffuse the light and spoil the image. Slides must be transparent.

Several years ago a magazine article [8] about the work of Boris Aronson suggested an imaginative use of projected images. Although Aronson worked with a model and a lens projector, the idea could be applied to Linnebach projection even more effectively. Not only did he make helpful suggestions concerning the preparation of slides, but he suggested breaking the surface of the image screen (cyclorama or drop) by applying different kinds of materials to the surface, such as opaque, open-mesh screen and fabric to break up and change the image in a variety of ways.

Thomas Wilfred has a Direct Beam Projector (his name for his version of the Linnebach projector) that is more completely described along with lens projectors in his monograph [9] on this subject. This is a Linnebach type projector with several unique features. The light source is a 2100 watt 60 volt lamp with a 6 volt control circuit, blower, and heat absorbing filter. While its maximum spread is only 90 degrees, its "color modifier" is an asset that puts this projector out of the homemade class. Strips of progressively graded colors are mounted in two motor driven frames which can be moved in opposite directions at very slow speeds. He suggests lighting the cyclorama with this projector even without slides, since his "color modifier" will change sky from daylight, through sunset, to night. A motor-driven plastic drum (on which one can paint clouds or other objects) moves around the instrument to add to his sky effects. Mr. Wilfred suggests that "landscape" slides be set up in front of the projector with the distant portion of the scene nearer the projector, and the foreground on

[8] *The Magic Lantern,* "Interiors" (December, 1948).

[9] Thomas Wilfred, *Projected Scenery, A Technical Manual* (West Nyack, New York, Art Institute of Light, 1955).

a larger slide set further away so that this portion of the image will be sharper. He suggests painting the slides on glass when projecting on a drop. The Thomas Wilfred Direct Beam Projector is shown in Figure 108. Other Linnebach projections are shown in Figures 109 and 110.

While neither lens projections nor Linnebach projections have a place in every production, they are useful elements of scenery

FIG. 108. 2100 watt, 60 volt lamp direct beam scenic projector with sky drum by Thomas Wilfred, Art Institute of Light.

and lighting. Although no substitutes for canvas and wood, projected scenes or images make many productions more convincing and dramatically effective.

8. LIGHTNING AND RAINBOW EFFECTS

A number of effects can be produced, as explained in Section 5, by means of lens projections of painted, photographic, or paper-cutout lantern slides. Examples of these are a zigzag cutout made

FIG. 109. Original production of *Dark of the Moon*, by Howard Richardson, University of Iowa, showing use of Linnebach projection for background. Directed by H. D. Sellman and designed by John Boyt.

FIG. 110. Another scene from the original production *Dark of the Moon*, showing use of Linnebach projection for background.

in a piece of black paper for flashes of stylized lightning, tiny holes punched in a tin slide for stars, or a handpainted slide for a rainbow. Such a rainbow effect can be rented or purchased, but anyone familiar with the physics of light can assemble one for temporary use from parts found in almost any department of physics in a college or university. Lightning more naturalistic than that produced by a projected cutout is created by momentary contacts between a carbon and a metal terminal. This lightning effect, which is offered for sale, is properly enclosed to guard against fire. One type is operated by hand, and another is operated by a magnet so that it can be controlled electrically from a distance.

A Linnebach lightning effect can be convincing, too, under the right circumstances. The writer made one for the storm scene in Maxwell Anderson's *High Tor* in the following manner. The basic instrument was an arc floodlight with the white reflecting surface repainted black. The arc carbons rested against each other and when the switch was closed the carbons separated, striking the arc. Next, a piece of glass was cut to fit the color frame guides of the arc hood, and painted with a coat of thick black paint of a type that will not flake off. With a photograph as a guide, a forked lightning pattern was scratched with a sharp point through the black paint in a thin line. When the switch was closed momentarily, the movement of the carbon in the striking of the arc gave the projected image on the cyclorama enough movement to make the lightning very dramatic.

Since the development of the electronic flash for photography, the writer has been trying it for lightning on the stage. While this device produces the broad flash of light like the arc, it is at the same time much more convenient, compact, and probably safer. For a broad, open flash, two flashers work better. Some types work on batteries; others plug directly into 120 volt outlets. The price is about $30 to $40.

A Linnebach rainbow is well suited to a romantic folk play, such as Obey's *Noah*. One can cut a curved slot in a cardboard slide, cover the slot with a piece of transparent plastic, and paint the colored stripes with colored lacquer. Craftint transparent colors, made for painting on plastic materials, are good for this purpose.

9. FIREPLACE EFFECTS

Fireplaces offer opportunities for variety and beauty in lighting interior settings that are worthy of some consideration. The motivation—that is, the apparent source of light—must be a dimly illuminated, inconspicuous coal grate or set of fire logs, neither of which is difficult to assemble. To produce a coal-grate fire, one can borrow a metal basket and fill it with chunks of amber and black glass. In the bottom of the basket it will be necessary to clamp two receptacles containing lamps of small wattage, which will illuminate the chunks of glass and make them seem like glowing coals. This whole unit can be purchased or borrowed from a department store that uses the grate for window display. Fire logs are expensive to purchase but quite simple and cheap to construct. Taking a board of suitable size and shape as a base, first attach two lamp receptacles, and wire them to illuminate the logs. Then make a form from chicken wire in the shape of the group of logs, coals, and ashes, and attach it to the wooden base. Clearance, of course, must be left to allow the lamps to be placed in the receptacles. The next step is to cover the frame with papier-mâché. Dip strips of newspaper or paper toweling in cold water paste and smoothe it into place over the frame until it is completely covered. When this dries, it forms a durable surface that will stand fairly rough treatment. To complete the logs, punch some holes in appropriate places and cover them with colored cellophane or gelatin, and finally, paint the whole unit to resemble logs. Naturalistic detail is unnecessary, since fire logs are always partly concealed and are never seen at close range. If the fireplace is in a side wall downstage, one or two small spotlights with red and amber color media should be concealed where they can be focused on a chair or sofa to illuminate the actors in this area with the warmth of firelight in contrast, perhaps, to moonlight coming in a window. The amount of illumination from a fireplace should be rather low because of the position and angle of illumination that might produce objectionable shadows on the opposite wall.

10. INCANDESCENT LAMPS

An incandescent lamp consists of a base (the part that screws into the receptacle or socket), which is made in a number of sizes and shapes (Figure 111), a bulb of glass of various shapes, the lead-in wires, the filament with different forms (Figure 111), and the filament supports. Lamps with pear shaped (PS) bulbs are used in floodlights and striplights; lamps with globe shaped

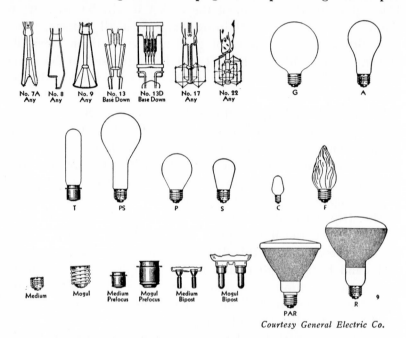

Courtesy General Electric Co.

FIG. 111. Incandescent lamps and their parts.

(G) and tubular (T) bulbs are used in spotlights. A small spotlight, such as the 6-inch Fresnel lens instrument, is equipped with a medium prefocus socket for the 250 watt or 400 watt G lamps, and the 500 watt T lamp, each of which is made with a medium prefocus base. As mentioned above in Section 3, lamps for spotlight service ordinarily have a prefocus base that places the filament in the most efficient position in relationship to the reflector and lens, when inserted in the receptacle in the spotlight. Larger lamps for spotlights, such as the 1000 watt with the G bulb, are provided with mogul prefocus bases.

It is unfortunate that some manufacturers of small ellipsoidal spotlights provide the common medium prefocus socket, while others believe that a medium bi-post (Figure 111) base and socket improve the characteristics of this instrument. In the 1000 watt and larger ellipsoidal spotlights, all of the manufacturers provide for the mogul bi-post lamp.

In fact, a number of special lamps for spotlights can be found only in stage lighting catalogues and in special lists, not in the printed folders of the lamp manufacturers. A helpful notation specifying the lamps that can be used with each spotlight can be found in some stage lighting catalogues. Both lamp catalogues and stage lighting equipment catalogues have lists of incandescent lamps, with complete data on details of sizes, shapes, and so forth, to help the user select the proper lamp for any use.

PS lamps of 1000 watts or less can be burned in any position, but G lamps cannot be burned within 45 degrees of vertically base up. Operators must be careful in mounting spotlights to see that the lamps are burning in the proper positions, because G and T lamps will burn out quickly if placed vertically base up. PS lamps have an average life of 1000 hours, while G and T lamps for spotlight service are limited to about two hundred hours. The ellipsoidal spotlight requires a tubular lamp which burns base up. It is made particularly for this instrument.

11. COLOR FRAMES

Frames for supporting color media used on spotlights, floodlights, and striplights are commonly made of sheet metal in two halves, with square or round openings large enough to prevent obstruction of light from the instrument for which the frame is intended. The best frames are those in which the two halves are hinged at one edge, and on the opposite edge there is riveted a fold of metal that clips the two parts together after the color medium has been inserted. Temporary frames can be cut from cardboard and held together with paper clips. One should be careful, when selecting lighting instruments, to reduce the number of color frame sizes necessary to be carried in stock.

12. MASKS AND FUNNELS

A mask is a piece of sheet metal or cardboard placed within the guides of a spotlight to change the shape or size of the illuminated area. A mask may be made of a single piece with a hole cut in it, or of two pieces, to allow an operator to change the size and shape of the illuminated area at will. One expensive professional mask (called an iris) is made like the iris diaphragm of a camera which allows one to change the diameter of a round opening from the full size of the lens down to a pinhole, or "blackout." An approximation of this can be made of two pieces of cardboard, with a triangular notch in one edge of each. Funnels are frequently used to modify or partly eliminate the diffuse or soft edge of the beam of a Fresnel lens. They are fairly successful if long enough. A funnel is a most useful accessory in preventing spill light (caused by reflections from the walls) from appearing outside the illuminated area, such as spill light from beam spotlights falling on the teaser or proscenium arch. The funnel is a cylinder of sheet metal from 12 to 30 inches long, with some arrangement for attaching it to the instrument for which it is intended. It must be painted black inside and out.

13. STAGE CABLE

A stage cable is a flexible twin conductor which consists of two bundles of fine wire, each twisted into a heavier wire like a cotton cord constructed from fine threads. Each of these conductors is covered with insulating material made of rubber or plastic. The two insulated conductors are finally covered together with more insulating material to form a single flexible cable. The safe size for use on stage in connecting spotlights, floodlights, and any other movable instrument whose total wattage is 1500 or less, is No. 14 wire, which safely carries a current of 15 amperes.[10] As 2000 watt lamps become more common, No. 12 wire is gradually replacing No. 14.

All nonprofessional workers should be warned against using cable of current-carrying capacity less than the current through the load. It is both illegal and unsafe. For example, No. 14 wire

[10] See definition in Ch. 13, Elementary Electricity.

is unsafe for arc spotlights because they draw from 25 amperes up to 100 amperes, or occasionally even more. Where the wire or cable is subject to heat, asbestos covered wire is essential. Any of the lighting equipment companies listed in the appendix, as well as the electrical wholesalers, can supply all sorts of stage cable.

Electrical codes in many cities, and even states, are requiring that outlets in public buildings, where extension cords are connected to electrical appliances, have a third "ground" connection, and that the cable have a third wire. In some cases this has been applied to theatres also, and while the change is expensive, it is definitely in the interest of safety. A short table of wire sizes with corresponding ampere capacities is listed here for convenience. A more complete table can be found in any handbook of wiring practice and in some catalogues of lighting equipment.

Wire Sizes Guage No.	Maximum Ampere Capacity
18	3
16	6
14	15
12	20
10	25
8	35
6	50

14. STAGE CABLE CONNECTORS

The common method of connecting stage cable and lighting instruments to a source of electrical energy is by means of connectors used for the stage, called pin connectors or pin plug connectors. They consist of small blocks of fiber with contacts on one edge and a cable entrance on the opposite edge. They belong in pairs, a line connector with a load connector. The line connector has two brass cylindrical openings that receive the brass prongs of the load connector. These connectors are used in splicing lengths of cable together, to connect the short asbestos leads from a spotlight or floodlight to a length of cable, and to make any sort of connection from portable equipment to the source of electrical energy. The line connector should always be on the "live" end (the one connected to electrical energy) of a cable, and the load connector is always placed on the short leads from the lighting instrument.

For school, college, and community theatres these connectors of 15 ampere size are recommended to take the place of stage plugs and plug receptacles ordinarily found in commercial theatres. The connectors are cheaper and their exclusive use in one size throughout the theatre greatly simplifies the handling of cable, because all cable will then be interchangeable. The 15 ampere size is sufficiently large to handle all ordinary incandescent loads.

To prevent connectors from pulling apart, the cable is frequently tied before the plugs are put together. This is impossible when plugging connectors into a wall or floor pocket. At the University of Iowa a hinged, rectangular metal yoke was dropped over the connectors after they were plugged in place. Some manufacturers make stage connectors with spring clips between the brass prongs that hold the connectors together. In the theatres at Stanford University, San Diego State College, and elsewhere, they have provided all of the cable and outlets with 15 ampere or 20 ampere twist-lock connectors. These are similar to common convenience plugs, but when rotated to the right after being plugged together they cannot be disconnected accidentally. The three-prong (one for the ground wire) twistlock of the 15 ampere or 20 ampere size makes a more rigid connection. The two-prong variety tends to loosen with age and cause flickers in the light if one touches the cable. The third prong (ground) is left unconnected when two-conductor cable is being used.

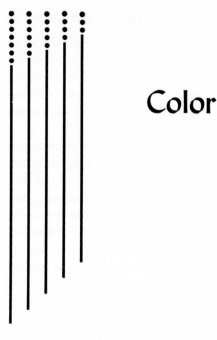

CHAPTER 12

Color

1. INTRODUCTION

"LIGHT IS THE aspect of radiant energy of which a human observer is aware through the visual sensations which arise from stimulation of the retina." [1] Light, defined in this way, is a psychophysical concept. It is safe to say that, in their broadest sense, color and light are practically synonymous. If radiant energy from the sun passes through water vapor and stimulates the retina of the eye of the observer, it is seen as a rainbow. When similar radiant energy is made to pass through a triangular prism of glass, we call the observed result, as it stimulates the retina, a spectrum or band of color composed of violet, blue, green, yellow, orange, and red. These colors have wave lengths from 400 millimicrons to 700 millimicrons, and thus form the visible spectrum.

According to the strict interpretation of our definition, it is not legitimate to attribute colors to objects but only to the light reflected from them. Radiant energy falls on an object, and its

[1] 1944 Report of the Colorimetry Committee of the Optical Society of America. In this chapter on color an attempt will be made to follow this report as far as definitions are concerned.

color is nothing more than its ability to modify the light incident upon it. The object absorbs certain wave lengths; others reach the retina of the observer. The color of an object, then, depends on (1) the spectral distribution of incident radiant energy, (2) selective absorption, (3) and the psychophysical functions of human vision.

When light falls on the surface of an object, one of three things can happen: the light is absorbed, reflected, or transmitted. When radiant energy falls on an object that is ordinarily called red (the way it appears in daylight), other wave lengths are absorbed, and red wave lengths (if any are present) are reflected to the eye of the observer who perceives the object as red. This is selective reflection. If the red material is transparent, less energy may be reflected from the surface, but essentially the material transmits red and absorbs the other wave lengths.

The Colorimetry Committee used the term *luminance* in referring to the effect on the eye of light direct from its source, and *reflectance* when the light comes from a surface that has reflected the light. *Brightness* is the technical term they have adopted when referring to the mental effect of light of a specific *luminance*. As brightness refers to luminance, so *lightness* refers to reflectance. *Luminance* and *reflectance* are psychophysical terms. *Brightness* and *lightness* are psychological terms.

Brightness (or lightness), then, is the attribute of a color which makes it equivalent to one member of an achromatic series, ranging from very dim to very bright (brightness), and from black to white.

There are innumerable color systems, some with color solids in which there is a vertical axis that forms a gray scale, with white at the top and black at the bottom. In the Munsell System [2] the three variables are hue, chroma, and value, which correspond roughly to the hue, saturation, and brightness (or lightness) of the Optical Society's Colorimetry Report. Munsell called his gray series a scale of value instead of a scale of lightness.

A German system of color, invented by Wilhelm Ostwald,[3] uses a double cone as a color solid with a gray scale through the

[2] Munsell, *Book of Color* (Baltimore, Munsell Color Company, 1929).
[3] Wilhelm Ostwald, *Color Science* (London, Winston & Newton, Ltd., 1931, 1933).

center, white at the upper apex and black at the lower. His gray scale corresponds to a series of illumination intensities which would make it behave according to psychophysical variables rather then psychological ones. These two systems help us to understand surface colors and their variables.

Returning to the definitions of the other two attributes of color, they are as follows: *Hue* is that attribute of color which permits it to be classified as red, orange, yellow, green, blue-green, blue, violet, and so forth. Chromatic colors are those possessing hue. Achromatic colors are those which have no hue; that is, they correspond to the gray scale mentioned above, and range from very dim to very bright. *Saturation* is that attribute of any chromatic color which determines its degree of difference from the achromatic color that it resembles most closely. These three, *brightness* (or *lightness*), *hue,* and *saturation,* are the most common terms for the attributes of color sensation.

2. ADDITIVE AND SUBTRACTIVE MIXTURES

As was mentioned above, when light strikes an object it is reflected, absorbed, or transmitted. If the object is transparent, a small amount of light is reflected, and certain wave lengths are absorbed while others are transmitted. This is considered a subtractive mixture. When white light falls on a transparent red color medium, a small amount of white light is reflected from the surface, the exact quantity depending on the angle at which the light strikes the surface. Red is transmitted, and the remainder of the white light is absorbed (subtracted). If a transparent green filter were placed in the path of the red light, the red would be absorbed by the green filter and nothing would be transmitted.

When two different lights (with different wave-length distributions), such as a red and a green, fall on the same surface and are reflected to the eye, they reach the eye as a single distribution, in this case yellow. Green is added to red and reaches the eye as yellow. This is called an additive mixture. All of the changes in light before it reaches the eye work according to the additive or subtractive process.

3. ADDITIVE PRIMARIES

White light (sunlight) is a mixture of the visible wave lengths from 400 to 700 millimicrons. When light passes through a prism to form a band of color, the separate colors are usually recognized as violet, blue, green, yellow, orange, and red. Sir Isaac Newton was the first to observe this, and later it was discovered that if three widely separated colors are projected to a white surface it is possible to match the appearance of any other part of the spectrum. All three of these together will produce white light. There are also a large number of pairs of colors which, when mixed, will produce white—for example, blue and yellow.

For an accurate mathematical specification, it would be well to follow the approach accepted by the Optical Society of America. This is the I.C.I. (International Commission on Illumination) system. This system involves the specification of a color in terms of the amounts of three I.C.I. standard primaries (standard lights). A complete description of this system is beyond the scope and elementary nature of this chapter, but can be found in a number of books on color systems.[4]

For practical use in the theatre it is possible to use three saturated glass or plastic (transparent) color filters, blue, green, and red, for the additive primaries. The principles involved in understanding the additive primaries can be illustrated best by reference to an equilateral triangle shown in Figure 112. Here, light is being mixed from two or three separate light sources, each with a primary color medium covering the incandescent lamp. In stage lighting terms, three color filters are each being placed in front of the lens of a spotlight, and are projecting their beams to a single area. Blue and green in various proportions will obviously produce all of the possibilities from a slightly bluish green to a slightly greenish blue. If we accept the name *magenta* for the half and half mixture of blue and red, then various proportions of red and blue might be purple, through magenta, to a scarlet red. Green and red additive mixtures are a little more surprising to those who are meeting this phase of color for the first time. Approximately equal parts of green and red produce yellow. With

[4] Ralph M. Evans, *An Introduction to Color* (New York, John Wiley & Sons, Inc., 1948), and in numerous technical periodicals.

more green than red, yellow-green is produced; and with more red than green, the result will be orange. Mixtures are inclined to be brighter and less saturated than the basic primaries. When two colors such as blue-green and red (or green and magenta, or blue and yellow) are projected to a white surface, the result will be white light. Such pairs producing white are called complementary colors, or complements. When all three of the primaries are mixed from three different light sources, a large number of other colors can be produced by varying the proportions of the three. After two colors are mixed and a third one is added, the third color be-

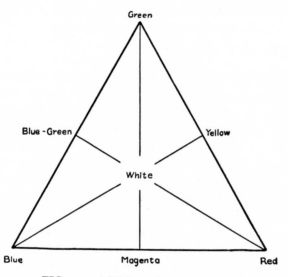

FIG. 112. Additive mixture of color.

comes diluted until the result is white light. This is common practice when the striplights are wired in three circuits and the lamps are covered with primary blue, green, and red color mediums. Projected to a light-blue cyclorama, an approximately equal mixture of the three reveals the cyclorama as a daylight sky. By adjusting the dimmer readings on these three color circuits one can produce the various tints and colors of a sunset, after which he can gradually dim out the red and green to the desired dark blue (or combination of dim blue and a small amount of green) for a color that resembles a night sky on this same cyclorama. Although primary colors are rarely used in spotlights for acting area lighting, light tints of blue, blue-green, yellow, violet, and red are common and are used in spotlights where two are focused on one area. This is an example of additive mixtures in specific illumination. It is possible under special circumstances to use more saturated colors in acting area spotlights. If, in a stylized production, one wishes to exaggerate the color in shade or shadows, he can use complementary saturated colors in spotlights, depending on the additive mixture to produce white highlights, and a white undistorting mixture on the make-up, while the saturated color falls in the folds of the costumes, one color on one side, the other on the opposite side.

4. SUBTRACTIVE MIXTURES

As mentioned above, when light is transmitted or absorbed selectively, some wave lengths are subtracted; so less light reaches the eye than the original amount emanating from the source. This is a subtractive process. Our general understanding of primary colors is that a few fundamental colors are capable of being combined to produce a great many others. The three that seem to produce the greatest number of nearly saturated colors are called cyan (or blue-green), yellow, and magenta. Referring to the superimposed circles in Figure 113, one can see that blue-green over magenta produces blue, magenta over yellow produces red, and blue-green over yellow produces green. Superimposing all three produces gray or black. One should think of this subtractive mixing as the placement of one transparent color medium, such as a colored gelatin filter, over another. In fact, this is actually done in stage lighting practice when one fails to find in stock the exact tint he needs. If a daylight blue filter seems to be too green (blue-green) for a particular costume or make-up color, a lavender (pale magenta) filter can be placed over it to produce a color that is nearer pure blue. Perhaps a yellow medium is too greenish (lemon yellow) for a pleasant sunlight color; a lavender or pink filter will subtract the green wave lengths and produce a more desirable straight yellow.

Dyes are transparent colors that mix subtractively, as do transparent water-color paints. While painters rarely limit themselves to three pigments, Dr. Herbert Ives [5] made a quantitive spectral analysis of many pigment colors and found that fairly good results could be obtained with the three primaries—blue-green, magenta, and yellow.[6] He concluded that there were certain deficiencies in available pigments and that at least four colors might be better than three.

Theoretically, a subtractive primary would have to transmit more than a narrow band of spectral energy in order to fulfill the

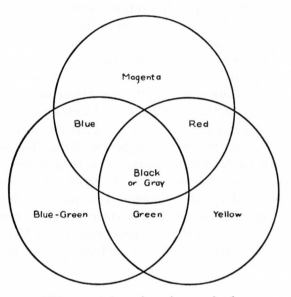

FIG. 113. Subtractive mixture of color.

requirement that two colors superimposed produce a third color. For example, both blue-green and magenta will transmit blue because they have blue in them, but blue and red have nothing in common to transmit; so theoretically they will transmit nothing when superimposed. In practice, however, there are few, if any, color filters that are so selective. Nearly all blue filters transmit a small amount of green or blue-green.

[5] Herbert Ives, "Thomas Young and the Simplification of the Artist's Palette," Proceedings of the Physical Society (January, 1934).

[6] The water colors suggested were prussian blue (pure ferric ferrocyanide), rhodamine 6G lake, and cadmium yellow.

5. PIGMENT MIXTURES

As mentioned in the last section, transparent water colors mix according to subtractive principles. There are, however, many pigments that are not transparent. Opaque pigment particles may cover each other and only the top layer will reflect certain wave lengths to the eye. Particles that reflect different wave lengths when placed side by side will produce results according to the additive mixture principle. If a surface is painted with small dots of two different colors and viewed at a distance, the eye does not see the separate dots. If the dots are blue and yellow, this surface will appear gray when seen at a distance in a white light. This is an additive mixture because the blue and yellow reflected from the dots mixes before it reaches the eye. While we might call this mixture white light, the lightness level of such a surface would not be high enough to call the surface white. It might be a medium gray, depending on the average lightness of the blue and yellow. Since the behavior of pigment mixtures may be either additive or subtractive, it is difficult to predict the results of mixtures except by experience with specific pigments. The spatter method of scene painting is essentially an additive mixture, unless the pigments are transparent and some of the dots cover others, in which case light can pass through transparent dots and this part of the result is subtractive.

6. THE LIGHT SOURCE

The use of the common incandescent lamp, modified by selective transmission and absorption in the form of color filters, is our basic method of revealing and changing the appearance of objects and people on the stage. Although the incandescent lamp is not entirely satisfactory in spectral distribution, it is a fairly small source that can be dimmed satisfactorily. The spectral distribution leaves much to be desired, since it is quite low on the violet and blue end, and high on the orange and red. The mixture of wave lengths is a pale yellowish white that changes gradually into red as the lamp is dimmed until almost no blue energy is produced. Sources with more blue, such as fluorescent lamps, are more efficient but are more difficult to dim and cannot be used in spotlights. They are used in open-pan floodlights for television to a limited extent, but are not gaining in popularity. Carbon arcs produce a white light with a smaller source but cannot be dimmed.

7. COLOR MEDIA

Color filters currently accessible are far from satisfactory. The following sections will show simple comparisons of such qualities as range of color, durability, fading, and cost. Better materials at lower cost would be made in this country if there were greater demand.

Transparent lacquer. Transparent lacquer that can be applied directly to the bulb of an incandescent lamp is available in five or six colors, and these can be mixed to produce others. It fades easily and is burned off rapidly in lamps larger than 50 watts. It is useful in coloring a few lamps for backing striplights and for painting slides for projection.

Glass. Colored glass roundels that fit over individual lamps or reflectors in borderlights, footlights, and striplight sections have been common for many years. They are made of heat-resistant glass in different sizes and shapes, but are limited to a few colors like red, green, blue, yellow, and clear. The so-called primary colors are quite satisfactory for mixing the other colors needed for the cyclorama, including sunsets, and for toning and blending the acting area with general illumination. Although the roundels are expensive, their colors do not fade. Various tints in glass strips, framed in the usual color frame sizes for spotlights, have been available for several years. These are expensive and heavy, but with good care will last a long time. Since they are handled much more than roundels in striplights, breakage is much higher.

Gelatin. Colored sheets of gelatin are still the most popular for use in spotlights and have survived a number of newer materials. Gelatin is available in about one hundred hues and tints in sheets approximately 20″ x 24″. The cost is around 30 cents a sheet. Its only advantages are its low cost, large variety of colors, and flame-proof quality. It fades easily, is easily dehydrated in dry climates or in heated storage places. When dry, it is brittle and fragile, its usual condition after a short time in a hot spotlight. All the colors

Two settings at the University of Iowa. Above: *Doctor in Spite of Himself,* designed by Andy Loshbaugh. Below: *Mr. Roberts,* designed by B. J. Kidd. Supervised by Arnold S. Gillette.

seem to fade, especially the blues and blue-greens, which last no more than six or eight hours when in use.

Cinabex and cinemoid. Two new color filters, imported from England, have appeared on the American market in recent years. The two are not identical, but they are quite similar in some of their names and numbers. Although the number of colors is perhaps fewer than the number available in gelatin, there are certainly more than most of us need. The material is thicker and stiffer than gelatin, but still not thick enough to use without color frames. The sheets are about 20″ x 24″ and the price is slightly over a dollar a sheet. These materials are flameproof and mechanically strong, but fade about as fast as gelatin.

8. LIGHT AND COSTUME

Although it is rarely done, the color of the light in which the costume will be worn by all means should be considered when the costume is designed. Using colored light in the dye room, or looking at the material through small pieces of color media will help a great deal to prevent re-dyeing after the first dress rehearsal. In general, unsaturated colors in light are much safer than saturated ones for period costumes that are made of several colors, but even with such acting area colors as daylight blue and amber, light colored costumes can be considerably affected. For example, a yellow costume can be grayed or neutralized by daylight blue light, and it will be black in saturated blue light. The reverse is also true. A blue costume is grayed by light amber illumination, and yellow-orange light will make the blue look absolutely black. Generalizing, one can say that light of a complementary hue will make a costume appear gray, but light of a similar hue will enhance the beauty of a piece of fabric and make it more prominent. Blue light on blue velvet or satin makes it seem to glow from within. In dimly illuminated scenes costumes should be of tints if possible, because they need to reflect more light than the background, while in well-lighted scenes saturated hues and shades may also be included. The designer of costumes, all will agree, should have a thorough understanding of color in light as well as color in fabrics.

9. LIGHT AND MAKE-UP

One who is responsible for the lighting of a play is often held responsible for deficiencies in make-up, but make-up is really the actor's problem, and he should include in his training some consideration of the way light affects his appearance. In general, foundation make-up has more red in it than normal flesh color, because much amber light has been common in stage lighting. Heavy foundations now are out of style, because more suitable colors in light, like daylight blue, very light amber, and pink, are in more general stage use. Illusion pink (a highly unsaturated violet) is a flattering color medium that passes all of the spectrum but is low in yellow. For this reason, it takes away sallowness and emphasizes the pink pigment in the actor's complexion.

The following simple suggestions about make-up and colored light may prove useful.

Amber light adds a yellow tonality that tends to make the complexion sallow, and reduces the contrast between rouge and foundation. More rouge, or rouge with less orange in it, is necessary.

Red light is reflected by rouge and foundation equally, leaving the actor apparently with no rouge. More rouge slightly toward the blue is necessary in red light.

Blue light has the opposite effect. Red reflects little or no blue light; therefore in blue light, rouge on the cheeks appears as two black spots. A very light foundation, with only a trace of rouge, is best in blue light.

Green light gives the face an unearthly appearance and should be avoided unless the play demands such an effect.

Professional actors and some experienced nonprofessionals are very familiar with these suggestions, but a surprising number of players lack even a trace of information of this sort.

10. LIGHT AND SCENERY

The radical lighting artist is of the opinion that scenery is merely one of the reflectors that he needs in making a design in light. While most scenic artists would probably disagree, this is, from a technical view at least, essentially true, and in this way it will be considered for the moment. Ideally, acting area light should be kept off the scenery, but reflections from the floor and spill light influence its appearance to some degree. As in the case of costumes, scenery must be designed and painted for a specific color in lighting. Otherwise it will never look as it was intended. Scenery, as most people in the theatre know, should almost never be painted in a flat color, but by one technique or another several colors should be applied, so that definite spots or small areas of each color lie near each other (see Chapter 6). When light falls on the whole surface, each small area reflects certain parts of the spectrum, and the reflected light mixes additively before it reaches the eye some distance away in the auditorium. If the primaries blue, green, and red were painted on the surface in this way and illuminated with white light, the surface at a distance would appear gray, but very different from one with a uniform gray paint covering the whole surface. The one with the three colors would have texture, variety, and beauty, while the solid color surface would be monotonous. If the three colors were illuminated with red light, the blue and green would reflect no light, and the appearance at a distance would be that of a dark red, uneven surface, uneven because of the areas reflecting no light. By changing the light to blue, the color of the surface would appear as dark blue. Changes in the color of light frequently assist in scene changes, but the painting must be done with this definite intention. It is not, however, so simple as it sounds. The primaries are rarely used, if ever, but several colors more appropriate to the particular design are used, along with a color in the general illumination that will emphasize the dominant color in the paint. Three-circuit striplights, with blue, green, and red filters, mounted on the bridge or first pipe along with the acting area spotlights, can serve the purpose of toning and blending the walls of an interior set. The footlights can also assist in this way. As the mood changes from act to act in a single set production, this mood can be suggested by progressing from a warm to a cool tonality (or vice versa) by varying the mixture of the three colors in the general illumination. The set, of course, must be painted to reflect this change.

Monk's cloth, hemp, and other neutral (gray) materials used as draperies for the stage are easily colored by means of striplights and floodlights with appropriate color media. Because of their sheen and the interesting highlights and shade when they are hung in folds, silk, satin, and rayon look well in colored light. All of these materials should be hung in folds in order to attain variety in light and shade. If light from opposite directions is of different colors, one can have shadows of two different colors and an additive mixture of these colors in the highlights.

By carefully selecting pigments that have a distinctly different appearance in two or more colors in light, spectacular and comic effects are possible for the right occasion (not usually for drama). As an illustration, one can draw two sketches on white paper, one with blue chalk and one with orange or red chalk. In blue light the blue chalk and the white paper are equally blue because each reflects blue light to about the same degree; so the blue sketch essentially disappears. The orange chalk, reflecting little or no blue light, appears black and stands out boldly. In red light the orange or red chalk disappears and the blue sketch appears. Very amusing cartoons can be made in this way and changed by changing the color of the light. One might paint a drop according to these principles and change a woodland scene from summer to winter. If the sky were light blue and the leaves of the trees green or blue-green, the leaves could be made to disappear by using green or blue-green light. Such things have to be very well done to have any measure of success, and such a drop could not be shown in its entirety. If only a part of it were seen through windows, it might be satisfactory. In general though, such things are too spectacular for drama, and belong to musical comedy and revues, where smart effects are always in demand.

Good designers should know the relationship of light to pigment so thoroughly that they think in terms of light even when using pigments. Sorrowful is he who paints a set for amber light and discovers later that his set will be clothed in daylight blue.

Color symbolism. The use of light for emotional and psychological purposes was discussed briefly in Chapter 10. Although this function is somewhat intangible, its usefulness and definite place in lighting on the stage are established. Research in this field is needed but is difficult to approach. The related subject of color symbolism is fraught with many contradictions, and its use with many pitfalls. For certain plays, nevertheless, there is a definite place for symbolism in costumes and lighting. In such cases, if it is used with clarity and simplicity, it should be successful. True, there is considerable divergence of opinion, and colors certainly do affect people in a great variety of ways.

For these reasons it has been considered of sufficient importance to mention some of the ideas and to present a list of the things which colors are said to symbolize and suggest. In some cases there is substantial agreement. Red, orange, and yellow are commonly called warm hues, and blue and green are said to be cool. A certain hue of red may suggest murder because blood is associated with murder. It also suggests anger, perhaps because a bull is supposed to be angered by red. Green is generally agreed upon as suggesting envy under certain conditions.

Color on the stage is used primarily, of course, for other reasons, but it has been discovered, sometimes by accident, that color affects an audience emotionally—at times objectionably so. The atmosphere of a scene or complete play often suggests certain hues to an artist. To be sure, the same play probably suggests entirely different hues to another artist, and it is difficult to say who is right. For example, red, orange, and yellow light might be used for the drinking scenes in *Twelfth Night* and *Henry IV*. Purple and red would suggest royalty and power in throne-room scenes. The projection of dagger-like shafts of red light for a murder scene in *Macbeth* is obviously symbolic.

This brings us to a clue to the mystery of the many conflicting ideas associated with various hues. Color can be used with so many other things that influence the impression it makes on an audience, that one can never state arbitrarily what a hue symbolizes unless the circumstances are included. For example, form alone can change the emotional or symbolic value of a hue entirely. A dagger pattern of red light surrounding Macbeth when he says, "Is this a dagger, which I see before me, the handle toward my hand?" could hardly suggest anything but Macbeth's state of mind as he plans to murder Duncan. On the other hand, a red costume for a king might well indicate royalty and power. To use color effectively for this purpose, one must always consider form, associated hues, and all of the surrounding elements that influence the emotional and symbolic value of a color.

A glance at the following list will show what a diversity of ideas is associated with a single hue. These have been taken from count-less literary sources of all ages, and are included here as a possible aid in designing costumes, scenery, and lighting.

White is the symbol of light, purity, chastity, innocence, truth, modesty, peace, femininity, delicacy, sacrifice, and infirmity. White is cold, hard, cruel, and sometimes a symbol of mourning.

Black in many respects is opposed to white. It expresses gloom, darkness, woe, night, death, dread, mystery, horror, terror, evil, wickedness, crime, and mourning.

Gray, one of the black and white series, is less severe than black. Gray symbolizes humility, melancholy, resolution, solemnity, age, penance, sadness, and mature judgment.

Red, classed as a warm hue, suggests blood, heat, fire, anger, hatred, cruelty, murder, tragedy, shame, and destruction. On the other hand it can symbolize power, vigor, health, and passion.

Orange is a warm hue. It is a symbol of autumn, harvest, warmth, plenty, laughter, and contentment.

Yellow is also a warm hue. It suggests heat, liveliness, gaiety, gaudiness, and in some instances cowardice, indecency, decay, de-ceit, and sickness.

Brown signifies autumn, harvest, plenty, warmth, contentment, and happiness.

Green suggests youth, vigor, spring, immaturity, contemplation, faith, immortality, peace, solitude, life, victory, and sometimes jealousy.

Blue symbolizes coldness, melancholy, the sky, the sea, heaven, hope, constancy, fidelity, serenity, generosity, intelligence, truth, spirituality, and aristocracy. Blue is opposed to its complement, yellow.

Violet signifies sadness, quietness, purity, love, sentimentality, royalty, and wealth.

Purple suggests royalty, heroic virtue, and wealth.

CHAPTER 13

Elementary

Electricity

1. INTRODUCTION

THIS SHORT CHAPTER can hardly prepare one to take an examination for an electrician's license. But even the simplest of outlines for electricity in lighting circuits can help the beginning student of technical practice on the stage to protect himself, his fellow workers, and the equipment they will handle in lighting a play. A better understanding of the principles of this subject will add to the student's confidence and efficiency.

According to contemporary theory, electricity in metallic substances is a flow of electrons, a current in a wire being something like the flow of water in a pipe. It takes pressure to push water through a pipe, this pressure being measured sometimes in pounds per square foot. A current of water can be measured in gallons per minute. Flow of electricity or current might be measured as the number of electrons passing a certain point in an electrical circuit in one second. The common unit of current is called an *ampere*. The unit of electrical pressure, or electromotive force, is the *volt*. Carrying the water analogy a bit further, it might be said that a current of water in a pipe encounters a certain amount of friction or resistance to flow, depending on the internal surface of the pipe, its length, and its diameter. A current of electricity in a wire encounters friction, or resistance, depending on the nature of the material of the wire, its length, diameter, and its temperature. The unit of electrical resistance is the *ohm*.

The term conductivity is the antonym of resistance. If a material has a high resistance, it has low conductivity. If it has high conductivity, it has low resistance. There is a simple but very important relationship between the electromotive force (volts), the current (amperes), and the resistance (ohms) in an electrical circuit. This relationship, called Ohm's Law, which applies to the whole or any part of an electrical circuit, can be expressed in this way. *The electromotive force is equal to the product of the current and the resistance.* Using the symbols E for voltage, I for current, and R for resistance

$$E = IR$$

or $$I = \frac{E}{R}$$

or $$R = \frac{E}{I}$$

where I is expressed in amperes, E in volts, and R in ohms.

Example I: Determine the resistance of a lamp which carries a current of 2 amperes flowing under an applied e.m.f. of 110 volts.

$$R = \frac{E}{I}$$

$$R = \frac{110}{2} = 55 \text{ ohms, resistance of lamp.}$$

Example II: Find the current that will flow through a dimmer or rheostat (see footnotes in Section 4) having a resistance of 25 ohms, if the applied voltage is 125 volts.

$$I = \frac{E}{R}$$

$$I = \frac{125}{25} = 5 \text{ amperes, current passing through the dimmer.}$$

2. SERIES AND PARALLEL CIRCUITS

Electrical circuits may be divided into two general classes, series and parallel. All circuits found in practice consist of either series elements, parallel elements, or a combination of the two. A series circuit is one in which the current follows a single path through the several elements, and has the same value in all parts of the circuit (see Figure 114).

Problem. Each of the 6 lamps in Figure 114 has a resistance of 10 ohms, and the generator maintains an e.m.f. of 110 volts. Determine the current.

10 ohms per lamp x 6 = 60 ohms total resistance.

$$\frac{E}{R} = I$$

$$\frac{110}{60} = I = 1.83 \text{ ampere current in the circuit.}$$

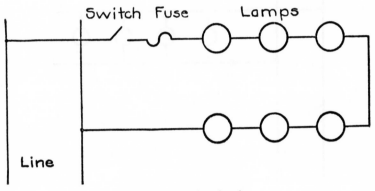

FIG. 114. Series circuit.

In a series circuit the applied voltage of the whole circuit is equal to the sum of the voltages across the components of that circuit. We can illustrate this with the same example. Each lamp was assumed to have a resistance of 10 ohms, and a current of 1.83 amperes was found to be flowing through it. Assuming for the moment that we do not know the voltage, let us determine the voltage necessary to maintain that current. The voltage drop across each lamp is, by Ohm's law, $E = IR = 1.83 \times 10 = 18.3$ volts. Adding the voltage drop across each lamp to get the total drop, or the total voltage the generator must maintain, we have 6 lamps of 18.3 volts each, 6 x 18.3 = 110 volts.

The resistance of a series circuit is the sum of the resistances of the components. This also was illustrated in the above example.

Six lamps of 10 ohms each possessed a total resistance of 60 ohms. If the connecting wire is long (half a mile for example), it might have an appreciable resistance that would then be added to the total resistance of the lamps.

A parallel circuit, occasionally called a multiple or shunt circuit, is one whose elements are connected in such a way that the current is divided among the several branches. That is, the current passing from the generator through the circuit and back to the generator will go through as many paths as there are branches in the circuit (Figure 115). The parallel circuit is of great impor-

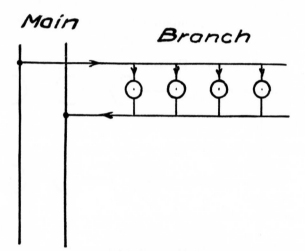

FIG. 115. Parallel circuit. Arrows indicate paths of current.

tance in theatre lighting, as well as in all interior lighting, because incandescent lamps are commonly connected in parallel.

The voltage across the group of lamps connected in parallel (Figure 115) is the same as the voltage across each lamp, provided that the resistance of the connecting wires is so small that it may be neglected. This is certainly true in the usual theatre lighting circuits.

3. POWER

Power is required to maintain a current of electricity, whether it is direct or alternating. The practical unit of power is the *watt*, the product of volts and amperes.

$$P = EI$$
Watts = volts x amperes.

Since by Ohm's law $E = IR$, then by substitution $P = I^2R$.

Lamps are rated by the number of watts they consume at a definite voltage.

Example: 100 watts at 120 volts. This information, used in the formula $P = EI$, gives the current passing through the lamp. Thus

$100 = I$ x 120 or $I = \dfrac{100}{120} = .85$ ampere, current through the lamp.

With this we are able to determine the resistance of the lamp.

Example 2: What is the resistance of a 1500 watt lamp rated at 110 volts?

$$P = EI$$
$$I = \frac{1500}{110} = 13.6 \text{ amperes, current through the lamp.}$$

Since

$$R = \frac{E}{I}$$

$$R = \frac{110}{13.6} = 8.07 \text{ ohms, resistance of lamp.}$$

From these two examples it is clear that the greater the power consumed by a lamp, the greater the current that will flow through it, and the lower will be its resistance.

4. APPLICATION TO THE STAGE

The problem of changing the intensity of illumination is of fundamental importance in stage lighting. The simplest method of changing intensity is accomplished by placing a *rheostat* [1] (a *dimmer* [2] in the technical language of the theatre) in series with a lamp or group of lamps (Figure 116). When the variable contact

[1] *Note:* An electrical instrument consisting of an insulated base on which is mounted a length of wire of higher resistance than the usual copper conductor, and having terminals at each end, constitutes an electrical resistance. In cases where the resistance may be varied at will, the device is known as a rheostat.

[2] For a description of a dimmer, a rheostat made expressly for use on the stage, see Chaper 14, Sections 7 and 8.

is in a position that places the smallest part of the resistance in the circuit, very nearly the maximum current in the circuit is passing the small part of the wire in the rheostat. The resistance wire from which the rheostat is made must be, accordingly, of such size that it will not overheat when the maximum current of the circuit is passing through it. A rheostat is rated in amperes, the maximum current which will not overheat it (it is also rated in ohms, total resistance). Obviously, when a larger part of the wire is included in the circuit, by Ohm's law the current will be proportionally smaller.

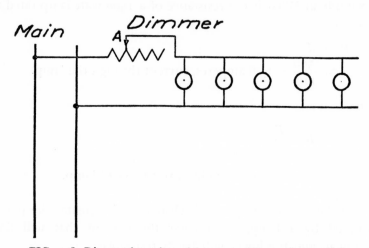

FIG. 116. Dimmer in series, with group of lamps in parallel.

In determining the proper rheostat to be employed in a given instance, first one must determine the current in the lamp circuit. This may be done as follows:

Problem. Suppose each of the 5 lamps in Figure 118 has a rating of 100 watts at 110 volts, and we wish to know the current-carrying capacity and the resistance of a dimmer capable of dimming these lamps to black.

The total lamp load is

$$5 \times 100 \text{ watts} = 500 \text{ watts.}$$

Then by $P = EI$, we have $500 = 110\,I$

$$\text{or } I = \frac{500}{110} = 4.5 \text{ amperes.}$$

This is the amount of current flowing through the line when there is no dimmer in the circuit. Accordingly, for this circuit we select a rheostat or dimmer with a rated capacity of about 4.5 amperes.

The other important consideration is to have sufficient resistance to dim the lamps completely. Knowing the voltage and the current, we can find the total resistance of the lamp load. Thus:

$$R = \frac{E}{I}$$

therefore, $R = \dfrac{110}{4.5} = 24$ ohms (approximately).

It has been determined by experiment that the resistance required to dim a lamp completely is about three times the resistance [3] of the hot lamp load. Multiplying 24 ohms by 3 gives us 72 ohms, which is the amount of resistance necessary to dim a lamp load of 500 watts. For this purpose we need a rheostat rated at not less than 4.5 amperes and 72 ohms.

Theatrical dimmers are rated in watts: for example, a 1000 watt dimmer can be safely connected in series with a 1000 watt lamp, or with a group of lamps whose total wattage is 1000. If a larger load were connected to the dimmer, it would overheat and, more than likely, burn out. A smaller load is safe, of course, but a smaller load requires a greater resistance to dim it completely out. For these reasons a resistance dimmer should be connected to a load equal, approximately, to the rating of the dimmer. The discussion and explanation above concerning the current-carrying capacity and resistance necessary for dimming has been included not only to enable the reader to understand the principles involved, but also to serve as a possible guide in the construction of homemade dimmers and in employing rheostats not intended for theatrical use. Producing groups in colleges and high schools can usually borrow rheostats from departments of physics and of electrical engineering when the rheostats are to be used for a day or two only. In such cases, a calculation of maximum resistance and current-carrying capacity should always be made to prevent dam-

---

[3] The resistance of the wire from which lamp filaments are made varies with its temperature. Its resistance is much higher when the lamp is bright than when it is dim.

age to the apparatus. Since resistance dimmers are becoming obsolete, the importance of this discussion lies mainly in helping the reader to understand the electrical circuits.

5. TRANSFORMERS

A transformer is an alternating current device for changing alternating current voltage to a higher or lower value. It will not work with direct current. It consists of two separate and insulated copper wire coils wound around a common soft iron core, and so arranged that electrical lines of force around one winding will pass through the other by way of the iron core. There is no electrical connection in the usual sense between the two coils of wire (see

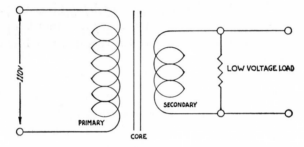

FIG. 117. Simple stepdown transformer.

Figure 117). One winding, called the primary, is connected to a source of alternating current energy. The other winding, which is available to give out energy, is called the secondary. If there are 100 turns of wire in the primary coil and 10 turns in the secondary, this would be called a step-down transformer. If 100 volts are applied to the primary, then 10 volts are available at the secondary winding. It can work in the opposite way, with more turns in the secondary and fewer in the primary. Such a transformer is a step-up transformer. Small bell-ringing transformers are made to connect to 120 volt power sources, and the secondary provides 6 volts for a door bell.

For certain applications the primary winding of a transformer does not have to be insulated from the secondary. In fact, the secondary is a part of the primary, and two secondary wires lead away from the primary winding. This type can step the voltage up (usually not much higher than the primary voltage) or down (see Figure 118). The autotransformer dimmer, discussed in Chapter 14, is a dimmer operating on this principle. The primary coil, insulated and wrapped around its iron core, has a small portion of each turn of the coil bared so that it may make contact with a sliding device that connects to the lamp or group of lamps to be dimmed. When the slider is at the top of the coil, the 120 volt power goes directly to the lamps, bringing them up to full brightness ("full up"). As the slider is moved down, fewer and fewer turns are connected to the lamps and they are dimmed because the secondary has fewer turns, and accordingly is applying less voltage to the lamps. When the slider is halfway down, the transformer has a step-down two to one ratio of turns producing half voltage (60), and the lamps are, roughly, half bright.

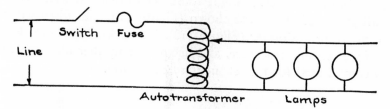

FIG. 118. Method of connecting an autotransformer.

6. REACTANCE

If a coil of insulated wire is wrapped around an iron core and designed with the proper number of turns and the right amount of iron in the core, current will tend to flow when the coil is connected to a 120 volt source of energy. Since the core is within the coil, however, there is set up, in the opposite direction, an electromotive force that bucks the original voltage and prevents current from flowing. If lamps are connected in series with this coil, the lamps will be very dim. No voltage remains to push current through their filaments. If the iron core could be removed, the lamps would be bright again. In applying this principle to the dimming of lamps for the stage, it was discovered that a sort of secondary winding could be applied to the same core. The coil becomes a control coil when energized with direct current, and neutralizes the back electromotive force, allowing the normal line

voltage to apply a gradually changing alternate current voltage to
the lamps as the direct current is varied in the control coil. This
makes a very satisfactory dimmer in its present form. At first, direct current generators and large resistance dimmers had to be
added to the control circuit, making the reactance dimmer useful
for very large loads only. At present, as explained in Chapter 14,
the direct current is supplied by an electronic tube and the same
basic reactance dimmer (improved in design) is very good for a
remote control system.

7. SIMPLE WIRING

Explanations and simple diagrams for connecting lamps in
series or in parallel (Figures 114 and 115) have already been discussed in this chapter. A single resistance dimmer in series with a
small group of lamps was shown (Figure 116) and discussed, as
was an autotransformer (Figure 118), in the section above. Electronic, electronic reactance, and magnetic amplifier diagrams are
too complicated for this elementary discussion.

8. THREE-WIRE SYSTEM

Power comes into a building from a transformer on a pole near
the street, or from a transformer in a vault in a remote part of a
public building such as a theatre. In a metal pipe, called a conduit,
a heavy three-wire cable runs to the remote part of a remote
control system or the rear of a direct control board. As shown in
Figure 119, the secondary from the transformer, which provides
220 volts between the two outside wires, has a center tap that is
called the neutral. From either outside wire to this neutral there
will be an electromotive force of 110 volts. The lines under the
gnd in Figure 119 indicate that this neutral is connected to the
ground. By connecting this neutral wire and also the frames and
housing of various kinds of electrical equipment, including control boards and spotlights, to the ground, they are made safer for
operating personnel. As mentioned in the last chapter under the
discussion of electrical cable, city and state electrical codes are being changed to make the grounding of power tools and other electrical equipment required by law.

Figure 119 illustrates a single-phase [4] system for lighting circuits. Figure 120 illustrates a four-wire, three-phase system that is used where lighting loads are more important than power loads. When this system is used for motors, 208 volts are obtained between any two of the "outside" wires, but lighting loads of 120

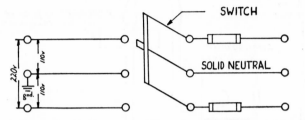

FIG. 119. A three-wire power system. The tubes in the top and bottom wires at the right represent cartridge fuses.

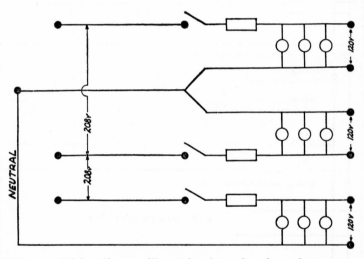

FIG. 120. Wiring diagram illustrating four-wire, three-phase system.

volts are connected between any one of the "outside" wires and the fourth, or neutral (grounded), wire.

Figure 121 shows three-wire power coming into a lighting control board main switch, and continuing through a group master switch and dimmer that has two individual dimmers and switches

[4] If the student is interested in phase or phase relationships, he should refer to any elementary text on electrical engineering.

going to some type of plugging panel. From here it goes to an outlet where a spotlight with cable is plugged in at the top center of the diagram. At the group master switch two fuses are shown. The more recent practice does not use a second fuse shown in the

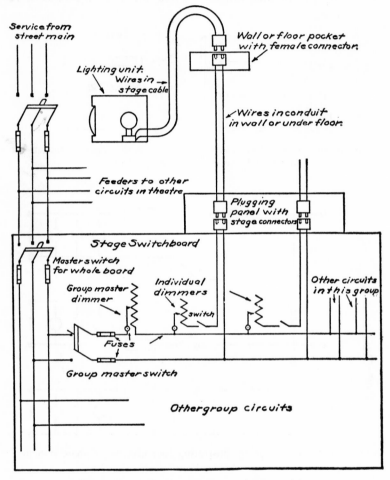

FIG. 121. Schematic diagram of stage wiring.

neutral. As explained in the following chapter under control board parts, in most instances the fuses would be replaced by a circuit breaker and this would be in the "hot" (ungrounded) line only, not in the neutral.

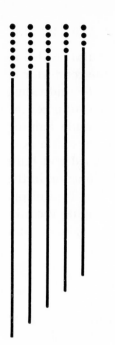

Lighting Control

1. INTRODUCTION

FROM THE ANALYSIS of light and its functions in Chapter 10, and the discussion and description of lighting instruments in Chapter 11, we have seen that instruments cannot, either optically or mechanically, control the properties of light perfectly. Many years ago, David Belasco said, "Without perfect control, lighting in the theatre, instead of being an irresistible means to every end of dramatic effect, would be continuously a hindrance and a stumbling block." [1] Belasco was thinking of the electrical control board where the brightness of each lamp can be changed individually and in a variety of group combinations. Many improvements in instruments and control have been added since the important contributions of Belasco in the early part of the century. What did he mean by "perfect control"? Since light is the medium of expression that we know least about, probably we still do not know what perfect control is.

Perfect control seems to be complete control of the properties of light—quantity, color, and distribution—from a single posi-

[1] *Theatre Lighting Past and Present* (Ward Leonard Electric Co., Mt. Vernon, N.Y., 1923).

tion. From this position the control operator must also be able to see the entire stage, and the actors on it. Just as the conductor of an orchestra co-ordinates the contributions of the individual musical instruments, a lighting control operator co-ordinates the contribution of each lighting instrument to the whole lighting plan. As in the case of different musical instruments in a symphony orchestra, each lighting instrument is designed and built for a definite purpose and is selected for a specific function in the lighting design of one scene of a play. The lighting control operator has these instruments at his finger tips, bringing them in and out according to the lighting "score." Quantity, color, and distribution may be continually changing.

2. CONTROL LOCATION

If it is important for an organist to hear what he is playing as he sits at the organ console, it is equally important for the lighting control operator to see what light is doing to the actor and the production as he moves his fingers over the lighting controls. To place lighting control backstage in a new theatre is a throwback to horse and buggy days. At the Metropolitan Opera House and the Music Hall (Rockefeller Center) in New York, and in such college and university theatres as those at Stanford, Iowa, Oregon, Yale, and San Diego State, to mention only a few, the lighting controls are out front. Viewing the stage from the footlight position gives one a somewhat distorted impression because he is too close to see the performance in normal perspective. A better place is one farther away from the stage, such as in the rear of the auditorium, which is the position of the control board in the University Theatre at the University of Iowa, and in the smaller theatre at Stanford University. If the balcony is not too high, a place almost equally good is in the rear of the balcony, as in the case of the University Theatre at the University of Oregon. From either of these last two positions an excellent view of the stage is presented to the operator, who can follow every change in mood and movement as easily as the audience. The only disadvantage in the out-front position is the necessity for communication by telephone with the stage manager and head of the light crew, but this rarely, if ever, causes any difficulties. The more conventional and tradi-

Two interior settings from San Diego State College. Above: *The Chalk Garden,* and below: *Idiot's Delight.* Designed by Don W. Powell.

tional location for the control board, left or right backstage near the proscenium arch, may be satisfactory for road-show theatres, but for repertory or production theatres, as well as for college, school, and community theatres, a location that affords complete visibility for the operator greatly multiplies the opportunity for effective lighting.

In spite of the awareness of the advantages of the out-front position for control boards among educators in college and university theatres (with a few notable exceptions), the commercial theatre production is provided with a complete layout of rented lighting equipment, including portable control equipment, placed in the usual offstage location. The antiquated stationary board, which may have been a part of the original equipment of the theatre in 1910, is completely ignored—a fate that might also befall the latest model installed last week, the theatre owner tells us. The footlights and auditorium lighting are the exceptions, and are commonly controlled from the theatre's own stationary board. Many good theatres in New York City have been converted to television production (and a few reconverted, like the Belasco, back to drama) where modern portable control boards have been designed for this purpose, and in a few instances the latest electronic controls have been used in stationary form.

3. GENERAL CLASSIFICATION—PERMANENT AND FLEXIBLE

There are two methods of lighting control, permanent and flexible. Permanent control is the one in which the wiring from any outlet on the stage, such as the wiring for a border-light circuit, to a switch and dimmer on the control board, is permanently fixed with no provision for connecting that outlet or instrument to any other circuit on the board. This method of control has developed out of antiquated lighting practice and the associated tradition of equipping theatres with stock lighting instruments, such as footlights, borderlights, and stage pockets for spotlights or floodlights. In the past, these were thought to be the backbone of all stage lighting, and accordingly were always permanently connected to the control board. As a result, in recent years the majority of road companies have carried their own lighting instruments and portable control boards, and have completely ignored the permanent stage-lighting equipment in the theatres on the road.

Modern practice in stage lighting requires much more variety and flexibility in an equipment layout, especially for experimental theatres, than the permanent method of control affords. For a number of reasons, then, a method of control has come into use that is far better suited to college or community theatres. It is called flexible control, which means that between the control board and the outlets where instruments are connected, there is some means of connecting any outlet to any dimmer and switch on the control board. Furthermore, any number of outlets can be connected to one dimmer if desirable, as it often is.

4. INTERCONNECTING PANELS

The means of connecting dimmers to outlets is called by various names, including interconnecting panel, cross-connecting panel, interplugging panel, or even patching panel. The engineers of the Hub Electric Company of Chicago, who have had considerable experience in building these panels, classify them into five types— dial selector, bar, separable cord, counterweighted fixed cord, and suspended fixed cord.

The bar type, illustrated in Figure 122 (planned by the writer and built by the Hub Electric in 1931), consists of vertical copper bars in the rear connected to the dimmer control circuits, and horizontal bars in front connected to the outlets. A clothespin type bronze plug slides along the outlet bar and clips over the appropriate dimmer bar to connect a specific outlet to a dimmer circuit. This is a simple way to connect any outlet to any dimmer; furthermore, any number of outlets can be placed on one dimmer bar. This type is simple, not expensive, unlimited in range, but illegal under certain circumstances because of its "live" front. That is, one can get an electric shock from it easily.

In the separable cord panel, a male jack is wired to each stage outlet circuit, while each dimmer control circuit is represented on the panel by two or more female jacks. Cord sets, each with a male plug at one end and a female at the other, are provided to make the connection between outlet and dimmer. With an elaborate system consisting of perhaps 80 outlets and 48 dimmer control circuits, the separable cord type can become a confused mass of cable, and if one of them is accidentally knocked out, tracing it and properly replacing the jacks can be very troublesome.

Instead of having a number of separate cords that must be hung up and are frequently lost, it seems preferable to have fixed cords. That is, each cord is permanently attached to the outlet circuit and has some type of jack or plug on the free end. The

FIG. 122. Interconnecting panel (bar type).

dimmer control circuit is represented by two or more receptacles, as shown in Figure 123. This one was planned by the writer so that each dimmer can control as many as four lighting instruments when the need arises. This is especially desirable when the total number of controls is small. Behind the panel a small sash weight is suspended on each cord to take up slack and keep the front of the board as neat as possible.

If the panel in Figure 123 were essentially a suspended cord type, all of the cords would be like the five cords in the right center section of the panel. In this particular panel, five auditorium

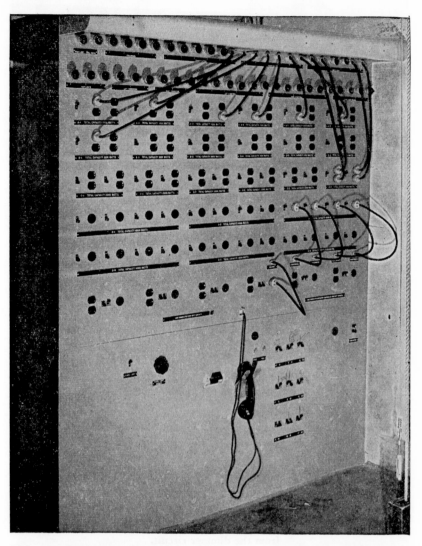

FIG. 123. Interconnecting panel built for Little Theatre at San Diego State College. Panel was built on the campus from standard twistlock parts.

FIG. 124. Retractable cord type interconnecting panel as made by Kliegl, called "Safpatch" because the circuit breaker opens before the plug is removed from the dimmer circuit.

luminaries were connected to short cords to plug into dimmers above them during stage performances, and to direct line outlets below for class room and other uses of the auditorium. In the latter case all five are controlled by the push button on a magnetic contactor below.

The patch-plug type, shown in Figure 124, is good but the shelf portion takes up valuable space. The Ariel Davis Company

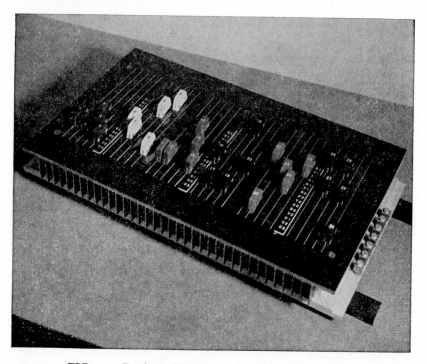

FIG. 125. Davis Quick-Connect interconnecting panel.

makes a Quick-Connect type, shown in Figure 125. As the slide is tilted, the connection is broken until it is released from the hand at the proper control bar. This type, while expensive, is compact and safe. Its one disadvantage seems to be that it can only be made in units of fifty outlets or less. If one has more than fifty outlets, it must be made in two parts, and the control (dimmer) circuits are duplicated in each half. This requires checking both halves to prevent overloading the dimmers.

5. ADVANTAGES OF FLEXIBLE CONTROL

By means of one of the interconnecting arrangements mentioned above, flexible control saves time and money and adds to convenience of operation. When connecting instruments to stage outlets, in order to conserve stage cable, and to avoid excess cable getting in the way of the actors and the shifting scenery, it is necessary to have considerably more stage outlets than are ever needed for one production. These outlets are located in convenient places about the stage so that instruments can be plugged in wherever they are needed. On the other hand, it does not follow that one needs an equal number of dimmer circuits on the control board; in fact, the number of dimmer circuits is often only half the number of outlets, but these figures must be determined by workers in their own theatres who know from considerable experience the actual needs for the sort of plays commonly produced there. The number of dimmer circuits never should be determined by a manufacturer or dealer who thinks he knows what the theatre needs. If the most useful wattages are selected, from twenty to thirty dimmer circuits take care of a fairly elaborate production on a small stage. The number of stage outlets is determined somewhat by the size of the stage, but fifty to sixty is a rough estimate of a convenient number.

The following advantages are important. In this kind of control, a dimmer of any wattage found on the board (many good ones have dimmers of different wattages) is available to any outlet, and a single dimmer can be connected to two or more outlets, a practice which is frequently necessary. Furthermore, a flexible control board is much cheaper because fewer dimmer circuits are necessary than in permanent control, in which several dimmers may be idle because they are permanently connected to an instrument not in use at the time. Finally, flexible control allows the operator to arrange the controls into groups according to the needs of each production, so that he can handle the switches and dimmer handles with maximum speed and facility and with minimum danger of error.

6. DIRECT AND REMOTE CONTROL

Control boards are classified, also, as direct or remote control. In direct control, the switches and dimmers which the operator actually handles carry the total current that passes through the lamps. When a single circuit carries a large group of lamps, or a master switch or dimmer handles the whole board, the space occupied by such a switch or dimmer becomes quite large. Dimming under these circumstances is less subtle and not as smooth as it is with small parts. In remote control the large switches and dimmers are placed in some remote place, such as a basement room, where space is not at a premium. These large parts are controlled by small switches and dimmer handles on a compact pilot console (manually operated control board) out front where the operator can see the entire production.

7. PRESET OR MULTI-SCENE CONTROL

For the past twenty-five years a method of setting up the switches, and later the dimmer readings, for several scenes in advance has been developing. Today it has reached a relatively high state of refinement in contemporary electronic control systems, described in Section 12, and more elaborately elsewhere.[2] In plays with a large number of short scenes with only a few seconds between scenes, it is helpful to have all of the scenes set on the board in advance, up to the intermission of ten minutes or so, when the operator can set up another group of scenes. Faders are provided on these control boards to smoothly change the individual readings on a group of instruments to another set of dimmer readings on the second preset, and so forth to the last preset available. In the opinion of some, two presets are sufficient, because after one has faded to the second, an assistant can help reset the first preset readings in time for the fade to the third scene, and so on. This argument falls down if the control board has from fifty to one hundred individual controls to be reset during a 30-second scene. A representative of the Strand Electric Company of Lon-

[2] See Century Lighting Inc. control board catalogue, and many articles in periodical literature during the early nineteen-fifties.

don said recently that in England good control boards had at least 144 individual controls. While this sounds like a beautiful dream compared with the average board in an American theatre, it is desirable to have more than the usual twenty-four to sixty controls commonly found in American theatres. Our controls cost about five times as much as those made in England.

Another point of view concerning presets is that at least twenty or more are needed on the assumption that changing the distribution of light from one scene to another is not nearly so important as the use of presets in establishing a large number of specific distributions of light within a scene, then allowing a motor-driven fader to blend slowly from one distribution to another while the scene is in progress. This could be done in an exciting sunset that lasted for ten minutes, while changing continually in color, quantity, and distribution. Control boards of this kind cost from $25,000 to $50,000. A sensitive and interested student can create this effect manually with the individual controls on a much simpler piece of equipment.

8. CONTROL BOARD PARTS

A discussion of the way in which control boards operate is difficult without a brief mention of the essential parts of which these boards are composed. The vital essentials for controlling the intensity of an incandescent lamp are a switch to open and close the circuit, a fuse or circuit breaker to guard against short circuits or excessively high current, and a dimmer for the purpose of changing the amount of illumination.

Switches. The smallest durable switch which is silent in operation, easy to operate manually, and which meets the requirements of the electrical code, is usually the best for stage control boards. Mercury switches are very good but are not common for the stage. Silent mechanical switches seem to be preferred by control board manufacturers. Toggle switches are much too noisy.

For remote control, a small, compact, silent switch on the pilot console does not carry the full current, nor does it directly energize a large lamp (or lamps) on the stage. It controls a large magnetic switch (contactor) on a control panel in a remote room containing the actual load-carrying switches, fuses, circuit breakers, and dimmers. This small pilot switch energizes an electromagnet that opens and closes a large switch. In many contemporary control systems the large magnetic switch is not provided in each circuit, but is used only as a blackout switch for a large number of controls, that is, as a master switch for the whole control board. Each no-dim circuit on a remote control board must have a magnetic switch in the remote portion of the control system. Individual dimmer circuits can be opened or closed without the expense of these magnetic switches by merely opening or closing a part of the pilot current.

Fuses. Either plug or cartridge fuses are satisfactory for stage lighting. The plug type, which screws into place like a lamp, has the advantage of displaying the fact that it is either intact or blown. This fuse, however, is not made in sizes above 30 amperes. Cartridge fuses are small cylinders of fiber with brass contacts on the ends. Their size varies with the current to be carried. Circuits should never be over-fused; in other words, a circuit carrying current for 500 watts should have a 6 ampere fuse, not a 10 ampere one. The 6 ampere fuse will "blow" if a 1000 watt lamp is connected to a 500 watt dimmer, warning the operator that an overload has been placed on the dimmer; the 10 ampere fuse will not give this warning.

Circuit breakers. Now replacing fuses in branch circuits (such as individual circuits on a control board) is a thermal device that opens the circuit when excessive current overheats it. This device is provided with a handle to open and close it manually, and a great many models of this type resemble the common toggle switch. Over a period of time the circuit breaker is a good deal cheaper than fuses if the fuses have to be replaced often, and the circuit breaker prevents the dangerous practice of putting pennies behind fuses when they are blown. Either a fuse or a circuit breaker is required by law in each circuit, and anything that interferes with its normal operation is a serious and dangerous matter.

Dimmers. Almost every person actually associated with the production of plays appreciates the supreme importance of being able to change the intensity of light on the stage. Those who need to be convinced are local architects and electrical contractors, school principals, and superintendents. The architect and school administrator are often more concerned with combining the cafeteria with the auditorium than they are with making the stage and its equipment effective for producing plays. In twenty-five years there has been some improvement, but dimming control is neglected all too often.

Dimmers are usually classified according to the electrical principle on which they operate. The ones in common use today are resistance, autotransformer, electronic reactance, electronic, and magnetic amplifier. Since the last four have so many advantages over the resistance dimmer, it might be considered obsolete for permanent installations where alternating current is available. Since the resistance dimmer is the only one that will operate on direct current, the portable control boards used in Broadway productions contain almost no other type. Not only are some Broadway theatres provided with direct current only, but each production, unless it is extremely elaborate, plans to tour, either for a "warm up" period preceding its opening in New York, or a road tour following the New York run, or both. In a few places on the road they might run into direct current, and the resistance type operates on both direct and alternating current.

Resistance and autotransformer dimmers are essentially direct control in their operation unless they are motor driven. Since a motor drive with variable speed is impracticable, in the opinion of the writer a motor-driven dimmer is unsatisfactory for stage lighting. Electronic, electronic reactance, and magnetic amplifier dimmers are associated with remote control because the dimmers themselves, and their supplementary parts, are rather large and have no moving parts; in this case it is ideal to place them in a remote place from the stage and have the manually operated part of the system, where parts are small and sensitive, in the rear of the auditorium or some other out-front position. Remote control systems cost from two to four times as much as direct control. For many small schools and colleges a remote control system is too expensive to consider.

9. RESISTANCE DIMMERS

In shape, resistance dimmers are either square or round plates, varying in height from about 12 to 20 inches. The round-plate type (Figure 126) can be interlocking or non-interlocking. Interlocking means that the handles which change the intensity can be connected in such a way that two or more dimmers set in a row can be operated together by a single handle called the interlock-

FIG. 126. Ward Leonard resistance dimmer (interlocking type).

ing handle. Figure 127 shows how interlocking dimmers (both resistance and autotransformer types) are mounted in rows in a steel frame with a large interlocking handle near the end of each row. These dimmers (if resistance) have 110 steps, so that they will dim very gradually, and each handle is provided with a scale of 10, so that the desired quantity of illumination controlled by the dimmer can be noted and recorded for succeeding rehearsals, and for the performance. The non-interlocking dimmers have about 30 or 40 steps only, which does not produce such smooth dimming, and there is no scale provided for noting a dimmer-reading. The price of non-interlocking dimmers, however, is only about half that of the interlocking ones. When the most rigid economy must be practiced even at considerable sacrifice in result, the cheaper ones are recommended if used with master dimmers.

Resistance dimmers waste energy in the form of heat, and the load must be fairly closely matched to the capacity of the dimmer.

FIG. 127. Interlocking dimmers by Ward Leonard. Resistance and auto-transformer dimmers can be interlocked in the same way.

A 500 watt dimmer will not dim out a load smaller than about 450 watts.

Multicapacity resistance dimmers. For stage outlets into which spotlights or floodlights of various loads are plugged, dimmers of various ratings are needed. This is taken care of somewhat with a flexible control board, but if the circuits are permanently connected, a multicapacity dimmer is needed. These so-called dual or multicapacity dimmers have, for example, resistance enough to dim a 500 watt lamp and will carry enough current for a 1000 watt lamp. They are also made in 250 to 500 watt and 1000 to 2000 watt capacities. The disadvantage, however, is that the control handle will have moved only two-thirds of its travel when it has completely dimmed a lamp of maximum wattage for the dimmer. This restricts gradual dimming to some extent. Nevertheless, some of these, especially those from 250 to 500 watts, are highly recommended for flexible control boards on a small stage provided with direct current, although all of the dimmers on the board should not be of this type.

10. AUTOTRANSFORMER DIMMERS

Some years ago a new dimmer appeared using the autotransformer principle that has been common in electrical engineering practice for many years. It consists of a coil of copper wire surrounding an iron core. At one end of its cylindrical form is a dial (much like a large dial of an early model radio), to which is fastened a carbon brush, or sliding contact, which is manually moved around the coil of wire (see diagram in Figure 118). In this piece of apparatus there is no heat loss, and practically no energy is used by the dimmer. Its chief advantage, however, is that it has complete variable capacity. That is, a 1000 watt dimmer will dim completely and gradually any wattage, even a 5 watt lamp, up to its maximum capacity (1000 watts).

The large manufacturers of resistance dimmers (and others) soon realized that the autotransformer principle was much superior to resistance for lighting control, and they have designed autotransformers to fit into their standard interlocking frames. The new dimmers are well built and rugged, and have a capacity up to 8000 watts on a single unit. While they have complete variable capacity, they are even more expensive than resistance dimmers, and offer no improvement over these in compactness and subtlety of operation. Autotransformers similar to those in Figure 128 are made by the large transformer companies also (see Appendix). Autotransformers operate on alternating current only, whereas resistance dimmers can be used with either direct or alternating current.

Some years ago an autotransformer dimmer that had a number of sliders on a single coil appeared in European theatres. Instead

Courtesy General Radio Company

FIG. 128. Autotransformer dimmers. Ward Leonard, left; General Radio, right.

FIG. 129. Davis dimmer with six sliders.

of a coil for every circuit, one coil was provided for every six circuits. This seemed to be a good idea and was later developed in
this country by the Ariel Davis Manufacturing Company. This
Davis dimmer is made in two sizes, 6000 and 12,000 watts, and
each has six sliders, any one of which will carry 2500 watts, but of
course the total wattage 6000 or 12,000 must not be exceeded by

FIG. 130. Ward Leonard electronic reactance control board at Brooklyn
College Theatre.

all six. This unit of control is available with six outlets and circuit breakers to serve as a small portable control board, and also
can be combined into groups for stationary installations (Figure
129).

11. ELECTRONIC REACTANCE DIMMERS

As made by the Ward Leonard Electric Company, the electronic reactance dimming circuit consists of the basic reactance

coil and the supplementary controls which they call a Hyster Set. Included are a thyratron electronic tube that produces the direct current, and miscellaneous transformers, potentiometers, and so forth. The reactance coil is in reality two coils, one in series with the lamp to be dimmed, and the other a control coil connected to the direct current produced by the electronic tube. All of this (placed in a remote part of the theatre) is connected by electrical

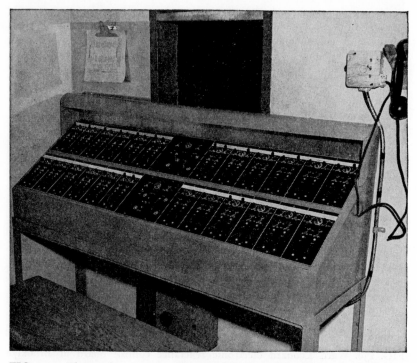

FIG. 131. Electronic reactance control board at San Diego State College (Little Theatre), assembled from Ward Leonard parts.

cable to the small manually operated parts on a compact pilot control board (console) placed where the operator can see the stage. As is shown in Figure 130, the parts are small and sensitive, readily lend themselves to subtle operation, and are usually within reach of a single operator. Master and submaster dimming (Section 14) are very simple and are accepted as essential parts of this type of control. Two or more presets are usual, too. The most recent improvement in this system is the quick response noticeable in larger sizes from 4000 watts up. The actual change in brightness corresponds exactly with the movement of the pilot dimmer handle. The lag that was so annoying in earlier models has been eliminated completely. The loading range, or degree of multicapacity, is 80 per cent, that is, a 1000 watt dimmer will completely dim a 200 watt lamp.

12. ELECTRONIC DIMMERS

An electronic dimmer, a more recent development in dimmer design, is one in which the large thyratron tubes themselves act as

FIG. 132. Century-Izenour electronic control board for Brussels World Fair.

a dimmer, of course with a number of accessory transformers, potentiometers, and so forth. The more elaborate of the two competing electronic control boards, the Century Izenour board, was invented by George Izenour and is manufactured by Century Lighting, Inc. It is illustrated in Figure 132, showing the control console at the center and the preset panel on each side. This model

has ten presets for each control, and the fading and master control can be done automatically by motor drive at a pre-selected
speed, or by manual operation.

The other electronic control board is manufactured by Kliegl
Brothers. It, too, uses a thyratron type tube, which actually consists of three tubes in each circuit that serve as the dimmer along
with their supplementary parts. This system has a more conventional console with the presets associated with the individual controls and switches, or they can be arranged in scene groups. The
necessary fading devices and master dimmers can be arranged to
suit the purchaser, since this, as well as the Izenour board, is a
custom made item. Electronic dimmers are completely flexible in
their loading range, that is, they have complete multicapacity.
A 6000 watt dimmer will completely dim the smallest lamp. The
Kliegl board is illustrated in Figure 133.

13. MAGNETIC AMPLIFIERS

When the ultimate in dimming characteristics (with minimum
maintenance) can be justified, even at a slightly higher price, the
magnetic amplifier should be preferred. This dimmer resembles
the reactance coil in the electronic reactance dimmer, but the
wiring circuit is quite different and it is controlled not by electronic tubes, but by dry disc selenium rectifiers (Figure 134).
Like the last two mentioned, the magnetic amplifier is of the remote control type, with pilot controllers resembling those of the
electronic reactance dimmers. This magnetic amplifier dimmer
will dim out any load, from its rated capacity down to $\frac{1}{30}$th of that
amount. They are made in a number of sizes from 2000 watts to
25,000 watts. For loads greater than 6000 watts one must use this
type or the electronic reactance. Autotransformers and electronic
tube dimmers are not made in larger sizes. The control wiring of
a magnetic amplifier is simplified and reduced in cost by a low
voltage control circuit. At present the manufacturers are Vickers,
Metropolitan, Superior, and Ward Leonard. Prospective purchas-
ers should study all three for cost and dimming characteristics
before specifying any one. The trend is toward magnetic amplifiers, the best dimmers for remote control. Since the magnetic

FIG. 133. Kliegl electronic two-scene control board, above. Tube bank, below.

amplifier is more expensive, many people do not agree that it should be chosen over the electronic type.

14. MASTER DIMMERS

One hand with a master dimmer can do more than a dozen hands using individual dimmers. If the individual dimmers can be interlocked, it is true that one hand will serve to dim them all

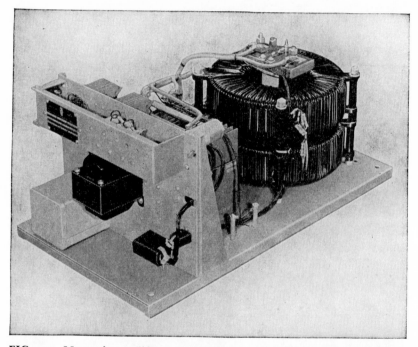

FIG. 134. Magnetic amplifier type of dimmer. Consoles for this remote type dimmer can be similar to any of the electronic or electronic reactance consoles.

at once, but interlocking requires a much greater pull, and accordingly affords less smooth and subtle dimming. The real advantage that justifies the expense of a master dimmer is something called proportional dimming. Suppose a master dimmer were connected (electrically) to four individual dimmers, with dimmer readings of each at full up (that is 10, on a scale of 10), 7, 5, and 2. By changing the handle of the master only, all four individuals will begin dimming at the same time, and all will dim out at the same time. The relative intensities of the four lamps will be the same whether the master is at 10 or 5 or any other setting. This is called proportional dimming, an important element in control board planning and design. A group master is useful for dimming a smaller group, such as one consisting of six antiproscenium spotlights that go up as the curtain goes up. Another

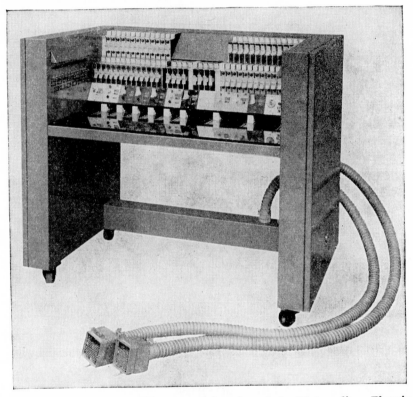

FIG. 135. Magnetic amplifier control board made by Metropolitan Electric Mfg. Company.

group master may dim an entire sky consisting of five or six different circuits controlling three colors in the cyclorama base lights, and light and dark blue groups of floodlights for the upper part of the cyclorama. When dimming down a late afternoon sky, unity and proportion must be kept in mind. And last, a whole group of area instruments must be able to go up or down when an actor pushes a wall switch button, which may be a cue for the grand master, leaving only a few instruments constant for backings and sky.

Although master dimmers for direct control are quite expensive because their size must be equal to the total load connected to them, in remote control the matter is much simpler and the cost very little beyond that of the individual controls. In mastering remote controls, the master dimmer is only mastering the small individual pilot controls on the manually operated console, and may consist of a small autotransformer or variable resistance carrying a very small current like that in all of the parts on the console. No additional parts need to be added to the heavy remote equipment.

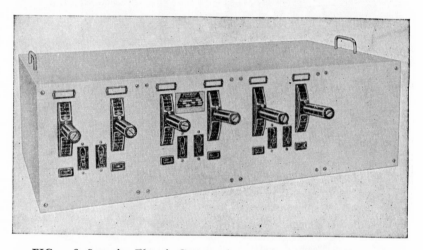

FIG. 136. Superior Electric Company's portable "package" dimmers.

15. PORTABLE CONTROL BOARDS

A portable control board is what its name implies—a control board light enough to be either carried about by hand or rolled on casters. It consists of the usual parts associated with stationary boards—dimmers, switches, circuit breakers, wiring, outlets, and sometimes an interconnecting panel. Almost any stage lighting equipment manufacturer will make control boards of the portable variety according to the customer's specifications or can provide certain stock sections. Many theatre groups buy parts and assemble their own portable controls. While the basic function of such a board, by definition, is control that is portable, this type of equipment appeals also to those seeking lighting control that is reasonable in price.

Theatre groups starting with little equipment have accumulated dimmers in small numbers and have assembled them in boxes of wood or steel, planning to add more dimmers later. Both the Ward Leonard Electric Company and the Superior Electric

FIG. 137. Century portable control board.

Company have "packaged dimmer" units, illustrated in Figure 136, in standard "packages" of three, four, five, and six dimmers of the autotransformer type, including circuit breakers, switches, and outlets for plugging lighting instruments directly into the portable board. A type assembled by Century Lighting, Inc., for the professional theatre is illustrated in Figure 137. An interesting variation built by the Ariel Davis Manufacturing Company is intended particularly for schools and colleges. Such a portable dimmer was discussed in Section 9. It was mentioned earlier in the chapter that most theatrical producers in New York rent portable control boards. Many such pieces of control equipment are used in television studios, particularly in New York City.

16. TELEVISION LIGHTING CONTROL

Similar to control equipment for stage lighting, television lighting control equipment includes the whole range of possibilities

FIG. 138. Century direct control board with autotransformers for an NBC television studio.

from elaborate electronic controls to the simplest of portable arrangements of dimmers, switches, and outlets. Figures 138 and 139 are typical of the simpler portable direct control variety. If the television studio has been adapted from a theatre, the lighting controls have often included the old stage control board, revised or used without modification.

Since television programs often require fairly numerous and

elaborate scenes, only a small number of spotlights and floodlights set up for the whole program can be connected to dimmer
circuits at any one time. By means of an interconnecting panel
(see Section 4), the control operator can change his board
quickly from instruments for one scene to instruments for another; or he can change instruments from dimmed to undimmed
circuits, and vice versa. As new television studios are built and

FIG. 139. Direct control board by Kliegl is designed so that the operator can
see over the top.

older ones are revised, the direction in control equipment seems
to be toward better quality and a larger number of dimmer circuits. Electronic controls are gaining in favor, but autotransformer
and resistance types are more common at present in New York.
On the West Coast, where new television studios are multiplying
rapidly, the electronic and magnetic amplifier control boards are
being provided as permanent pieces of equipment.

17. CONTROL BOARD DESIGN

There are several fundamental questions involved in planning a lighting system for a theatre old or new. The answers depend somewhat on the personality and personnel of the theatre organization. If the artists in the theatre work well together, they usually develop a group personality and philosophy of production. This could be true even if the group is composed of just two people. A college group will have a different philosophy from a community group. A theatre organization in a large university in a small community will have a different point of view from that of a similar organization in a college in a large city. The important thing to remember is that attitudes and production methods vary considerably from group to group, and they should be reflected in the planning of lighting control.

It goes without saying that one should have flexible control that requires an interconnecting panel. A large stage requires a large number of outlets, perhaps 80 to 140; a medium sized stage could use 60 to 80, and a small one, 40 to 60.

The number and type of dimmers is a more difficult decision. For a large stage and a liberal budget, remote control using magnetic amplifier dimmers is preferred, although a number of well-informed people are satisfied with the electronic type at a slightly lower cost. In either case it would be better to have about 64 individual dimmer controls; 48 should be the minimum, with about half of the dimmers of 6000 watts and half of them of either 2000 or 3000 watts.

A medium sized theatre should have 36 to 48 individual control circuits of about the same wattages. A small theatre needs a minimum of 24 individual controls, but 32 to 36 would be much better if its staff prefers elaborate productions. Wattages can be somewhat smaller for this theatre; perhaps six dimmers of 4000 or 6000 watts each, and the rest of 2000 watts would be satisfactory. If for economy the demand is for direct control, the auto-transformer is the type of dimmer to specify; and the best wattages would be 6000, with a saving in cost possible if half of the dimmers were 2000 or 3000 watts.

During the first two decades of this century there developed the curious practice of organizing a control board (then called

Above: an example of flat plane design. The church in *Dark of the Moon,* devised by R. L. Scammon, Indiana University. Below: scenery for a children's production, *Alice in Wonderland,* designed by Wendell Josal, University of Minnesota.

switchboard) into three rows of switches and dimmers, one for red, one for white, one for blue. Rather than for patriotic reasons, it may have been based on a crude attempt at realism or naturalism —white for daylight, red for the rosy glow of sunset, and blue for night. Lighting was essentially from footlights and borderlights wired for these three colors with floor pockets marked red, white, and blue also. There one could plug in olivettes (floodlights) between the wings or send some amber light through the window of an occasional box set. Some years ago Robert Edmond Jones said that we are now in the spotlight era. The red, white, and blue system belonged to the foot and border era, and we must not plan lighting control systems that are obsolete. They become obsolete all too soon without beginning that way.

A modern control board should be arranged in the simplest possible way that conforms to present-day lighting practices. Furthermore, there are certain limiting factors, such as the reach of the average person's arm as he sits in front of a console. The space between controls should be suited to the anatomy of the hand, and the space between rows of handles should be such that minute changes in the dimmers can be done with the hand resting as the fingers move the controls. If there are reasons why the console cannot be of a desk type and must have a vertical face, then the height must be low enough to see over it. The operator should be able to reach the lower row of controls without stooping and still be able to see the stage. A dim operating light is a necessity and the phone should be within easy reach. A headset phone is desirable. A clock either built into the board or near it is very useful.

A flexible system with an interconnecting panel makes it possible to arrange the board, to a degree at least, in the best way for each production. Some people feel that this is confusing, but when students are learning, the operator or operators are usually new for each production.

If the operator sits or stands at the center of the controls so that he can reach in both directions, it seems reasonable to place the master controls in the center of the console (see Section 14). In a remote system, master controls are relatively simple and do not add greatly to the expense. In a direct control system, the master dimmers have to be very large, equal in wattage to the sum of the individual dimmer wattages. For example, if there were twenty-four 2000 watt individual (autotransformer) dimmers, the single master would have to be of 48,000 watts. Since there is no such thing, we could have two masters of the magnetic amplifier type available in 25,000 watts. These would have to be remote control and would have two miniature pilot control handles on the manually operated board. If desired (not necessary), a third handle could be provided so that a single dimmer handle could dim the whole board. Another useful arrangement is to have a group master dimmer for each group. This size (24) can be divided into four groups of six each, in which case the magnetic amplifier group masters would be of 12,000 watts each, with four miniature controls and a fifth grand master pilot dimmer to dim the whole board. Four 12,000 watt remote dimmers would be somewhat more expensive than two of 25,000 watts each, but would provide greater flexibility of control. This combination makes this control board a direct type for individual dimmers but remote for master dimmers. There are two possibilities for complete direct control. If the loads are small, such as twenty-four 1000 watt autotransformers, one could have a group master autotransformer of 6000 watts if the board were divided into four groups. An interlocking device might be helpful to connect the four direct control group masters. The second, and inferior, alternative would be to interlock all of the dimmers and have no master dimming.

Keeping in mind the relationship of the arrangement of the face of the console and the lighting of the play as a whole, the size of each group is important. The six individual dimmers in a group are related to the six spotlights commonly distributed over the upstage or downstage areas. Referring to the description of area lighting in Chapter 15, one can see how the six basic acting areas can be lighted and controlled by two groups of six dimmers, one above the other, arranged on the console as they are on the stage (upstage and downstage). With a larger number of dimmers, say 32, one might have four groups of eight, adding to the basic six instruments two special instruments controlled by the two extra controls in the group. If one is doing a play requiring a higher proportion of special instruments, an arrangement can be made whereby six basic instruments in one group are supplemented by six specials, each placed just below or above the specific place on the control board to which it relates. From these examples one can see how certain divisions into groups, along with the opportunities of change through the patch panel, can connect the planning of the console with the planning of the lighted areas. Light coming from the right (stage right) to the right side of the stage would be connected to dimmers on the same side (left) of the console out front.

The planning of the individual control unit is important too. It will always have an off-on switch, and usually a three position (individual-master-preset) switch. The latter allows one to remove one or more individual circuits from the preset or master dimmer and allows it to remain constant while others are being dimmed by the master. If the board is not of the multiscene type (see Section 7), the individual control will probably have nothing more than one dimmer, one switch, and a pilot light. The pilot light indicates to the operator at a glance whether the circuit is on or off. If this is a multiscene board there will be a dimmer handle (and sometimes a switch) for each scene.

In the central section of the console one usually finds a grand master control (with switch), a scene master control for each scene, and, if there are more than two scenes, a fader to dim from one scene to another is desirable. A blackout switch that will throw all of the controls on or off instantly is a standard part of every console.

There are many variations of the general plan suggested here. If there are no preset dimmers, it is well to have a group master dimmer for each group of six or eight, with a switch to make it independent or connect it to the grand master. An alternate master is a useful addition in that, in a sense, it makes a single scene board into two scenes. An alternate master is provided below the grand master, and the individual control unit has a switch that connects the individual control to either its group or directly to the alternate master. If the group masters are switched to the grand master, then any part of the board can be controlled by the grand master and the remainder by the alternate master. In other words, a scene could be set up in advance on the alternate master and when ready for the change, the grand master (connected to the other scene) could be dimmed down while the alternate is dimmed up. Any lighting instrument that is the same in both scenes would have to be put in its independent position (separate from both masters) if one wanted it to continue from one scene to the other.

Since a control board is an expensive item in any list of stage equipment, the planning of it should be given a great deal of thought and discussion. The representatives of the better manufacturers are helpful in discussing various types and possibilities, and even in writing specifications. Sometimes completely unbiased advice is needed. The suggestions here are intended to be an outline for the student and a guide for those considering the purchase of new control equipment.

CHAPTER 15

Lighting Practice

1. INTRODUCTION

THE PRECEDING CHAPTERS have presented an analysis of the philosophy of light in the theatre, a survey of light-producing instruments and their accessories, the fundamentals and the application of color, and the methods and equipment of lighting control. This chapter is concerned with the application of these things in lighting plays, both in general practice and in specific productions. In the discussion of specific instruments, their various uses have been mentioned. Here, these suggestions will be gathered together in review and in elaboration to complete the story of lighting on the stage.

2. THE BALANCE OF ILLUMINATION

The effective lighting of any play or scene depends upon a properly proportioned mixture of the two kinds of illumination, general and specific. As was mentioned in Chapter 10, specific illumination brings variety to the stage, and because it is shadow producing, it is also form revealing. In contrast to this, general illumination softens shade and shadow, modifies excessive con-

342

trasts in specific illumination, and creates the general color tonality of the whole area.

When lighting a play, one must not forget that his first duty is to the actor. If the actor is not lighted effectively, he is not being supported and reinforced in his effort to interpret the play for an audience. When one is concerned with the co-ordination of scenery and lighting, of instrument placement in relationship to the scenic elements in the ground plan, and in the co-operative efforts to share limited space, it is easy for him to forget that in lighting the acting area, the actor comes before the background.

A set of photographs (Figure 140, *a* through *h*) was made to call attention to the simplest matters concerned with lighting the actor's face. The first shows the face reduced to a skull-like appearance by a spotlight directly overhead. The second (Figure 140*b*) is the same, with footlights added. By partly illuminating the eyes, the result is an emaciated or gaunt expression. In Figure 140*c*, with footlights alone, the shadows are reversed from the usual direction and a surprised but not unpleasant expression results. In Figure 140*d* a rather hard or severe look is achieved by a single spotlight about 45 degrees above the horizontal, and directly in front. Notice the dark frame of shadow on the sides of the face. The right ear looks detached. In Figure 140*e* the face is lighted by two spotlights at a vertical angle of 45 degrees. The horizontal angle between them is about 60 degrees. This is more effective, but the eyes are too dark to be expressive. The face lighting is improved in Figure 140*f* by the addition of footlights that bring out the eyes. By adding more footlight illumination in Figure 140*g*, face shadows are wiped out to the extent that a rather bland, naïve expression is the result. Figure 140*h*, with footlights and a spotlight from one side, is interesting for a static pose, but too much is lost when the actor moves. If the actor were static, like a piece of sculpture, lighting him effectively would be comparatively simple. After studying a static pose, one would place a source of specific illumination at that ideal horizontal and vertical angle which would cause areas of shade and shadow to contrast most effectively with highlights. Then one would add general illumination of just the right amount to soften the contrast between highlight, shade, and shadow and to produce a desirable color tonality in

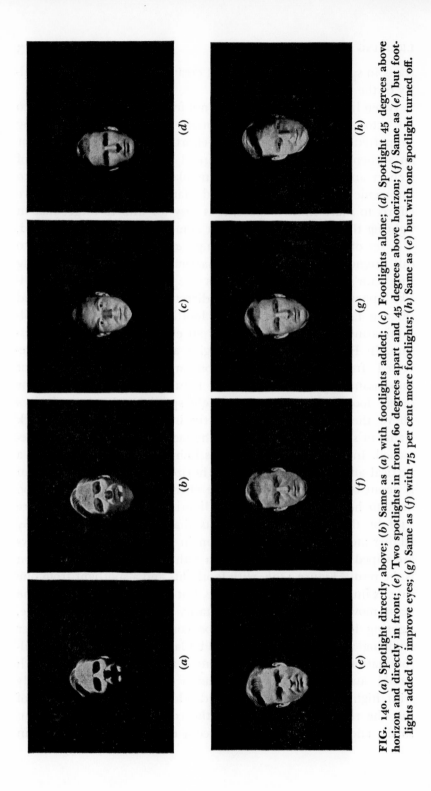

FIG. 140. (a) Spotlight directly above; (b) Same as (a) with footlights added; (c) Footlights alone; (d) Spotlight 45 degrees above horizon and directly in front; (e) Two spotlights in front, 60 degrees apart and 45 degrees above horizon; (f) Same as (e) but footlights added to improve eyes; (g) Same as (f) with 75 per cent more footlights; (h) Same as (e) but with one spotlight turned off.

the areas of less illumination. In this way, a single actor remaining immobile in one area might be effectively lighted; but alas, the problem is not so simple. The actor is in almost constant movement within an area, and he ordinarily uses all of the areas in a setting. Thus a degree of complexity is introduced.

3. INSTRUMENTS FOR SPECIFIC ILLUMINATION

A large number of instruments might seem to be necessary to produce specific illumination from various angles, according to the position of the actor; but this is impracticable for reasons that will soon be obvious. Two instruments separated by a horizontal angle of about 90 degrees (the size of this angle is controlled to considerable extent by physical conditions) will light the actor adequately in a single area. Since the stage is commonly divided into six areas, a total of twelve instruments is needed for the specific illumination on the whole acting area as a basic pattern (see Figure 141). The downstage areas are properly lighted from a position in the auditorium ceiling. Because the instruments for these areas are often placed in false beams that form a part of the auditorium ceiling, they are ordinarily called beam lights or antiproscenium lights. The vertical angle at which the light from these sources strikes the acting area varies from 35 to 60 degrees, but there are a number of circumstances that influence one in choosing the right angle. The building may impose limitations; the distance from the source to the stage may be greater than the efficiency of a spotlight will permit; and an angle as low as 35 degrees may make shadows of the actors on the wall of the set, unless the set is very deep. If, however, no footlights are used, the vertical angle of the beam lights should not be over 40 degrees, because a higher angle will make the shadows and shade too dark in the eye sockets and under the nose and chin. If the set is shallow and footlights are available, an angle of approximately 55 degrees is satisfactory. At this angle shadows on the rear wall are eliminated, and the deep facial shadows can be softened with the general illumination from footlights. On the other hand, a low teaser height may require a very low beam angle. In any case, footlights are necessary when players wear hats with broad brims. Instruments to be used as beam lights should be large conven-

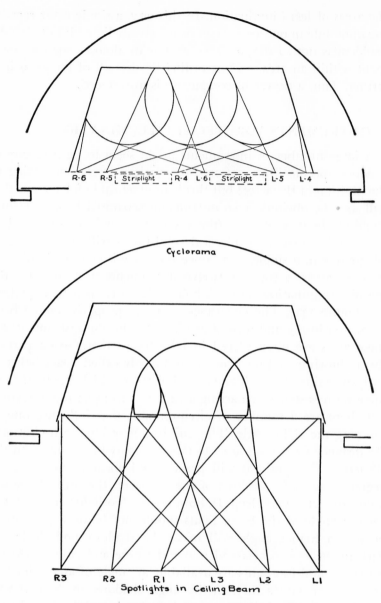

R·6   R·5 ⌐Striplight⌐   ⌐R·4 L·6⌐   Striplight   ⌐ L·5   L·4

Cyclorama

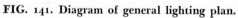

R3   R2   R1   L3   L2   L1

Spotlights in Ceiling Beam

FIG. 141. Diagram of general lighting plan.

tional spotlights (with 8-inch lenses), sufficiently well ventilated to hold 1000 watt or 1500 watt lamps, or even better, ellipsoidal spotlights with 750 to 1500 watt lamps (see Chapter 11).

Anyone familiar with the technical side of the theatre will have noticed that lighting the downstage areas from the beam position is not common in the commercial theatre in New York City. The road companies from New York follow the same practice of lighting the front of the stage from spotlights hung from frames on the front of the balcony. Some of the commercial theatres in New York supplement this with spotlights partly concealed in boxes fastened to the side walls of the auditorium. The front of the balcony places the spotlight at a much lower angle than the beam position, causing the eye sockets to be more easily illuminated without footlights. This has certain advantages to the mature matinee idol who is desperately trying to look twenty-eight. An important disadvantage of this low vertical angle is in the large shadows of the actors that appear on the wall of an interior, or on the cyclorama in an exterior. The usual method of removing these objectionable shadows is to pile on light from so many angles that the shadows are at least partly wiped out. In order to accomplish this result, sometimes as many as twenty to thirty balcony front spotlights are used, and the result is not flattering but flattening, giving the actors' faces a washed-out appearance.

Similar circumstances obtain in the upstage areas, and six instruments are used to cover these three areas just as they are on the downstage areas. In this case, however, the vertical and horizontal angles are both much larger and the length of throw is considerably shorter. The upper diagram in Figure 141 and the lighting layout in Figure 142 show the two common mounting positions for the instruments covering the upstage areas. In either case, the instruments are mounted on the teaser batten; that is, in the position farthest downstage next to the teaser. This batten ordinarily hangs a little higher than the ceiling of the set. Shadows of the actors and areas of greater brightness on the walls of the set are inevitable if the actors play close to the walls. These shadows, as well as those in the faces of the players, are modified in part by general illumination from striplights on the teaser batten (see Figure 141). General illumination from these same striplights helps also to smooth out the spottiness in the acting area from all twelve of the instruments producing specific illumination.

In addition to these basic twelve, a number of special area instruments may be added for several purposes. If the six basic instruments for the upstage areas are focused low to keep spill off the walls of a set, a special spotlight, probably mounted on bridge or first pipe, will be needed to focus on all doors or entrance openings. If the brightness is too high when the door is shut the control operator can handle a change in brightness on cue for actors' entrances or exits. Other special spotlights are used for a single actor, or even two or three, when the distribution of the area instruments is too broad for a specific scene or effect. The director may place his actors in a position that could be called "between areas." In such a case, large area dimming might be desired while one or more faces are kept brighter. Specials would be needed for the faces. Another use of specials is for modeling light from special spotlights in the rear; it is called back or rim lighting in television. These are sometimes placed directly overhead for certain kinds of highlighting. A picture on the wall or any unusual property is sometimes made to stand out by a special instrument. Finally, specials are used to build up around motivating light sources, as explained in the next section.

Separate control of each of these twelve or more instruments allows considerable flexibility and variety of distribution. In this way, any area can be brought into prominence or reduced to obscurity by changes in quantity of illumination. Variety in color is often obtained by having one cool color and one warm one in the two instruments that light a single area. If moonlight is coming through windows on one side, then the instruments covering the acting area from that direction should produce cool light. Pink, illusion pink, orange pink, light violet, and daylight blue are the most useful acting area color media (see Chapter 12, Section 9). Since general illumination from both footlights and the striplights on the teaser batten affects the tonality of the walls of the set, the color of this light must be determined by the color of the set.

4. MOTIVATIONS FOR ACTING AREA LIGHTING

When interiors appear to be illuminated by artificial light from floor lamps, table lamps, candles, and other sources of very low intensity in themselves, they serve as motivation for area instruments of greater illumination and variation in color. Exterior motivations, such as sunlight, can be produced by spotlights or special instruments producing parallel rays. These may add to the visibility at times, but are useful chiefly to produce highlights and to justify the use of certain colors and higher levels of illumination in certain places on the acting area. In this way such sources of light accomplish several functions at the same time.

All visible sources of light, such as table and floor lamps, bracket lamps, candles, lanterns, and torches, should contain small incandescent lamps of very low wattage. Nothing is more annoying to an audience than to be forced to look at a bright source of light on the stage. Even a wax candle is frequently too bright. Obviously, any lighting instrument must be so masked that it is not visible from any seat in the house.

Around the backings of the set, illumination should be much less than on the acting area; in these locations short compartment striplights (Chapter 11, Section 4) are adequate. They can be attached to the offstage side of the set itself. These striplights, moreover, are very useful on the floor to illuminate ground rows.

5. LIGHTING THE WALLS OF A SET

The actual walls of a set should have very little light on them, probably not more than from a twentieth to a twenty-fifth part of the light on the acting area. This keeps the emphasis and the attention of the audience on the actors instead of on the background. More fundamental than the matter of relative emphasis is the fatigue that follows looking at large areas of bright light. In fact, a good play could fail because the set was as bright as the acting area. An important reason why illuminating a play by means of borderlights and footlights alone is wrong is that the background receives the same amount of light as the actors receive. Since a setting that is high in brilliance would probably reflect more light than the average make-up, it would appear brighter than the actors' faces. Sometimes, however, it is necessary to increase the amount of illumination on the wall of a set beyond an appropriate degree. For example, if actors play up against the wall, the specific illumination must be high enough for adequate visibility, and this will cause spottiness on the wall that will have to be smoothed out by increasing the general illumination. The practice of using Fresnel lenses in upstage area spotlights has helped smooth out this difficulty to a large extent. Even if this objectionable increase is necessary, the upper part of the set can be kept darker by directing the striplights down. Then very little illumination other than footlighting will fall on the upper portion of the set. Since this light should be dim, it will add a pleasing color tonality to the set without making it too light. In general, one should always regulate and distribute the light on the setting so that the intensity decreases gradually from the bottom to the top.

6. BACKGROUND LIGHTING

The last element to be considered in the setting is the background. For this discussion the principal background elements are sky cycloramas and drops, and the period revival drop painted for a particular production. A cyclorama is the most difficult element in the setting to light effectively, probably because stage space is nearly always so limited that instruments have to be placed too close to the surface of the cyclorama. This condition makes an even distribution very difficult to maintain.

While a cyclorama ordinarily extends from an offstage position near one side of the proscenium arch to a similar position on the other side of the stage, seldom must the whole of it be lighted at once. From a half to two thirds of the surface is as much as is commonly used for any one play. The size of the area has little to do with the difficulty or simplicity of the task of lighting a cyclorama. The difference is largely in the number of instruments necessary. The whole problem, then, is that of producing general illumination evenly distributed over a smooth surface. Of course, variations in quantity and color in this distribution are necessary. The base of the cyclorama, including an area extending about 10 or 12 feet up, can be lighted best by short striplights from 6 to 9 feet long. Such instruments, with a maximum wattage in each lamp of 150 with the reflectors on 6-inch centers (see Chapter 10, Section 4), are the right size for all cyclorama base lighting in common practice in an average theatre. Employing an instrument with reflectors on 6-inch centers, one should use 150 watt lamps, although there is much more blue needed than green or red. With such instruments color mixing is close to the instrument, so that an 18-inch ground row is high enough to mask the mixing, and the instrument can be placed within a foot of the cyclorama surface. For a better distribution of light, however, the instruments should be at least 5 or 6 feet from the surface. Larger instruments can be used where greater wattage is necessary, if space allows them to be placed 6 feet from the surface and if taller ground rows are used to mask them. This condition will obtain in large theatres only. The reader is no doubt familiar with the fact that these instruments produce the changes in color necessary for sunsets and sunrises. By the use of the primary colors in three circuits, subtle changes in quantity and color can be made at the control board to produce beautiful sunrises and sunsets of the cloudless variety. The short striplights are connected end to end in an arc-like formation in front of the cyclorama. As explained in Section 4 in Chapter 11, the striplight without the reflectors, using R40 and PAR 38 lamps and 55-degree spread roundels, gives a better distribution than the other type in which the striplights are forced too close to the surface.

The upper part of the cyclorama is lighted by floodlights mounted on a batten or frame, as explained in Chapter 11. To accomplish changes from daylight to night, or vice versa, it is necessary to have these in two circuits. If space is limited and the instruments have to be within 5 or 6 feet of the surface, they must be very close together in a row with every other instrument on the same circuit. A more nearly even distribution can be acquired, however, if the instruments are placed 15 or 20 feet from the surface. Floodlights of 500 watts are large enough for almost any cyclorama.

Again in the case of cycloramas, we find that the errors in lighting fall on the side of too much light rather than too little. The cyclorama needs no more than between a twenty-fifth and a fiftieth of the illumination on the acting area. In color the daylight sky can be produced with light-blue color medium (see Chapter 12). It should be neither toward the green nor toward the violet. A dark blue that transmits no red is hard to obtain in cheap color media, but for a night sky the medium must be neither green-blue nor purple. Only a strictly pure blue, so far as the eye is concerned,

Above: *Hippolytus,* designed by Don W. Powell and lighted by Hunton D. Sellman, San Diego State College. Below: *Amahl and the Night Visitors,* designed by Professor Powell and lighted by Donald Parnell.

will carry the illusion of sky. One rarely sees a stage sky that is dim enough and of the proper hue.

While only sky cycloramas have been discussed above, any surface that partly encloses the acting area of the stage might, generally speaking, be called a cyclorama. In fact, a drapery of monk's cloth, velour, or any other material hung in folds might be considered in this general class. The method of lighting these is much the same as that described above, but much more variety in color is often used over the whole surface, depending on the purpose to which the drapery is put. Floodlights on stands are used as supplementary sources if the height of the material is not more than 12 or 14 feet, and the width 20 feet or less. Flat surfaces of material hung from battens, called drops, are really substitutes for cycloramas. When a drop is used as a sky backing, the lighting is done according to the method described above or by means of a borderlight; striplight sections connected end to end serve the same purpose. On the other hand, in producing plays from the nineteenth century or earlier, painted drops, wings, and borders are often made a part of the setting if the play is done in the style of its original production. These drops and their companions, the wings and the borders, look best in dim general illumination produced with a borderlight placed parallel to the drop and about 6 or 8 feet from it. A row of floodlights is a satisfactory substitute, but spotlights cannot be used because shadows and an uneven distribution distort the painting. Even with borderlighting, however, shadows may appear if the actors are allowed to play very near the drop. Natural shadows produced by light are always incongruent with painted ones. When painted drops must be used, the only satisfactory light for them is general illumination that is as nearly shadowless as possible.

7. PRELIMINARY PLANS FOR PRODUCTION

If one is now familiar with the general approach, he is ready to begin planning the lighting in the production of a specific play. The obvious way to begin is with a good knowledge of the text. If one is planning or designing the lighting, he must read the script, first for its general emotional impact and mood, and then again for its detailed requirements that concern light. Before the next step, which is consulting with the director and designers of scenery and costumes, the lighting designer might ask himself several questions. What is the mood; what is the emotional effect of the play? What is the playwright trying to say? Is this a serious play, a comedy, a tragedy, or a melodrama? What is its style? Can these general matters be expressed in terms of quantity, color, and distribution of light? Should the light be evenly distributed, with subtle tints of color, such as one might use in many of Chekhov's plays? What are the time, place, and season in each scene? How is light to be motivated; that is, shall the light on the actor and the set seem to come from the sun or sky? Or should the light seem to come from artificial sources such as table and floor lamps, candles, or gas luminaires? And finally, which functions of light should be emphasized? These questions are a part of the lighting designer's thinking as he studies the play in detail and makes appropriate notes. Some of the answers will be found in the text. Others will come from the designer's imagination and analytical ability, or from consultations with the director and other designers. If the theatre staff consists of several people, the planning of a production becomes a co-operative matter led by the director. In a one man organization he may have to answer all of these questions alone, but in the educational theatre we can assume that the production of a play is a learning process for students and that those with experience and imagination will have a part in the lighting plans under discussion.

After consultation with his fellow artists and an examination of the scene and costume sketches, the lighting designer is ready to make the detailed plans commonly called the lighting layout, or a light plot. The light plot includes a floor plan of the set, such as the one in Figure 142, a section (Figure 143), an instrument schedule, and a control board cue sheet. The plan and section show the position of each instrument and the area lighted by that instrument. The instrument schedule, using the same symbols, shows the type, wattage, outlet, dimmer, color and so forth, for each instrument. While the section is not always necessary, it is helpful in indicating instrument heights above the floor and the vertical angles of the beams of light. Although the control board cue sheets must be prepared in part before the lighting rehearsals, the

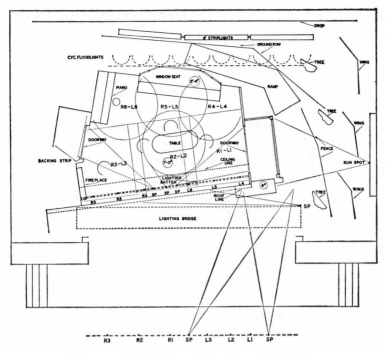

FIG. 142. Lighting layout for *Beautiful People*.

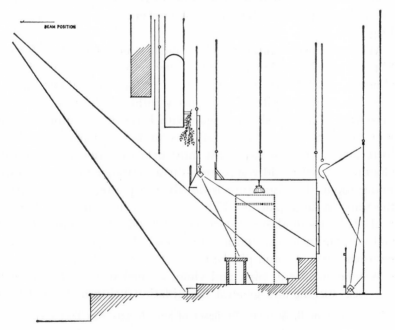

FIG. 143. Longitudinal section for *Beautiful People*.

dimmer readings may be changed frequently before the final dress rehearsal.

Complete communication and proper co-ordination of the work of all of the artists concerned is highly essential to the success of any dramatic production. Lighting is sometimes easier to change than scenery and costumes. But it must light the actor even if holes have to be cut in the scenery to allow light to reach the acting area. Refocusing, changing a color filter, and even moving a lighting instrument during the dress rehearsal period are not too difficult. On the other hand, good mounting positions for the instruments at the proper angles to light the actor most effectively need consideration from the beginning. Careful early planning prevents last minute difficulties.

8. LIGHTING AN INTERIOR

A production of William Saroyan's *Beautiful People,* designed and directed by Don W. Powell,[1] has been selected as an example of interior lighting with some interesting problems. Since Powell designed an interior that shows some of the exterior of the house, the lighting problem becomes less conventional and more challenging.

William Saroyan has shown particular concern and love for the "little" people of America. This play is no exception, with its almost childlike faith in humanity and in the essential goodness of the characters in spite of their petty foibles. The mood and atmosphere of a play about people with little or no ambition, but with faith and love for their fellow man, is rather hard to express in terms of light. In fact, light must overcome the impression of gloominess that could result from the appearance of the rundown living room. The furniture is dowdy and plaster has fallen from the walls in large patches. The railing that decorated the outside wall of the room above is starting to fall off. Still, there is humor and wit, and a happy ending. The general tone in lighting must be warm, delicate, and pleasant.

A general tone of pink and violet seemed suitable for the acting area, specific and general illumination being motivated by a

[1] Don W. Powell, Associate Professor of Speech Arts, San Diego State.

pinkish yellow sunlight in Act I, and Scene 1 of Act II. The photograph is actually of the Act II, Scene 2 lighting, where moonlight is coming into the room from down left and making shadows of the foliage on the upper story wall. The motivating warm source in the last scene was the old luminaire shown hanging from the ceiling.

As shown now in the ground plan, the following set elements are indicated in relationship to the symbols for lighting instruments and their distribution of light. The main living-room area has door openings, right to a hall with a stairway and left to a porch. Upstage is a large bay window. For the sky a portion of the cyclorama is shown where needed, that is, outside the window and around left as far as sight lines demand. Down right is a tree trunk with foliage above and a piece of fence near it. The properties and fireplace are clearly indicated in the photograph and on the ground plan.

The instrument layout needed in this play is as follows:

The downstage areas in the room are conventionally lighted with six 6-inch, 750 watt ellipsoidal spotlights, with an additional special ellipsoidal from the same general position in the auditorium ceiling to light the porch (Figure 142). The upstage areas are lighted with six 6-inch, 500 watt Fresnel spotlights mounted on the bridge, as shown in Figure 142. The door opening down right was used infrequently and seemed to be sufficiently lighted from L3 in the "beam" position, but the more important entrance and exit down left required a special instrument (6-inch, 500 watt Fresnel) framed to fit the door and focused high enough to help light the porch area. It was mounted on the bridge, as shown in Figure 142. Two table specials (T Sp R and T Sp L) added variety in angle and allowed regular area instruments to be dimmed during the early evening scenes. These two specials were motivated by the central overhead luminaire and the moonlight special mounted at the left end of the bridge. It illuminated the upper part of the house and made shadows of the tree foliage as shown in the photograph in Figure 144. This moonlight spotlight might have been made into a slide projector with a foliage slide (see Chapter 10, Section 6), but the set was too close to the bridge to make this practicable. In fact, this set was rather deep in propor-

did not correspond to Act I and Scene 3 corresponded to II. The photograph is usually of the Act II, Scene 4 lighting, when normally in

FIG. 144. San Diego State College production of William Saroyan's *Beautiful People*, designed and directed

Chapter 39, Section I), but the set was too close to the bridge to make this practicable. In fact, this set was rather deep in perspec-

tion to the shallow stage (17 feet), making shadows on the cyclorama, caused by the area instruments, inevitable and impossible
to eliminate completely.

The cyclorama, lighted by eight 500 watt floodlights above and
three 6-foot color striplights below, was much too close for an ideal
distribution of light on its surface. The floodlights are shown on
a dotted line to indicate that the batten is hanging in the flies. A
small two-lamp backing striplight was hung on a stage brace down
right to light the hallway during the daylight scenes. For the same
scenes a "sun" spotlight (1000 watt, 8-inch lens) was mounted
down left on the wall of the stage to highlight the roof, tree trunk,
and porch post, as well as the actors entering from outside. The
color frame was changed to blue-green in the same instrument
for the evening scenes to add to the moonlight mentioned above.

This is an example of a simple interior with very few special
instruments and other complicating factors. The chief difficulty
in lighting plays on this stage is lack of room. Cramped conditions
make spills and undesirable shadows difficult to prevent or conceal.

9. AN EXTERIOR

One scene from the first revival production of James K. Paul-
ding's *The Lion of the West* will be used as an example of a simple
exterior. This play was written in 1830 and sold to James H.
Hackett, who played it successfully for twenty years. It also played
in England under another title. Until 1951 it was one of America's
famous lost plays. After four years of searching, Professor James
Tidwell of San Diego State College found a copy in the British
Museum. Dr. Tidwell edited the published version in 1954. Although the author denied it, the public always associated the leading character, Nimrod Wildfire, with the "similarly uninhibited"
David Crockett.

The play is a two-act farce, containing much satire and carica-
ture, and was treated as such in this production with appropriate
scenery and costumes. The lighting suggested the period with the
footlight reflectors, shown in Figure 145, and period luminaires in
other scenes. This scene, Act II, Scene 3, is the final one and the
only exterior in the play.

The intention here, as one might expect, was to produce the

FIG. 145. San Diego State College production of *The Lion of the West*, designed by Don W. Powell

illusion of period lighting, certainly as far as its effect on the scenery was concerned, but at the same time doing more than that for the actor. More light was used in this production than Hackett probably had in his, and the area was lighted with spotlights to make the actor stand out from his background and to give him a three-dimensional quality. Originally (1831 to 1850?) it was un-

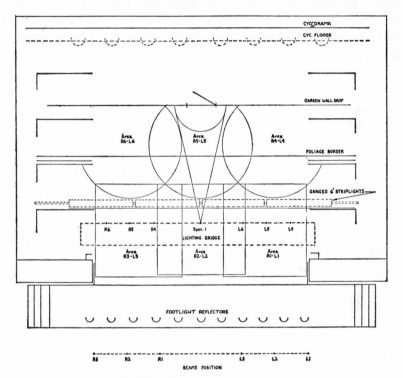

FIG. 146. Lighting layout for *The Lion of the West.*

doubtedly lighted by gas footlights and borderlights, and perhaps a limelight spotlight for Mr. Hackett himself.

Beginning with the acting area, the three downstage areas are lighted by six 6-inch lens ellipsoidal spotlights (see Figure 146). The footlight reflectors suggest candle light but actually produce some general illumination by means of 40 watt lamps, one behind each reflector. These were dimmed quite low but did produce an orange glow from below that helped the period illusion. The upstage areas were lighted as usual with six 6-inch lens Fresnel spotlights, with one special (C Sp) focused somewhat higher for actors in the gate opening. A borderlight, comprised of four 6-foot three-color striplight sections, lighted the foliage border and wings, and was dimmed down for the night scene in the photograph (Figure 145). Since the garden wall was fairly high (5 to 6 feet) lighting the cyclorama from below was unnecessary, but the upper portion was lighted with eight 500 watt floodlights, four with light blue and four with dark blue color filters. They were on two separate circuits to allow a mixture of the two for the evening scene.

APPENDIX

GLOSSARY OF STAGE, SCENERY, AND LIGHTING TERMS

(For more elaborate definitions and descriptions of the following terms and others in the text, see the index.)

Acting Area: That portion of the stage enclosed by scenery which is used by the actors during a performance.

Alzak: A patented method of processing aluminum reflecting surfaces to increase reflectance and to prevent deterioration. It is now used in many lighting instruments.

Ampere: The common unit of current or rate of flow of electricity.

Autotransformer: A transformer in which a single coil of wire wound around an iron core is used as both primary and secondary. As used in the theatre for a dimmer, it has a brush that can be rotated around the coil, thus changing the voltage applied to the lamps.

Baby Spotlight: A small spotlight intended for a 100 watt, 250 watt, or 400 watt lamp. Its lens is ordinarily 5 inches, 4½ inches, or smaller, in diameter.

Backing: A flat, a series of flats, a drop, a border, or a tab used to limit the view of the audience through an opening (e.g. a doorway or window) in a set of scenery.

Backing Striplight: A short, light striplight about three feet long or less, wired in one circuit and used to light backings behind doors, and so on. It is sometimes used between ground rows.

Balcony Spotlight: A spotlight mounted somewhere in the balcony of the auditorium, frequently on a railing or in a box at the front of the balcony.

Base: (1) The part of an incandescent lamp that screws into, or is fastened in, the socket or receptacle. (2) A cast-iron disc that can be attached to the yoke of a spotlight to make the spotlight sit on a flat surface.

Batten: A length of rigid material, usually wood. The 1″ x 3″ lumber strips used to construct scenery are battens. The strips of wood fastened to the top and bottom of a drop are battens. The length of wood or iron pipe on a set of lines, to which scenery is often fastened for flying, is a batten.

Beam. The cone of light from a lens or a parabolic reflector.

Beam Light: A spotlight mounted in a false beam, or otherwise concealed in the auditorium ceiling for the purpose of lighting the downstage acting areas from above. Antiproscenium light is a synonym.

Blackout: A rapid change in illumination produced by opening a switch, usually a master switch, to control all or nearly all of the illumination on the stage.

Board: See *Control Board.*

Boomerang: A box attached to a lighting instrument to hold color frames. Its purpose is to make color changes convenient, and frequently the frames can be changed electrically or mechanically at a distance.

Border: An abbreviated drop, used to represent overhead foliage or to mask the flies. (See Figures 44 and 45.)

Borderlight: A striplight, usually as long as the width of the proscenium arch, hung overhead from the gridiron to produce general illumination on the stage. Many older theatres have three or four of them hung at intervals of 10 or 12 feet.

Brace Cleat: A small metal plate attached to the frame of a flat. Into it a stage brace is hooked to prop up the flat. (See Figures 28 and 59.)

Bridge: A narrow platform, as long or longer than the width of the proscenium arch, hung from the gridiron or sometimes supported from the side walls or on legs. Various kinds of lighting instruments are mounted on the upstage side of the bridge, and an operator can adjust them or change color frames from the platform just behind the instruments. If a theatre has only one bridge it is usually hung just upstage from the teaser.

Brilliance: Brilliance is that property of any color that allows the color to be classified according to a series of grays ranging from black to white. Lightness is used as a synonym.

Bulb: The glass part of an incandescent lamp containing the filament, supports, and so on.

Cable: An electrical conductor (two wires in each cable is the usual practice on the stage) containing one or more copper wires properly insulated with cotton and rubber or plastic and further protected on the outside with a very tough rubber or neoprene sheath to withstand rough treatment.

Ceiling: A large, horizontal, canvas-covered frame hung on two or three sets of lines, used to close in the top of an interior set. (See Figure 42.)

Ceiling Plate: A metal plate with a ring, used in bolting together and flying ceiling frames. (See Figure 42.)

Circuit: A complete path of good conductors leading from the source of electrical energy to a useful device, such as a lighting instrument, and back again to the source.

Circuit Breaker: A more modern device for opening a circuit automatically, taking the place of a fuse.

Clamp, or Pipe Clamp: A brass, aluminum, or steel device that connects the yoke or pipe arm of a spotlight or other instrument to a pipe batten. (Two kinds are shown in Figures 88 and 89.)

Code: Refers to the National Electrical Code, or to the city electrical code that has been enacted into law and based on the National Electrical Code.

Color: In general, refers to all sensations arising from activity of the retina. Color may be chromatic or achromatic, the latter including white, grays, and black.

Color Frame: A metal, wood, or cardboard holder to keep the color filter rigid and to protect it when placed in a lighting instrument.

Color Medium or Filter: A transparent material such as glass, gelatin, or sheet plastic used to obtain color from incandescent light by a process called selective transmission.

Complements, or Complementary Colors: Two colors possessing hue that may be mixed to produce white light. Transparent complementary pigments mixed together produce gray.

Connector: A small block of insulating material with metallic contacts connected to the ends of cable or to lighting instruments, so that power may be conducted from an outlet on the stage through one or more cables to a lighting instrument. Connectors are of two kinds, the *line* connector, which is at the "hot" or power end, and the *load* connector, which is fastened to an instrument or the instrument end of a cable. The twistlock connector is now common.

Contactor: A magnetically operated switch, located in a remote place to save space and to keep the noise of closing the contactor from being heard on the stage. A small switch on the manually operated pilot control board is used to energize the magnet that closes the contactor.

Control Board: The distribution point of electrical energy where the amount of energy, going to the various lighting instruments on the stage, may be controlled. It is composed of switches and dimmers, as well as necessary wiring for the proper distribution of power.

Corner Block: A small piece of ¼-inch 3-ply veneer board, cut in the shape of a triangle and used to reinforce joints in scenery. (See Figure 30.)

Counterweight System: A mechanical system for flying scenery with a counterweight that runs up and down a track at the side of the stage. In contrast with the pin rail system, which is usually operated from the fly floor, the counterweight system is operated from the stage floor. (See Figure 66.)

Cue Sheet: A record of the dimmer readings and changes for each scene of the play, placed on the control board where the operator can see it during the progress of a performance.

Current: Rate of flow of electricity is called current of electricity. It is expressed in amperes.

Curtain Line: The line across the stage behind the proscenium which marks the position of the front curtain when it is closed.

Cyclorama: A large curtain of canvas, or other material—single or in sections—hung from a horizontal U-shaped wood or metal frame suspended by sets of lines from the gridiron. (See Figure 46.)

Diffuse Reflection: Reflection in all directions.

Dim: To change the amount of illumination, either by increasing it or decreasing it.

Dimmer: Any means for changing the amount of light, but usually an electrical device operating on the principle of resistance, reactance, autotransformer, electronic tube, or magnetic amplifier.

Door Frame Unit: A solid wood door frame made to fit into a flat. (See Figure 35.)

Dope: A mixture of glue and whiting that sticks to canvas.

Downstage: Any position on the stage near the footlights.

Draw Curtain: A type of curtain suspended from sliding or rolling carriers running in a track overhead. The curtain is opened by being drawn off to the sides. (See Figure 4.)

Drop: A large sheet of canvas, fastened to a batten at top and bottom and hung on a set of lines from the gridiron. It is commonly used to represent the sky. (See Figure 44.)

Effect Machine: See *Sciopticon.*

Electrician: A name applied in the professional theatre to a union stagehand who is capable of operating the control board and of making connections between instruments and the electrical outlets. The term is correctly applied to one who is capable of wiring buildings and of making and repairing various kinds of electrical apparatus.

Ellipsoidal Reflector: A reflector used in spotlights and floodlights that has two focal points. When a light source is placed at one focal point, light falling on the surface of the reflector converges to the other focal point.

Fireplace Unit: A fireplace frame made to fit into a flat. (See Figure 40.)

Flat: A unit section of flat scenery. A tall screen made of wood and canvas. (See Figure 33.)

Flies: The space above the stage occupied by sets of lines and hanging scenery.

Flipper: A small piece of flat scenery hinged to a larger piece of flat scenery.

Floodlight: A lighting instrument composed chiefly of a large reflector and a fairly high wattage lamp. It is used to produce general illumination. (See Figure 97.)

Floor Pocket: A metal box in the stage floor, its top flush with the floor surface, in which the stage electrical outlets are placed.

Fluorescence: Some substances have the property of absorbing invisible light and emitting visible light. This property is called fluorescence. Because the emitted light is very dim it can be noticed only in dark surroundings.

Fly: To lift scenery up above the level of the stage floor (usually out of view of the audience) by means of lines run from the gridiron.

Fly Floor, or Fly Gallery: A narrow gallery extending along a side wall of the stage some distance above the stage floor. The ropes used in flying scenery are operated from this gallery.

Flyman: A man employed to fly scenery.

Focus: The point to which parallel rays of light converge after passing through a lens. As a verb it is frequently used on the stage to refer to the adjustment of a spotlight to make the illuminated area larger or smaller, or to change the position of the area.

Foot-Candle: A unit of illumination. The illumination on a surface when there is a luminous flux of one lumen on an area of one square foot. It is also the illumination on a surface one foot from a source of one candle.

Foot Iron: A piece of hardware used to secure scenery to the floor. (See Figure 28.)

Footlights: One or more striplights placed in a recess or trough outside of the curtain line to produce general illumination from below. (See Figure 95.)

Funnel: A sheet metal hood, circular or square in section, from 1 to 3 feet long, intended to absorb spill or stray light that would otherwise fall outside the illuminated area. The funnel is fastened to the front of a spotlight.

Fuse: A protective device used in main circuits and branch circuits to prevent overloads and short circuits that might damage electrical equipment. When an overload happens, the small strip of fusable metal (within the fuse) melts and breaks the circuit.

Gelatin: The most common color medium. It is made of ordinary gelatine in thin sheets with an aniline dye producing the color.

Glare: The cause of the sensation of discomfort experienced when observing a surface or light source that is very bright. It depends on contrasts as well as the intrinsic brightness of a source or surface.

Grand Master: A term applied to a switch or dimmer that controls all of the individual switches or dimmers. It is used in contrast to a group master which may master a smaller number of individual controls.

Gridiron, or Grid: The framework of steel or wooden beams above the stage which supports the rigging employed in flying scenery. (See Figures 61 and 62.)

Ground Cloth, or Floor Cloth: A large piece of waterproof duck canvas frequently used to cover the stage floor.

Ground Row: A low, flat profile of ground foliage, a bank of earth, a distant mountain range, or the like, designed to stand up independently on the stage. (See Figure 52.)

Hanger Iron: A piece of hardware attached to the frame of a hanging flat, or other unit, for flying purposes. It has a ring at one end into which the line from the gridiron is tied.

Head Block: See *Lead Block.*

House Lights: Auditorium lighting.

Hue: That property of any color that distinguishes it from gray of the same brilliance.

Illumination: Strictly, it is the density of the luminous flux on a surface and is expressed in foot-candles. In a general way it is often used as a synonym for lighting.

Illuminometer, or Illumination Meter: A meter that measures illumination, usually read in foot-candles.

Instrument, or Lighting Instrument: A synonym for lighting unit, as a spotlight, striplight, floodlight, and so on.

Insulation: Materials, such as fabric, rubber, fiber, porcelain, and so forth, that are very poor conductors of electricity and are used to prevent conductors of opposite polarity from coming in contact with each other, and to prevent contact with individuals who must handle the conductors.

Intensity: The power of a light source, which is measured in candles.

Interlock: To move several dimmer handles up or down together. The usual method is to have a catch that temporarily connects each handle to a single shaft. A single handle permanently fastened to the shaft will then control any of the individual handles connected to it.

Jack: A triangular device made of wood, which is hinged to the back of a ground row or other set piece for the purpose of propping up the scenery from behind. The end of the jack is fastened to the floor by means of a foot iron and a stage screw. (See Figure 60.)

Keystone: A small piece of ¼-inch 3-ply veneer board, cut in the shape of a keystone and used to reinforce joints in scenery. (See Figure 30.)

Lamp, or Incandescent Lamp: Refers to the complete unit, including bulb, base, filament, lead-in wires, and so forth.

Lamp Dip, or Colored Lacquer: A colored transparent or frosted lacquer used on clear or frosted incandescent lamps when it is difficult to place color media in front of them.

Lash Cleat: A small metal hook on the frame of a flat over which a lash line is thrown to bind the flat to the edge of another flat. (See Figures 28 and 32.)

Lash Line Eye: The metal eye on the frame of a flat to which the lash line is attached. (See Figures 28 and 32.)

Lead Block, or Head Block: Three or more sheaves framed together and attached to the gridiron directly above the outer edge of the fly door. The sheaves may be framed in a line, or parallel to each other on a single shaft. The ropes from the three or more loft blocks in a set come together at the lead block and pass on down together to the pin rail. (See Figures 61 and 62.)

Left Stage: Any position on the stage to one's left when facing the audience. (See Figure 1.)

Lens: A piece of transparent material, such as glass, frequently having one or two spherical surfaces and sometimes having cylindrical surfaces. Lenses are used on the stage to converge the rays of light from a small source and concentrate the light to a narrow beam. They are used also to produce an image from a lantern slide or of moving objects. The latter are called objective or projection lenses; the former, condensing lenses.

Lighting Unit: See *Instrument.*

Linnebach Projector, or Shadowgraph Projector: A sheet metal hood painted black inside, using a concentrated source of light and a painted or cut-out slide.

Loft Block: A sheave (pulley wheel) in a steel frame bolted to the gridiron, used to run a fly rope. There is one block for each line in a set. (See Figures 61 and 62.)

Louvers, or Spill Shields: A series of thin cylindrical sections of sheet metal or parallel strips, placed in front of a reflector to eliminate spill light or direct emanation that would fall outside the beam produced by the reflector.

Lumen: The unit of luminous flux. The flux through a unit solid angle (steradian) from a source of one candle. It is also the flux on a surface, one square foot in area, one foot from a source of one candle.

Mask: To conceal a lighting instrument from the audience, usually by means of scenery.

Masking, or Masking Piece: A piece of scenery used to cut off from the view of the audience any part of the stage space which should not be seen. (See *Backing.*)

Master Dimmer, or Switch: See *Grand Master.*

Multiple, or Parallel Circuit: A circuit in which there are several paths through which the current may flow, as in all stage lighting circuits. and in fact, nearly all lighting circuits except street lighting.

Objective Lens: See *Lens.*

Offstage: Any position on the stage outside of the acting area.

Olivette: A box floodlight that can be mounted on a stand or hung by means of chains from a pipe batten.

Onstage: Any position on the stage within the acting area.

Operating Light: Usually a work light built into the control board to illuminate the handles and the cue sheet.

Operator: Any person who handles lighting instruments and equipment on the stage, or changes color frames between scenes. A person in charge of the control board for a production is frequently called the control board operator.

Outlet: A receptacle into which a plug or connector is inserted in order to connect a lighting instrument to the source of electrical energy. A floor pocket or wall pocket may contain one or more outlets.

Parabolic Reflector: A concave reflector whose surface is in the form of a paraboloid. When a source of light is placed at the focus, reflected rays of light tend to go out in straight lines. It is used in floodlights and striplights.

Parallel: The collapsible frame support for a stage platform. (See Figure 48.)

Parallel Circuit: See *Multiple Circuit.*

Phosphorescence: A substance is said to exhibit the property of phosphorescence if, after exposure to light, it continues to give off visible light when the stimulating source has been removed.

Picture-Frame Hook and Socket: Small pieces of hardware used to hang a lightweight unit of scenery, or a property, on another unit. (See Figure 28.)

Pilot Light: A small incandescent lamp, frequently covered with a colored cap, placed in the face of a control board to indicate that a circuit is turned on. One is frequently placed beside the switch and dimmer handle of each individual circuit.

Pin Rail: The double rail holding belaying pins on which fly ropes (sets of lines) are tied. The pin rail is generally located along the outer edge of a fly floor. (See Figure 62.)

Pipe Clamp: See *Clamp.*

Pipe Batten: A length of pipe suspended on a set of lines. Flied scenery is frequently attached to a pipe batten by means of snatch lines instead of being tied directly to a set of lines. A pipe batten is a standard part in a unit of the counterweight system. (See Figure 66.) It is also used to carry lighting instruments.

Platform: A collapsible and portable frame platform constructed in unit sections. (See Figure 48.)

Plug: A standard stage plug is a fiber block with heavy copper contacts rated for 50 amperes. It fits into a standard stage outlet. Especially in the nonprofessional theatre these plugs and outlets are being replaced by 15 or 30 ampere stage connectors or twistlock connectors.

Plywood: Veneer board in three or more plies, made from basswood, whitewood, fir, or other soft wood. Sometimes called *profile board.*

Pocket: See *Floor Pocket.*

Portable Control Board: A control board intended to be moved about, especially from one theatre to another. (See Figure 137.)

Practical: Practicable—capable of being used by the actor. A door with a swinging shutter, or a window with movable sashes, is "practical."

Primary Colors: The primary colors in light are usually called blue, green, and red. The primary colors in pigments are commonly considered to be blue-green, yellow, and magenta.

Profile Board: See *Plywood.*

Projector: A floodlight with a polished parabolic reflector and concentric louvers producing a beam of light is often called a floodlight projector, or sometimes a spot flood. See also *Lens* or *Linnebach Projector.*

Proscenium: The wall which divides the stage from the auditorium. The opening through which the spectator views the stage is termed the Proscenium Opening. (See Figure 1.)

Quality: In light it is sometimes used as a synonym for color.

Rail: A cross piece in the frame of a flat. In a flat 12 feet or less there are a *top rail,* a *bottom rail,* and one *toggle rail* (which braces the center of the flat). In a flat over 12 feet there are two or more *toggle rails.* (See Figure 33.)

Ramp: An inclined platform, sloping up from the level of the floor.

Receptacle: See *Outlet.* Frequently used as a synonym for socket.

Reflectance: The reflected light divided by the incident light, usually expressed in per cent.

Reflector: Any surface that reflects light, but this term usually refers to a definite piece of equipment, such as a spotlight reflector.

Regular Reflection: Reflection in which the angle of incidence is equal to the angle of reflection. Examples are highly polished metals and glass mirrors.

Remote Control: Control in which the current through the lamps does not pass through the manually operated control board, but through dimmers and switches in some remote place such as the basement of the theatre. Its purpose is to make possible the use of small and compact parts in the manually operated pilot control board.

Resistance: A characteristic of materials concerned with their ability to conduct electricity. Insulating materials are said to have very high resistance, and conductors very low resistance.

Rheostat: A variable resistance. Sometimes a synonym for resistance dimmer.

Right Stage: Any position on the stage to one's right when facing the audience.

Saddle Iron: A narrow strip of iron used to brace the bottom of a door flat across the door opening. (See Figures 34 and 37.)

Saturation: That property of any color possessing hue which determines its degree of difference from gray of the same brilliance. A measure of amount of hue.

Sciopticon: A spotlight to which has been added a supplementary condensing lens, moving effect holder, and an objective lens. Such moving effects as clouds, rain, rippling water, and so on, are accomplished with this instrument.

Series Circuit: A circuit with a single path in which the same current passes through every element. (See Figure 114.)

Set: A group or series of scenery units which suggests a single locale.

Set: To put up or assemble scenery for use. This word is generally combined with other words in a phrase—to *set the stage,* or to *set the scene.*

Set of Lines: A unit group of ropes hanging from the gridiron, used to fly (lift) scenery. There are commonly three or four lines in a set. (See Figures 61 and 62.)

Shade: In reference to color, a shade is a color below median gray in brilliance and frequently, but not necessarily low in saturation.

Sheave: A grooved pulley wheel.

Shift: To change scenery and properties from one setting to another.

Short Circuit: When two wires of opposite polarity and low resistance come in contact, the current tends to become excessive and dangerous, possibly causing fire or damage to electrical equipment and wiring. Fuses or circuit breakers are used to prevent damage when this accidental condition obtains.

Size Water: A thin solution of glue which is mixed with pigment powders to make paint for scenery.

Spherical Reflector: A concave reflector that has the property of sending light back to the center of curvature when a source of light is placed at this center. It is used in spotlights and, combined with a parabolic shape, in striplights.

Spill, or Spill Light: Stray light outside a beam, or any light that is misplaced on scenery or other objects on the stage.

Spotlight: A lighting instrument with a condensing lens producing a beam of light; used for specific illumination. (See Figures 88, 89, 90, 93, and 94.)

Spot Line: A single line specially rigged from the gridiron to fly a piece of scenery which cannot be handled by the regular lines.

Stage Brace: An adjustable device made of two lengths of 1″ x 1″ wood held between clamps, used to prop up scenery from behind. A forked iron hook fastened to one end of the brace is hooked into a brace cleat attached to the unit requiring support, and an iron heel at the other end of the brace is secured to the floor by means of a stage screw. (See Figure 59.)

Stage Screw, or Peg: A large, tapered screw with a handle, used to secure foot irons and stage braces to the floor. (See Figures 28 and 59.)

Stand: A heavy round iron base to which is attached a vertical telescoping pipe and rod. Spotlights and floodlights can be attached to the end of the rod and directed toward the acting area from a position five or ten feet above the floor.

Stile: The long side piece in the frame of a flat. (See Figure 33.)

Strap Hinge: A hinge with long tapered flaps, used principally for hanging door shutters in their frames and for locking door and window frames into flats. (See Figures 28 and 37.)

Strike: To take apart and remove a set of scenery from the acting area after it has been used—generally at the end of an act.

Striplight: A long trough-like reflector with sockets for lamps of small wattage, or a row of individual reflectors properly housed in a rigid sheet metal structure. Striplights are made in any length from a few feet to 30 or 40 feet long. They are used for borderlights, footlights, and for cyclorama lighting to produce general illumination. (See *Backing Striplight* and Figure 96.)

Switch: A device used to open and close an electrical circuit. In modern stage lighting practice, switches are placed behind the face of a control board with the handle extending through to the front. A remote control switch is called a contactor.

Tab: A sheet of canvas or other material, framed or unframed, narrower than a drop but suspended like it—used chiefly for masking offstage spaces. (See Figure 44.)

Template: A special type of work bench used in the construction of flats.

Thickness: A width of lumber, or other material, attached to the edge of an opening (a doorway, an archway, or a window) to give the edge the effect of depth or thickness. (See Figure 39.)

Three-Fold: Three flats hinged together to fold inward, face to face.

Throw: Indicates the distance from a lighting instrument to the illuminated area.

Tint: A color higher in brilliance than median gray and of various degrees of saturation.

Toggle Rail or *Toggle Bar:* The cross piece in the frame of a flat. (See Figure 33.)

Tormentor Light: A spotlight mounted on a vertical pipe batten just offstage from either tormentor.

Traveller: A slotted steel or wooden track, used to hang draw curtains. (See Figure 4.)

Trim: The wooden facing, about 4 or 6 inches wide, which surrounds a door or window opening. It is usually ornamented with molding. (See Figure 39.)

Trim: To level off a flied piece of scenery at the right height for use during a performance.

Trip: To elevate the bottom of a drop, or other flied scenery, with an auxiliary set of lines in such a way as to make it occupy a space approximately half its height. Tripping is resorted to on stages where there is not sufficient fly space to get a unit out of sight by taking it straight up with one set of lines only. (See Figure 65.)

Two-Fold: Two flats hinged together to fold inward, face to face. A two-fold is also called a *wing.*

Upstage: Any position on the stage away from the footlights.

Veneer Board: See *Plywood.*

Volt: A volt is the unit of electromotive force or electrical pressure. Electrical pressure is often referred to as voltage.

Wagon: A low, rolling platform on which a section of a set may be mounted to expedite scene changes.

Watt: The unit of electrical power. Since it is a small unit, the term kilowatt, meaning 1,000 watts, is in common use.

Window Frame Unit: A solid wooden window made to fit into a flat. (See Figure 38.)

Wing: Two or three flats hinged together to fold inward, face to face. On the old-fashioned stage a "wing" was a painted, and usually profiled, screen, which was pushed onstage in a groove to represent part of the side wall of a set. Hence arose the practice of calling the offstage spaces to the right or left of the acting area the "wings." (See Figure 1.)

Wing Nut: A special type of nut which may be tightened with the fingers, without the aid of a wrench. (See Figures 28 and 32.)

Work Light: Illumination for the stage used for rehearsals, scene shifting and building. Work light is controlled ordinarily by a wall switch instead of a switch on the control board.

BIBLIOGRAPHY

SCENERY

ADAMS, John Cranford, *The Globe Playhouse: Its Design and Equipment* (Cambridge, Mass., Harvard University Press, 1942).

ALBRIGHT, H. D., HALSTEAD, William P., and MITCHELL, Lee, *Principles of Theatre Art* (Boston, Houghton Mifflin Company, 1955). Has nine valuable chapters dealing with the organization of the theatre structure, the nature and function of design, and the practical solution of various problems in staging.

ALTMAN, George, FREUD, Ralph, MACGOWAN, Kenneth, and MELNITZ, William, *Theater Pictorial* (Berkeley, University of California Press, 1953).

APPIA, Adolphe, *Adolphe Appia: A Portfolio of Reproductions* (Zurich, Orell-Fussli, 1929).

Architectural Forum, Theatre Reference Number (September, 1932).

ASHWORTH, Bradford, *Notes on Scene Painting,* Donald Oenslager, ed. (New Haven, Whitlock's, Inc., 1952). A small but valuable manual by a professional scenic artist of long experience.

BARBER, Philip, *The New Scene Technician's Handbook* (see Gassner, John, *Producing the Play*).

BEL GEDDES, Norman, COLE, Edward C., LAUTERER, Arch, CHERMAYEFF, Serge, and McCANDLESS, Stanley, "Theatre Planning: A Symposium," *Educational Theatre Journal,* Vol. II, No. 1 (March, 1950), pp. 1–7. Several controversial and stimulating ideas.

BOYLE, Walden P., *Central and Flexible Staging* (Berkeley, University of California Press, 1956).

BURRIS-MEYER, Elizabeth, *Color and Design in the Decorative Arts* (Englewood Cliffs, N.J., Prentice-Hall, Inc., 1935).

BURRIS-MEYER, Harold, and COLE, Edward C., *Scenery for the Theatre* (Boston, Little, Brown & Company, 1938). Unquestionably the most complete and detailed professional book on the construction and handling of scenery. Contains chapters on the organization of the professional and nonprofessional theatre, scenery planning and construction, stage machinery, rigging, properties, sound effects, the assembling and running of the show. Exceptionally well illustrated.

———, *Theatres and Auditoriums* (New York, Reinhold Publishing Corporation, 1949).

CHENEY, Sheldon, *Stage Decoration* (New York, The John Day Company, Inc., 1928).

COLE, Wendell, "Some Contemporary Trends in Theatre Architecture," *Educational Theatre Journal,* Vol. VII, No. 1 (March, 1955), pp. 16–21.

CORNBERG, Sol, and GEBAUER, Emanuel L., *A Stage Crew Handbook* (New York, Harper & Brothers, 1941). A handy, easily understood manual on scenery and lighting, using the question-and-answer method of presentation. Contains many good drawings and a glossary of technical terms.

CRAFTON, Allen, and ROYER, Jessica, *The Complete Acted Play: From Script to Final Curtain* (New York, Appleton-Century-Crofts, Inc., 1943). Contains several good chapters on scenery.

CRAIG, Edward Gordon, *Scene* (New York, Oxford University Press, 1923).

EVANS, Ralph M., *An Introduction to Color* (New York, John Wiley & Sons, Inc., 1948). A thoroughly practical discussion of color theories as they apply to both light and pigment colors.

FRIEDERICH, Willard J., and FRASER, John H., *Scenery Design for the Amateur Stage* (New York, The Macmillan Company, 1950). A useful, practical manual.

FRY, Roger, *Vision and Design* (London, Chatto & Windus, 1920). An old but stimulating book.

FUERST, Walter R., and HUME, Samuel J., *Twentieth Century Stage Decoration* (New York, Alfred A. Knopf, Inc., 1928), 2 vols.

GASSNER, John, *Producing the Play,* rev. ed. (New York, Henry Holt & Company, Inc., 1953). The last part of this encyclopedic volume is given over to the first publication in book form of Philip Barber's *New Scene Technician's Handbook,* formerly available only as a mimeographed syllabus. A detailed and excellently illustrated treatment of scenery and property construction, sound effects, and lighting. In addition, Gassner's book contains many useful chapters on all phases of theatre production, including styles of drama, acting, directing, theatre organization, stage management, costuming, lighting, make-up, the dance, and radio production, by some of the foremost authorities in the theatre.

GRAVES, Maitland, *The Art of Color and Design* (New York, McGraw-Hill Book Company, Inc., 1941). Line, direction, shape, proportion, texture, value, color, analyzed according to repetition, harmony, gradation, and contrast. Good illustrations.

GREENBERG, Edward M., and RUBIN, Joel E., "Production Aspects of the Music Circus," *Educational Theatre Journal,* Vol. IV, No. 1

(March, 1952), pp. 26–32. Technical information for the larger arena.

HALSTEAD, William Perdue, *Stage Management for the Amateur Theatre* (New York, F. S. Crofts & Co., 1937). Contains valuable information on backstage organization, scene shifting, handling of properties and costumes, lighting, and sound effects.

HEFFNER, Hubert C., SELDEN, Samuel, and SELLMAN, Hunton D., *Modern Theatre Practice,* 4th ed. (New York, Appleton-Century-Crofts, Inc., 1958).

HEWITT, Barnard, *Play Production* (Philadelphia, J. B. Lippincott Company, 1940). A rather general treatment of theatre production, but contains some specific discussions of styles of settings, lighting sound effects, and so on. Many good illustrations.

ISAACS, Edith J. R., ed., *Architecture for the New Theatre* (New York, Theatre Arts, Inc., 1935). Illuminating and stimulating articles on new trends in theatre design. Illustrated.

JACOBSON, Egbert, *The Science of Color* (Chicago, American Photo-Engravers Association, 1937).

JONES, Leslie Allen, *Scenic Design and Model Building* (Boston, Walter H. Baker Company, 1939).

JONES, Margo, *Theatre-in-the-Round* (New York, Rinehart & Company, Inc., 1951).

JONES, Robert Edmond, *Drawings for the Theatre* (New York, Theatre Arts, Inc., 1925).

KEPES, Gyorgy, *Language of Vision* (Chicago, P. Theobold, 1944).

KOMISARJEVSKY, Theodore, and SIMONSON, Lee, *Settings and Costumes of the Modern Stage* (London, The Studio, Ltd., 1933).

LEEPER, Janet, *Edward Gordon Craig: Designs for the Theatre* (London, Penguin Books, Ltd., 1948).

LUCKIESH, Matthew, *Light and Shade and Their Application* (New York, D. Van Nostrand Company, Inc., 1916).

MACGOWAN, Kenneth, *The Theatre of Tomorrow* (New York, Boni & Liveright, 1921).

——, and JONES, Robert Edmond, *Continental Stagecraft* (New York, Harcourt, Brace & Company, Inc., 1922).

MACGOWAN, Kenneth, and MELNITZ, William, *The Living Stage* (Englewood Cliffs, N.J., Prentice-Hall, Inc., 1955). Chapter 15 reviews contemporary trends in staging.

MILLER, James Hull, "Initial Factors in Theatre Planning," *Educational Theatre Journal,* Vol. VIII, No. 2 (May, 1956), pp. 89–96.

National Theatre Conference, *Are You Going to Build a Theatre? A Bibliography* (Cleveland, National Theatre Conference, 1946).

NELMS, Henning, *A Primer of Stagecraft* (New York, Dramatists Play Service, 1941). One of the best handbooks available. Concise and accurate discussions of all technical matters. Especially well illustrated. Easy for beginners to use.

NICOLL, Allardyce, *The Development of the Theatre,* rev. ed. (New York, Harcourt, Brace & Company, Inc., 1947).

OENSLAGER, Donald, *Scenery Then and Now* (New York, W. W. Norton & Company, Inc., 1936).

PHILIPPI, Herbert, *Stagecraft and Scene Design* (Boston, Houghton Mifflin Company, 1953).

POPE, Arthur, *The Language of Drawing and Painting* (Cambridge, Mass., Harvard University Press, 1949).

ROBINSON, Horace W., "An Approach to Theatre Planning," *Educational Theatre Journal,* Vol. I, No. 2 (December, 1949), pp. 96–99.

SCHOLZ, Janos, ed., *Baroque and Romantic Stage Design* (New York, Herbert Bittner & Co., 1950).

SHERINGHAM, George, and LAVER, James, *Design in the Theatre* (London, The Studio, Ltd., 1927).

SIMONSON, Lee, *The Art of Scenic Design* (New York, Harper & Brothers, 1950).

SMITH, Milton M., *The Book of Play Production: For Little Theatres, Schools and Colleges* (New York, D. Appleton–Century Company, Inc., 1926). A good elementary book on amateur stagecraft. Practical, well illustrated.

Stanley Tool Guide (New Britain, Conn., Stanley Tools, Inc., 1942). Loose-leaf sheets fitting 8½″ x 11″ binder. Complete directions for the use of all common woodworking tools. Splendid illustrations. This company also publishes a handbook entitled *How to Work with Tools and Wood,* a useful guide for the scenery technician.

TEAGUE, Walter Dorwin, *Design This Day* (New York, Harcourt, Brace & Company, Inc., 1940).

WATKINS, Charles Law, *The Language of Design* (Washington, D.C., Phillips Memorial Gallery, 1946).

WILFRED, Thomas, "The Projected Setting," *Educational Theatre Journal,* Vol. VI, No. 2 (May, 1954), pp. 136–144.

LIGHTING

BENTHAM, Frederick, *Stage Lighting* (London, Sir Isaac Pitman & Sons, 1950). A British text, particularly good on equipment.

BOWMAN, Wayne, *Modern Theatre Lighting* (New York, Harper & Brothers, 1957).

COLOR AS LIGHT, (New York, International Printing Ink Corp., 1935). An elementary monograph on the physics of color.

ENGEL, Alfred von, *Bühnenbeleuchtung* (Leipzig, Hachmeister, 1926). Profusely illustrated.

EVANS, Ralph M., *An Introduction to Color* (New York, John Wiley & Sons, Inc., 1948). A thorough, well written discussion of the physics and psycho-physics of color.

FUCHS, Theodore, *Home-Built Lighting Equipment* (New York, Samuel French, Inc., 1939).

————, *Stage Lighting* (Boston, Little, Brown & Company, 1929). A comprehensive treatment of the subject with special emphasis on equipment.

GASSNER, John, *Producing the Play,* rev. ed. New York, Henry Holt & Company, Inc., 1953). Several chapters on stage lighting.

HARTMAN, Louis, *Theatre Lighting: A Manual of the Stage Switchboard* (New York, D. Appleton–Century Company, Inc., 1930). Interesting reminiscences of the manner in which Belasco and Hartman achieved their effects.

HEFFNER, Hubert C., SELDEN, Samuel, and SELLMAN, Hunton D., *Modern Theatre Practice,* 4th ed. (New York, Appleton-Century-Crofts, Inc., 1959). As far as lighting is concerned, the text is a little more elementary than *Stage Scenery and Lighting.*

HEWITT, Barnard, FOSTER, J. F., and WOLLE, Muriel S., *Play Production: Theory and Practice* (Philadelphia, J. B. Lippincott Co., 1952).

KNAPP, Jack Stuart, *Lighting the Stage with Homemade Equipment* (Boston, Walter H. Baker Company, 1933).

KRANICH, Frederick, *Buhnentechnik der Gegenwart* (Berlin, 1929 and 1933). Profusely illustrated. One can learn much about German theatre practice from the illustrations in this and the Engel volume, even if he cannot read German. This volume covers every aspect of theatre engineering, including large sections on lighting.

Light Sources Past and Present, G. E. Bulletin, LS 139 (General Electric Co., 1956). Useful for those interested in lamp history and recent design.

LUCKIESH, Matthew, *Light and Shade and Their Application* (New York, D. Van Nostrand Company, Inc., 1917). Good general background material.

——, *Color and Its Application,* 2d ed. (New York, D. Van Nostrand Company, Inc., 1921).

McCANDLESS, Stanley R., *A Method of Lighting the Stage,* 3d ed. (New York, Theatre Arts, Inc., 1947).

——, *A Syllabus of Stage Lighting,* 9th ed. (New Haven, Conn., Yale University Press, 1958). A sound, thorough text.

MOYER, Jas. A., and WOSTREH, John F., *Industrial Electricity and Wiring* (New York, McGraw-Hill Book Company, Inc., 1943).

RIDGE, C. Harold, and ALDRED, F. S., *Stage Lighting Principles and Practice* (London, Sir Isaac Pitman & Sons, 1940). A good British text, interesting largely for British terminology.

RUBIN, Joel E., and WATSON, Leland H., *Theatrical Lighting Practice* (New York, Theatre Arts Books, 1954). Covers arena, outdoor production, and television as well as stage lighting.

STURROCK, Walter, and STALEY, K. A., *Fundamentals of Light and Lighting,* G. E. Bulletin LD 2 (General Electric Co., 1956). Contains a useful discussion of the physics of light.

WEITZ, C. E., *Lamp Bulletin,* GE Bulletin LD 1 (General Electric Co., 1956). Characteristics and applications of various incandescent lamps and other light sources.

WILFRED, Thomas, *Projected Scenery, A Technical Manual* (West Nyack, N.Y. Art Institute of Light, 1955).

WILLIAMS, R. Gillespie, *The Technique of Stage Lighting* (London, Sir Isaac Pitman & Sons, 1952). A British text, good on color and British practice.

——, *Lighting for Color and Form: Principles, Equipment and Applications* (London, Sir Isaac Pitman & Sons, 1954).

DIRECTORY OF MANUFACTURERS

Ariel Davis Co., Inc., 3687 South State, Salt Lake City, Utah. *Davis* dimmers.

Art Institute of Light (Thomas Wilfred), West Nyack, New York. Projectors and projection effects.

Bodde Screen and Projection Co., 8829 Venice Blvd., Los Angeles 39, California. Projectors and projection screens.

Brigham Gelatin Co., Randolph, Vermont. Colored, clear, and frosted sheet gelatin.

Century Lighting, Inc., 521 West 43rd Street, New York 36, New York. 1840 Berkeley St., Santa Monica, California. General lighting equipment and control boards.

Frank Adam Electric Co., St. Louis, Missouri. FA-Major stage control boards.

General Electric Co., Inc. Lamp Department, Nela Park, Cleveland 12, Ohio. Lamps.

General Radio Co., Cambridge 39, Massachusetts. *Variac* autotransformer dimmers.

Hub Electric Co., 2219 West Grand Ave., Chicago 12, Illinois. Control boards and general lighting equipment.

Kliegl Brothers, 321 West 50th Street, New York 19, New York. General lighting equipment and control boards.

Major Equipment Co., 4603–19 Fullerton Avenue, Chicago, Illinois. General lighting equipment.

Metropolitan Electric Mfg. Co., Long Island City 5, New York. Control equipment, especially magnetic amplifiers.

Mole-Richardson, 937 North Sycamore Avenue, Hollywood 38, California. Motion picture lighting equipment.

Paramount Cosmetics and Theatrical Make-up, 431 Fifth Ave., New York 16, New York. *Cinabex* color media.

Rosco Laboratories, 367 Hudson Avenue, Brooklyn, New York. Colored gelatin and plastic sheets.

Strand Electric and Engineering Co., Ltd., 29 King Street, London, W.C. 2, England. England's largest lighting equipment manufacturer. (Kliegl Brothers represent Strand in the United States.)

Strobolite Co., 35 West 52nd Street, New York 19, New York. Ultraviolet effects and materials.

STRONG ELECTRIC CORPORATION, 87 City Park Avenue, Toledo 2, Ohio. Arc and incandescent follow spotlights and slide projectors.

SUPERIOR ELECTRIC CO., Bristol, Connecticut. Powerstat dimmers and packaged control boards.

SYLVANIA ELECTRIC PRODUCTS CORPORATION, Lamp Division, Salem, Massachusetts. Lamps.

TRANS-LUX CORPORATION, 1270 Avenue of the Americas, New York 20, New York. Projectors and projection screens.

WARD-LEONARD ELECTRIC CO., 115 MacQuestion Parkway South, Mount Vernon, New York. Autotransformer and magnetic amplifier dimmers and other control devices.

WESTINGHOUSE ELECTRIC CORPORATION, Lamp Division, Bloomfield, New Jersey. Lamps.

VICKERS INCORPORATED, Electric Products Division, 1865 Locust St., St. Louis 3, Missouri. Lighting control, especially magnetic amplifiers.

INDEX